LINEAR ALGEBRAIC GROUPS

MATHEMATICS LECTURE NOTE SERIES

E. Artin and J. Tate	CLASS FIELD THEORY
Michael Atiyah	K-THEORY
Hyman Bass	ALGEBRAIC K-THEORY
Melvyn S. Berger Marion S. Berger	PERSPECTIVES IN NONLINEARITY
Armand Borel	LINEAR ALGEBRAIC GROUPS
Paul J. Cohen	SET THEORY AND THE CONTINUUM HYPOTHESIS
Eldon Dyer	COHOMOLOGY THEORIES
Walter Feit	CHARACTERS OF FINITE GROUPS
William Fulton	ALGEBRAIC CURVES
Marvin J. Greenberg	LECTURES ON ALGEBRAIC TOPOLOGY
Marvin J. Greenberg	LECTURES ON FORMS IN MANY VARIABLES
Robin Hartshorne	FOUNDATIONS OF PROJECTIVE GEOMETRY
J. F. P. Hudson	PIECEWISE LINEAR TOPOLOGY
Irving Kaplansky	RINGS OF OPERATORS
K. Kapp and H. Schneider	COMPLETELY O-SIMPLE SEMIGROUPS
Joseph B. Keller Stuart Antman	BIFURCATION THEORY AND NONLINEAR EIGENVALUE PROBLEMS
Serge Lang	ALGEBRAIC FUNCTIONS
Serge Lang	RAPPORT SUR LA COHOMOLOGIE DES GROUPES
Ottmar Loos	SYMMETRIC SPACES I: GENERAL THEORY II: COMPACT SPACES AND CLASSIFICATION
I. G. Macdonald	ALGEBRAIC GEOMETRY: INTRODUCTION TO SCHEMES
George W. Mackey	INDUCED REPRESENTATIONS OF GROUPS AND QUANTUM MECHANICS

Andrew Ogg	MODULAR FORMS AND DIRICHLET SERIES
Richard Palais	FOUNDATIONS OF GLOBAL NON-LINEAR ANALYSIS
William Parry	ENTROPY AND GENERATORS IN ERGODIC THEORY
D. S. Passman	PERMUTATION GROUPS
Walter Rudin	FUNCTION THEORY IN POLYDISCS
Jean-Pierre Serre	ABELIAN *l*-ADIC REPRESENTATIONS AND ELLIPTIC CURVES
Jean-Pierre Serre	ALGEBRES DE LIE SEMI-SIMPLE COMPLEXES
Jean-Pierre Serre	LIE ALGEBRAS AND LIE GROUPS
Sholmo Sternberg	CELESTIAL MECHANICS

A Note from the Publisher

This volume was printed directly from a typescript prepared by the author, who takes full responsibility for its content and appearance. The Publisher has not performed his usual functions of reviewing, editing, typesetting, and proofreading the material prior to publication.

The Publisher fully endorses this informal and quick method of publishing lecture notes at a moderate price, and he wishes to thank the author for preparing the material for publication.

LINEAR ALGEBRAIC GROUPS

ARMAND BOREL

Institute for Advanced Study
Princeton, New Jersey

Notes taken by Hyman Bass, Columbia University

W. A. BENJAMIN, INC.

New York 1969 Amsterdam

LINEAR ALGEBRAIC GROUPS

Library of Congress Catalog Card Number 70-81196
Manufactured in the United States of America
12345R32109

*The manuscript was put into production February 18, 1969;
this volume was published April 1, 1969*

**W. A. BENJAMIN, INC.
New York, New York 10016**

INTRODUCTION

These Notes aim at providing an introduction to the theory of linear algebraic groups over fields. Their main objectives are to give some basic material over arbitrary fields (Chap. I, II), and to discuss the structure of solvable and of reductive groups over algebraically closed fields (Chap. III, IV). To complete the picture, they also include some rationality properties (§§15, 18) and some results on groups over finite fields (§16) and over fields of characteristic zero (§7).

Apart from some knowledge of Lie algebras, the main prerequisite for these Notes is some familiarity with algebraic geometry. In fact, comparatively little is actually needed. Most of the notions and results frequently used in the Notes are summarized, a few with proofs, in a preliminary Chapter AG. As a basic reference, we take Mumford's Notes [14], and have tried to be to some extent self-contained from there. A few further results from algebraic geometry needed on some specific occasions will be recalled (with references) where used. The point of view adopted here is essentially the set theoretic one: varieties are identified with their set of points over an algebraic closure of the groundfield (endowed with the Zariski-topology), however with some traces of the scheme point of view here and there.

These Notes are based on a course given at Columbia University in Spring, 1968,(*) at the suggestion of Hyman Bass. Except for Chap. V, added later, Notes were written up by H. Bass, with some help from Michael Stein, and are reproduced here with few changes or additions. He did this with marvelous efficiency, often expanding or improving the oral presentation. In particular, the emphasis on dual numbers in §3 is his, and he wrote up Chapter AG, of which only a very brief survey had been given in the course. It is a pleasure to thank him most warmly for his contributions, without which these Notes would hardly have come into being at this time. I would also like to thank Miss P. Murray for her careful and fast typing of the manuscript, and J. E. Humphreys, J. S. Joel for their help in checking and proofreading it.

A. Borel

Princeton, February, 1969

(*) Lectures from May 7th on qualified as liberated class, under the sponsorship of the Students Strike Committee. Space was generously made available on one occasion by the Union Theological Seminary.

TABLE OF CONTENTS

CONVENTIONS AND NOTATION

1. Throughout these Notes, k denotes a commutative field, K an algebraically closed extension of k, k_s (resp. $\bar{k}$) the separable (resp. algebraic) closure of k in K, and p is the characteristic of k. Sometimes, p also stands for the characteristic exponent of k, i.e. for one if $\mathrm{char}(k) = 0$, and p if $\mathrm{char}(k) = p > 0$.

All rings are commutative, unless the contrary is specifically allowed, with unit, and all ring homomorphisms and modules are unitary.

If A is a ring, A^* is the group of invertible elements of A.

$\mathbb{Z}$ denotes the ring of integers, $\mathbb{Q}$ (resp. $\mathbb{R}$, resp. $\mathbb{C}$) the field of rational (resp. real, resp. complex) numbers.

2. References. A reference to section (x. y) of Chapter AG is denoted by (AG. x. y). In the subsequent chapters (x. y) refers to section (x. y) in one of them.

There are two bibliographies, one for Chapter AG, on p. 83, one for Chapters I to V, on p. 391.

References to original literature in Chapters I to V are usually collected in bibliographical notes at the end of certain paragraphs. However, they do not aim at completeness, and a result for which none is given need not be new.

3. Let G be a group. If (X_i) $(1 \leqq i \leqq m)$ are sets and $f_i : X_i \longrightarrow G$ maps, then the map $f : X_1 \times \ldots \times X_m \longrightarrow G$ defined by

$$(x_1, \ldots, x_n) \longmapsto f_1(x_1) \cdot \ldots \cdot f_m(x_m), \qquad (x_i \in X_i ; 1 \leqq i \leqq m) ,$$

is often called the product map of the f_i's.

Let N_i $(1 \leqq i \leqq n)$ be normal subgroups of G. The group G is an <u>almost direct product</u> of the N_i's if the product map of the inclusions $N_i \longrightarrow G$ is a homomorphism of the direct product $N_1 \times \ldots \times N_m$ onto G, with finite kernel.

If M, N are subgroups of G, then (M, N) denotes the subgroup of G generated by the commutators $(x, y) = x.y.x^{-1}.y^{-1}$ $(x \in M, \ y \in N)$.

4. If V is a k-variety, and k' an extension of k in K, then $V(k')$ denotes the set of points of V rational over k'. $k'[V]$ is the k'-algebra of regular functions defined over k' on V, and $k'(V)$ the k'-algebra of rational functions defined over k' on V. If W is a k-variety, and $f : V \longrightarrow W$ a k-morphism, then the map $k[W] \longrightarrow k[V]$ defined by $\varphi \longrightarrow \varphi \circ f$ is the <u>comorphism</u> associated to f and is denoted f_0.

5. Finally, we list some of the notation which is often used without reference, after it has been introduced in one of Chapters I to V.

CHAPTER AG

BACKGROUND MATERIAL FROM ALGEBRAIC GEOMETRY

This chapter should be used only as a reference for the remaining ones. Its purpose is to establish the language and conventions of algebraic geometry used in these notes. The intention is to take, in so far as is practicable, the point of view of Mumford's chapter I. Thus our varieties are identified with their points over a fixed algebraically closed field K (of any characteristic). It is technically important for us, however, not to require (as does Mumford) that varieties be irreducible.

For the most part definitions and theorems are simply stated with references and occasional indications of proofs. There are two notable exceptions. We have given essentially complete treatments of the material presented on rationality questions (i.e. field of definition), in sections 11-14, and of the material on tangent spaces, in sections 15-16. This seemed desirable because of the lack of convenient references for these results (in the form used here), and because of the important technical role both of these topics play in the notes.

§1. SOME TOPOLOGICAL NOTIONS
(Cf. [Class., exp. 1, no. 1].)

(1.1) Irreducible components. A topological space X is said to be irreducible if it is not empty and is not the union of two proper closed subsets. The latter condition is equivalent to the requirement that each non-empty open set be dense in X, or that each one be connected.

If Y is a subspace of a topological space X then Y is irreducible if and only if its closure $\overline{Y}$ is irreducible. By Zorn's lemma every irreducible subspace of X is contained in a maximal one, and the preceding remark shows that the maximal irreducible subspaces are closed. They are called the irreducible components of X. Since the closure of a point is irreducible it lies in an irreducible component; hence X is the union of its irreducible components.

If a subspace Y of X has only finitely many irreducible components, say $Y_1, \ldots, Y_n$, then $\overline{Y}_1, \ldots, \overline{Y}_n$ are the irreducible components (without repetition) of $\overline{Y}$.

(1.2) Noetherian spaces. A topological space X is said to be quasi-compact ("quasi-" because X is not assumed to be Hausdorff) if every open covering has a finite subcovering. If every open set in X is quasi-compact, or, equivalently, if the open sets satisfy the maximum condition, then X is said to be noetherian. It is easily seen that every subspace of a noetherian space is noetherian.

PROPOSITION. Let X be a noetherian space.

(a) X has only finitely many irreducible components, say $X_1, \ldots, X_n$.

(b) An open set U in X is dense if and only if $U \cap X_i \neq \phi$ $(1 \leqq i \leqq n)$.

(c) For each i, $X_i' = X_i - \bigcup_{j \neq i}(X_j \cap X_i)$ is open in X, and $U_0 = \bigcup_i X_i'$ is an open dense set in X whose irreducible and connected components are $X_1', \ldots, X_n'$.

Part (a) follows from a standard "noetherian induction" argument.

Since X_i is irreducible the set $X_i' = X - (\bigcup_{j \neq i} X_j)$ is open in X and dense in X_i. Hence every open dense set U in X must meet X_i'. Conversely if U is open and meets each X_i then $U \cap X_i$ is dense in X_i, so $\overline{U}$ contains each X_i and hence equals X. It follows, in particular, that $U_0 = \bigcup_i X_i'$ is open dense. Since the X_i' are open, irreducible, and pairwise disjoint, they are the irreducible and connected components of U_0.

(1.3) Constructible sets. A subset Y of a topological space X is said to be locally closed in X if Y is open in $\overline{Y}$, or, equivalently, if Y is the intersection of an open set with a closed set. The latter description makes it clear that the intersection of two locally closed sets is locally closed. A constructible set is a finite union of locally closed sets. The complement of a locally closed set is the union of an open set with a closed set, hence a constructible set. It follows that the complement of a constructible set is constructible. Thus, the constructible sets are a Boolean algebra (i.e. they are stable under finite unions and intersections and under complementation). In fact they are the Boolean algebra generated by the open and (or) closed sets.

If $f : X \longrightarrow X'$ is a continuous map then f^{-1} is a Boolean algebra homomorphism carrying open and closed sets, respectively, in X' to those in X. Hence f^{-1} carries locally closed and constructible sets, respectively, in X' to those in X.

PROPOSITION. Let X be a noetherian space, and let Y be a constructible subset of X. Then Y contains an open dense subset of $\overline{Y}$.

REMARK. Conversely, by a noetherian induction argument, one can show that if Y is a subset of X whose intersection with every irreducible closed subset of X has the above property, then Y is constructible.

PROOF. Write $Y = \bigcup_i L_i$ with each L_i locally closed. Then $\overline{Y} = \bigcup_i \overline{L_i}$, so, if $\overline{Y}$ is irreducible, $\overline{Y} = \overline{L_i}$ for some i. Moreover $L_i (\subset Y)$ is open in $\overline{L_i}$.

In the general case write $Y = \bigcup_j Y_j$ where the Y_j are the irreducible components of Y. The latter are closed in Y and hence constructible in X. Moreover the first case shows that Y_j contains a dense open set in $\overline{Y}_j$. Since the $\overline{Y}_j$ are the irreducible components of $\overline{Y}$ (see (AG.1.1)) it follows from (AG.1.2) that $Y = \bigcup Y_j$ contains a dense open set in $\overline{Y}$.

(1.4) <u>(Combinatorial) dimension</u>. For a topological space X it is the supremum of the lengths, n, of chains $F_0 \subset F_1 \subset \cdots \subset F_n$ of distinct irreducible closed sets in X; it is denoted

$$\dim X .$$

If $x \in X$ we write

$$\dim_x X$$

for the infimum of $\dim U$ where U varies over open neighborhoods of x.

It follows easily from the definitions and the properties of irreducible closed sets that $\dim \phi = -\infty$, that

$$\dim X = \sup_{x \in X} \dim_x X ,$$

and that $x \mapsto \dim_x X$ is an upper semi-continuous function. Moreover, if X has a finite number of irreducible components (e.g. if X is noetherian), say $X_1, \ldots, X_m$, then $\dim X$ is the maximum of $\dim X_i$ $(1 \leqq i \leqq m)$.

§2. SOME FACTS FROM FIELD THEORY

(2.1) Base change for fields (cf. [C.-C., exp. 13-14]). We fix a field extension F of k. If k' is any field extension of k we shall write

$$F_{k'} = k' \otimes_k F .$$

This is a k'-algebra, but it is no longer a field, or even an integral domain, in general. However, each of its prime ideals is minimal (i.e. there are no inclusion relations between them) and their intersection is the ideal of nilpotent elements in $F_{k'}$ (see (AG.3.3) below). We say a ring is reduced if its ideal of nilpotent elements is zero.

Here are the basic possibilities:

(a) k' is separable algebraic over k: Then $F_{k'}$ is reduced, but it may have more than one prime ideal.

(b) k' is algebraic and purely inseparable over k: Then $F_{k'}$ has a unique prime ideal (consisting of nilpotent elements) but $F_{k'}$ need not be reduced.

(c) k' is a purely transcendental extension of k: Then $F_{k'}$ is clearly an integral domain.

(2.2) Separable extensions. F is said to be separable over k if it satisfies the following conditions, which are equivalent: We write p for the characteristic exponent of k (= 1 if char(k) = 0).

(1) F^p and k are linearly disjoint over k^p.

(2) $F_{(k^{1/p})}$ is reduced.

(3) $F_{k'}$ is reduced for all field extensions k' of k.

Suppose, for some extension L of k, that F_L is an integral domain, with field of fractions (F_L). Then F <u>is separable over</u> $k \Longleftrightarrow (F_L)$ <u>is separable over</u> L. The implication $\Longrightarrow$ follows essentially from the associativity of tensor products, using criterion (3). To prove the converse we embed a given extension k' of k in a bigger one, k'', containing L also. Since $F_{k'} \subset F_{k''}$ it suffices to show that $F_{k''}$ is reduced. But $F_{k''} = F_L \otimes_L k'' \subset (F_L)_{k''}$ and the latter is reduced, by hypothesis.

(2.3) <u>Differential criteria</u>. (See [N. B., (a), §9], [Z.-S., v. I, Ch. II, §17], or [C.-C., exp. 13].) A k-<u>derivation</u> $D : F \longrightarrow F$ is a k-linear map such that $D(ab) = D(a)b + aD(b)$ for all $a, b \in F$. The set of them,

$$\mathrm{Der}_k(F, F)$$

is a vector space over F.

THEOREM. <u>Suppose</u> F <u>is a finitely generated extension of</u> k. <u>Put</u>

$$n = \mathrm{tr.deg.}_k(F)$$

<u>and</u>

$$m = \dim_F \mathrm{Der}_k(F, F) \ .$$

<u>Then</u> $m \geqq n$, <u>with equality if and only if</u> F <u>is separable over</u> k.

Let $D_1, \ldots, D_m$ be a basis of $Der_k(F, F)$ and let $a_1, \ldots, a_m \in F$. Then F is separable algebraic over $k(a_1, \ldots, a_m)$ if and only if $\det(D_i(a_j)) \neq 0$.

If $m = n$ then a set $\{a_1, \ldots, a_m\}$ as above is called a separating transcendence basis.

(2.4) PROPOSITION. Let G be a group of automorphisms of a field F. Then F is a separable extension of $k = F^G$, the fixed elements under G.

We shall prove that F and $k^{1/p}$ are linearly disjoint over k, i.e. that if $a_1, \ldots, a_n \in k^{1/p}$ are linearly independent over k then they are linearly independent over F. The action of G extends uniquely to $F^{1/p}$ and G acts trivially on $k^{1/p}$. Suppose $a_1, \ldots, a_n$ are linearly dependent over F, but not over k; we can assume n is minimal. Let $a_1 + b_2a_2 + \ldots + b_na_n = 0$ be a dependence relation. If some b_i, say b_n, is not in F then it is moved by some $g \in G$. Subtracting $a_1 + g(b_2)a_2 + \ldots + g(b_n)a_n$ from the relation above we obtain a shorter relation; contradiction.

§3. SOME COMMUTATIVE ALGEBRA

(3.1) Localization [N. B., (b)]. Let S be a multiplicative set in a ring A, i.e. S is not empty and $s, t \in S \Longrightarrow st \in S$. Then we have the "localization" $A[S^{-1}]$ consisting of fractions a/s $(a \in A,\ s \in S)$, and the natural map $A \longrightarrow A[S^{-1}]$ which is universal among homomorphisms from A rendering the elements of S invertible.

If M is an A-module we further have the localized $A[S^{-1}]$-module $M[S^{-1}]$, consisting of fractions $x/s (x \in M, s \in S)$, which is naturally isomorphic to $A[S^{-1}] \otimes_A M$.

If $x \in M$ and $s \in S$ then $x/s = 0$ in $M[S^{-1}]$ if and only if $tx = 0$ for some $t \in S$. It follows directly from this that, if M is finitely generated $M[S^{-1}] = 0$ if and only if $tM = 0$ for some $t \in S$, i.e. if and only if $S \cap \operatorname{ann} M \neq \phi$, where $\operatorname{ann} M$ is the annihilator of M in A.

The functor $M \longmapsto M[S^{-1}]$ from A-modules to $A[S^{-1}]$-modules is exact, and it preserves tensors and Hom's in the following sense: If M and N are A-modules then the natural map $(M \otimes_A N)[S^{-1}] \longrightarrow M[S^{-1}] \otimes_{A[S^{-1}]} N[S^{-1}]$ is an isomorphism, and the natural map $\operatorname{Hom}_A(M, N)[S^{-1}] \longrightarrow \operatorname{Hom}_{A[S^{-1}]}(M[S^{-1}], N[S^{-1}])$ is an isomorphism if M is finitely presented.

EXAMPLES. (1) Let S be the set of all non-divisors of zero in A. Then $A \longrightarrow A[S^{-1}]$ is injective, and the latter is called the full ring of fractions of A. When A is an integral domain it is the field of fractions.

(2) If $S = \{f^n \mid n \geqq 0\}$ for some $f \in A$ then we write A_f or $A[1/f]$, and M_f for the localizations.

(3) An ideal P in A is prime if $S_P = A - P$ is a multiplicative set. The corresponding localizations are denoted A_P and M_P. In this case A_P has a unique maximal ideal, PA_P, i.e. A_P is a local ring.

(3.2) Local rings. Let A be a local ring with maximal ideal $\underline{m}$ and residue class field $k = A/\underline{m}$. Let M be a finitely generated A-module.

(a) If $\underline{m}M = M$ then $M = 0$.

For let $x_1, \ldots, x_n$ be a minimal set of generators of M, and suppose $n > 0$. Write $x_1 = \Sigma a_i x_i$ $(a_i \in \underline{m})$. Then $(1-a_1)x_1 = \sum_{i>1} a_i x_i$. But $1-a_1$ is invertible, so $x_2, \ldots, x_n$ already generate M; contradiction.

(b) If $x_1, \ldots, x_n \in M$ then they generate M if and only if they do so modulo $\underline{m}M$. Hence the minimal number of generators of M is $\dim_k(M/\underline{m}M)$.

This follows by applying (a) to M/N, where N is the submodule generated by $x_1, \ldots, x_n$.

(c) If M is projective then M is free.

We can write $A^n = M \oplus N$, so that $k^n = (M/\underline{m}M) \oplus (N/\underline{m}N)$. Lift a basis of k^n to A^n so that it lies in $M \cup N$. The result is, by (b), a set of n generators of A^n. These must clearly be a basis of A^n, e.g. because the associated matrix has an invertible determinant. Hence M, being spanned by part of a basis of A^n, is free.

(3.3) Nil radical; reduced rings. The set of nilpotent

elements in a ring A is an ideal denoted nil A. We call A _reduced_ if nil A = (0).

If J is any ideal the ideal $\sqrt{J}$ is defined by $\sqrt{J}/J = \mathrm{nil}(A/J)$. Thus nil A = $\sqrt{(0)}$. Moreover, we have

$$\sqrt{J} = \text{the intersection of all primes containing } J.$$

If S is a multiplicative set then $\sqrt{J}\cdot A[S^{-1}] = \sqrt{J\cdot A[S^{-1}]}$. In particular this implies that _A is reduced if and only if the full ring of fractions of A is reduced._

(3.4) _spec_(A) [M, Ch. II, §1]. We let X = spec(A) be the set of all prime ideals in A, equipped with the _Zariski topology_, in which the closed sets are those of the following form for some $J \subset A$:

$$V(J) = \{P \in X \mid J \subset P\} .$$

If $Y \subset X$ we put $I(Y) = \bigcap_{P \in Y} P$, and then V(I(Y)) is just the closure of Y. Moreover, if J is an ideal of A it follows from (3.3) that

$$I(V(J)) = \sqrt{J} .$$

Thus closed sets correspond bijectively (with inclusions reversed) to ideals J for which $J = \sqrt{J}$. It follows that if A is noetherian then spec(A) is a noetherian space.

The map $P \mapsto \overline{\{P\}}$ is a bijection from X to the set of irreducible closed sets in X. Thus the irreducible components of X correspond to the minimal primes in A. Moreover the (combinatorial) dimension of X (measured by chains of irreducible closed sets) is called the (Krull) dimension of A, and it is denoted $\dim A$. Thus

$$\dim A = \dim X \ .$$

If $f \in A$ and $P \in X$ one sometimes writes $f(P)$ for the image of f in the residue class field of A_P (which is the field of fractions of A/P). With this notation the complement of $V(f)$ is

$$X_f = \{P \in X \mid f(P) \neq 0\} \ .$$

This is called a principal open set. For any J we have $V(J) = \bigcap_{f \in J} V(f)$ so the principal open sets are a base for the topology.

Suppose $\alpha_0 : A \longrightarrow B$ is a ring homomorphism. Then α_0 induces a continuous map $\alpha : Y = \operatorname{spec}(B) \longrightarrow X$, $\alpha(P) = \alpha_0^{-1}(P)$. In fact $\alpha^{-1}(V(J)) = V(\alpha_0(J))$.

EXAMPLES. (1) If J is an ideal then $A \longrightarrow A/J$ induces a homeomorphism of $\operatorname{spec}(A/J)$ onto $V(J) \subset X$.

(2) If S is a multiplicative set then $\operatorname{spec}(A[S^{-1}]) \longrightarrow \operatorname{spec}(A)$ induces a homeomorphism onto the set of $P \in X$ such that $P \cap S = \phi$.

(i) If $f \in A$ then we obtain a homeomorphism

$$\operatorname{spec}(A_f) \longrightarrow X_f.$$

(ii) If $P \in X$ it follows that $\dim_P X$
$= \dim \operatorname{spec}(A_P) = (\text{Krull})\dim A_P$.

(3.5) Support of a module. Let $X = \operatorname{spec}(A)$ where A is a noetherian ring, and let M be a finitely generated A-module. Then it follows from (3.1) that

$$\operatorname{supp}(M) = \{P \mid M_P \neq 0\}$$

is the closed set $V(\operatorname{ann} M)$. In particular $M = 0$ if and only if $\operatorname{supp}(M) = \phi$.

Let $f : L \longrightarrow M$ be a homomorphism of A-modules. Since localization is exact it follows that the set of P where f is an epimorphism is the (open) complement of $\operatorname{supp}(\operatorname{coker} f)$. Applying this to $\operatorname{Hom}_A(M, L) \longrightarrow \operatorname{Hom}_A(M, M)$, and using the fact that the Hom's localize properly (see (3.1)) we conclude that the set U of $P \in X$ such that f_P is a split epimorphism is open, and f is a split epimorphism if and only if $U = X$.

Suppose f is surjective and L is free. Then we deduce from the last remark and (3.2)(c) that:

$$U = \{P \in X \mid M_P \text{ is a free } A_P\text{-module}\}$$

is open, and M is a projective A-module if and only if $U = X$.

(3.6) Integral extensions ([N. B., (b), Ch. 5] or [Z. -S., v. I, Ch. V]). Let $A \subset B$ be rings. A $b \in B$ is said to be integral over A if A[b] is a finitely generated A-module, or, equivalently, if b is a root of a monic polynomial with coefficients in A. The set B' of all elements of B integral over A is a subring, called the integral closure of A in B. We say B is integral over A if B' = B. We say A is integrally closed in B if B' = A. We call A normal if A is reduced and integrally closed in its full ring of fractions.

Suppose $A \subset B \subset C$ are rings. Then C is integral over A if and only if C and B are integral over B and A, respectively.

Suppose B is integral over A. Then spec(B) $\longrightarrow$ spec(A) is surjective and closed. If B is a finitely generated A-algebra then B is a finitely generated A-module. If B is an integral domain then every non-zero ideal of B has non-zero intersection with A.

To see the latter let $b^n + a_{n-1}b^{n-1} + \ldots + a_0 = 0$ be an integral equation of minimal degree over A of some $b \neq 0$ in B. Then $a_0 = -b(a_{n-1}b^{n-2} + \ldots + a_1) \in bB \cap A$. Moreover $a_0 \neq 0$; otherwise we could reduce the degree of the equation.

(3.7) Noether normalization [M, Ch. I, p. 4]. A k-algebra A is said to be affine if it is finitely generated as a k-algebra. Such an A is a noetherian ring.

THEOREM. Let $R = k[y_1, \ldots, y_m]$ be an affine integral domain over k whose field of fractions, $k(y_1, \ldots, y_m)$, has transcendence degree n over k. Then there exist elements $x_1, \ldots, x_n \in R$, which are algebraically independent over k, and such that R is integral over the polynomial ring $k[x_1, \ldots, x_n]$. If $k(y_1, \ldots, y_m)$ is separable over k then $x_1, \ldots, x_n$ can be chosen to be a separating transcendence basis of $k(y_1, \ldots, y_m)$ over k.

Except for the last assertion this theorem is essentially identical in statement and notation with that in Mumford, page 4. With the following modification, the proof in Mumford gives also the last assertion as well.

First, choose $y_1, \ldots, y_m$ so that the last n of them are a separating transcendence basis. Next, choose the integers $r_1, \ldots, r_m$ (as well as their analogues at other stages of the induction) to be divisible by p, the characteristic exponent of k. The proof in Mumford requires only that the r_i's be large and increase rapidly, so our additional restriction is harmless.

This done, the $x_1, \ldots, x_n$ produced by the proof will be congruent, modulo $p^{\underline{th}}$ powers, to the last n of the y_i's. Thus each x_i has the same image under every k-derivation as the corresponding y (if $p > 1$; otherwise there is no problem). It therefore follows that the x's, like the y's, are a separating transcendence basis (see (AG.2.3)).

(3.8) The Nullstellensatz [M, Ch. I]. Let A be an affine

K-algebra, and let $X = \max(A)$ be the subspace of maximal ideals in $\operatorname{spec}(A)$.

If $e : A \longrightarrow K$ is a K-algebra homomorphism then $\ker(e) \in X$ so we have a natural map

$$\varphi : \operatorname{Mor}_{K\text{-alg}}(A, K) \longrightarrow X \quad .$$

THEOREM (Nullstellensatz).

(1) φ is bijective.

(2) X is dense in $\operatorname{spec}(A)$. Moreover $F \longmapsto F \cap X$ is a bijection from the set of closed sets in $\operatorname{spec}(A)$ to the set of closed sets in X. Therefore the analogous statement is valid for open sets also.

If $x \in X$ we shall write e_x for the homomorphism $A \longrightarrow K$ such that $x = \ker(e_x)$. If $f \in A$ we shall also use the functional notation

$$f(x) = e_x(f) \quad .$$

Thus each $f \in A$ determines a function $X \longrightarrow K$. If f represents the zero function then $f \in I(X) = \bigcap_{x \in X} x$. It follows from part (2) that $I(x) = I(\operatorname{spec}(A)) = \operatorname{nil} A$. Thus, in general, the function on X associated with f determines f modulo $\operatorname{nil} A$. If A is reduced we can therefore view A as a ring of K-valued functions on X.

We shall use for X the same notational conventions introduced for $\operatorname{spec}(A)$. For example, if $f \in A$ then $X_f = \{x \in X \mid f(x) \neq 0\}$. These principal open sets are a base for the topology on X.

If M is an A-module we also write $\mathrm{supp}_X(M) = \{x \in X \mid M_x \neq 0\}$, or simply supp(M) when the meaning is clear. In view of part (2) of the Nullstellensatz all the remarks of (3.5) remain valid with X in place of spec(A).

The correspondence in (2) also matches irreducible closed sets, clearly, and hence irreducible components. If $x \in X$, then $\dim_x X = \dim_x \mathrm{spec}(A) = \dim A_x$. Moreover $\dim X = \dim \mathrm{spec}(A)$.

(3.9) Regular local rings [Z.-S., v. II, Ch. VIII, §11]. Let A be a noetherian local ring with maximal ideal $\underline{m}$ and residue class field $k = A/\underline{m}$. Then the minimal number of generators of $\underline{m}$ is (see (3.2)) the dimension over k of $\underline{m}/\underline{m}^2$. It is a basic fact that

$$\dim_k(\underline{m}/\underline{m}^2) \geqq \dim A \quad ,$$

where dim A is defined as in (3.4). When this inequality is an equality the local ring A is said to be regular.

Regularity has rather strong consequences for A, for example the fact that A is then a unique factorization domain.

We shall see in (AG.17) that, when A is the local ring of a point x on a variety V, then regularity of A means that x is a simple point; hence the importance of the notion. A minimal set of generators of $\underline{m}$ then gives the right number of local parameters at x on V, and $\underline{m}/\underline{m}^2$ is the cotangent space (see (AG.16)) of V at x.

§4. SHEAVES [M, Ch. I, §4]

(4.1) Presheaves. Let X be a topological space. The open sets in X are the objects of a category, top(X), whose morphisms are inclusions. If C is a category then a C-valued presheaf on X is a contravariant functor $U \longmapsto F(U)$ from top(X) to C. Thus, whenever $V \subset U$ are open sets in X we have a C-morphism

$$\mathrm{res}_V^U : F(U) \longrightarrow F(V) ,$$

sometimes called "restriction." A morphism $\varphi : F \longrightarrow F'$ of presheaves is just a morphism of functors. Thus it consists of morphisms $\varphi_U : F(U) \longrightarrow F'(U)$ rendering the diagrams

$$\begin{array}{ccc} F(U) & \xrightarrow{\varphi_U} & F'(U) \\ {\scriptstyle \mathrm{res}_V^U}\downarrow & & \downarrow{\scriptstyle \mathrm{res}_V^U} \\ F(V) & \xrightarrow[\varphi_V]{} & F'(V) \end{array}$$

commutative.

Suppose C is a category of "sets with structure," like groups, rings, modules, ... Then we say F is a presheaf of groups, rings, modules, ..., respectively, on X. If $x \in X$ then

$$F_x = \operatorname*{ind\,lim}_{U \text{ nbhd. of } x} F(U)$$

is called the <u>stalk</u> of F over x.

If U is open in X then $\mathrm{top}(U)$ is a subcategory of $\mathrm{top}(X)$ to which we can restrict a presheaf F on X. The resulting presheaf on U is denoted $(U, F|U)$.

(4.2) <u>Sheaves</u>. Let F be a C-valued presheaf, on X, where C is some category of "sets with structure." Then F is called a <u>sheaf</u> if it satisfies the following "sheaf axiom": Given an open covering $(U_i)_{i\in I}$ of an open set U in X, the sequence

$$F(U) \xrightarrow{\alpha} \prod_i F(U_i) \underset{\gamma}{\overset{\beta}{\rightrightarrows}} \prod_{i,j} F(U_i \cap U_j)$$

of sets is exact.

Explanation: "Exact" means that α induces a bijection from $F(U)$ to the set of elements on which β and γ agree. Thus, if F is a presheaf of abelian groups, for example, exactness means that α is the kernel of $(\beta - \gamma)$.

The map α is induced by the restrictions $F(U) \longrightarrow F(U_i)$ $(i \in I)$. Similarly, the restrictions $F(U_i) \longrightarrow F(U_i \cap U_j)$ $(j \in I)$ induce $F(U_i) \longrightarrow \prod_j F(U_i \cap U_j)$. Taking the product of these over $i \in I$ we obtain β. The map γ is obtained similarly, starting from $F(U_j) \longrightarrow F(U_i \cap U_j)$ to obtain $F(U_j) \longrightarrow \prod_i F(U_i \cap U_j)$.

Explicitly, the sheaf axiom says that, given $s_i \in F(U_i)$ such that $s_i | U_i \cap U_j = s_j | U_i \cap U_j$ for all $i, j \in I$

(we write $s|V$ for $res^U_V(s)$) then there is a unique $s \in F(U)$ such that $s|U_i = s_i$ for all $i \in I$.

EXAMPLE. Let $F(U)$ be the ring of continuous real valued functions on U. Then, with respect to restriction of functions, F is clearly a sheaf (of commutative rings).

(4.3) Sheafification. Let F be a C-valued presheaf on X, where C is some category of "sets with structure." Then there is a sheaf, F', called the "sheafification" of F, or the sheaf associated with F, and a morphism $f : F \longrightarrow F'$ through which all morphisms from F into sheaves factor uniquely. In other words the map

$$\mathrm{Mor}(F', G) \longrightarrow \mathrm{Mor}(F, G)$$

induced by f is bijective whenever G is a sheaf.

Roughly speaking, F' can be constructed in two steps. First define $F_1(U)$ to be $F(U)$ modulo the equivalence relation which relates s and t if their restrictions agree on some open covering of U. Then form F' from F_1 by "adding" to $F_1(U)$ all elements obtainable from compatible local data on some covering of U. This process makes sense thanks to step 1.

If $x \in X$ the morphism of stalks $F_x \longrightarrow F'_x$ is bijective.

Presheaves of abelian groups or modules form an abelian category, with the obvious notions of kernel, cokernel, exact sequence, etc. Thus, if $f : F \longrightarrow G$ is a morphism of presheaves then (ker f)(U) = ker(F(U) ⟶ F(U)), and similarly for coker(f). If F and G are sheaves then ker(f) is also a sheaf. On the other hand coker(f) need not be a sheaf. The cokernel of f in the category of sheaves is the sheafification of the presheaf cokernel.

One can show that the category of sheaves of abelian groups is abelian. A sequence $F \longrightarrow G \longrightarrow H$ of sheaves is exact if and only if $F_x \longrightarrow G_x \longrightarrow H_x$ is exact for all $x \in X$.

§5. AFFINE K-SCHEMES; PREVARIETIES

(5.1) A K-<u>space</u> is a topological space X together with a sheaf $\mathcal{O}_X$ of K-algebras on X whose stalks are local rings. If $x \in X$ we write $\mathcal{O}_{X,x}$ for the stalk over x, or simply $\mathcal{O}_x$ if X is clear from the context. Its maximal ideal is denoted $\underline{m}_x$, and its residue class field by K(x). One often writes X in place of $(X, \mathcal{O}_X)$ if this leads to no confusion.

A <u>morphism</u> $(Y, \mathcal{O}_Y) \longrightarrow (X, \mathcal{O}_X)$ of K-spaces consists of a continuous function $\alpha : Y \longrightarrow X$ together with K-algebra homomorphisms

$$\alpha_V^U : \mathcal{O}_X(U) \longrightarrow \mathcal{O}_Y(V)$$

whenever $U \subset X$ and $V \subset Y$ are open sets such that $\alpha(V) \subset U$. These maps are required to be compatible with the respective restriction homomorphisms in $\mathcal{O}_X$ and $\mathcal{O}_Y$. For $y \in Y$ we can pass to the limit over neighborhoods V of y and U of x = f(y) to deduce a homomorphism $\alpha_y : \mathcal{O}_x \longrightarrow \mathcal{O}_y$. It is further required of a morphism that this always be a "local homomorphism," i.e. that $\alpha_y(\underline{m}_x) \subset \underline{m}_y$.

(5.2) <u>The affine</u> K-<u>scheme</u> $\text{spec}_K(A)$. An <u>affine</u> K-<u>algebra</u> A is one which if finitely generated as an algebra. For such an algebra the subspace X = max(A) of maximal ideals in spec(A) will be denoted

$$\text{spec}_K(A) \ .$$

Recall from the Nullstellensatz (AG. 3. 8) that there is a canonical bijection $x \longmapsto \ker(e_x)$

$$X = \text{spec}_K(A) \ \text{ onto } \ \text{Hom}_{K\text{-alg}}(A, K) \ .$$

Moreover we adopt the functional notation

$$f(x) = e_x(f) \qquad\qquad (x \in X, \ f \in A) \ .$$

The resulting function $f : X \longrightarrow K$ (for $f \in A$) determines f modulo the nil radical of A (see (AG. 3. 8)) so, if A is reduced, we can thus identify A with a ring of K-valued functions on X.

We now introduce the K-space $(X, \widetilde{A})$, where $\widetilde{A}$ is the sheaf associated to the presheaf $U \longmapsto A[S(U)^{-1}]$. Here, for U open in X, S(U) is the set of $f \in A$ vanishing nowhere on U. It is easy to see that the stalk of $\widetilde{A}$ at $x \in X$ is the local ring A_x, so that $(X, \widetilde{A})$ is a

K-space. The symbol $\mathrm{spec}_K(A)$ will be used both for X and for the K-space $(X, \tilde{A})$. A K-space isomorphic to one of this type will be called an affine K-scheme.

In case A is an integral domain with field of fractions L then the A_x's are subrings of L and we can describe $\tilde{A}$ directly by: $\tilde{A}(U) = \bigcap_{x \in U} A_x$.

A homomorphism $\alpha : A \longrightarrow B$ of affine K-algebras induces a continuous function $\alpha' : Y \longrightarrow X$, where $Y = \mathrm{spec}_K(B)$. If $U \subset X$ and $V \subset Y$ are open and $\alpha'(V) \subset U$ then $\alpha(S(U)) \subset S(V)$ so there is a natural homomorphism $A[S(U)^{-1}] \longrightarrow B[S(V)^{-1}]$. These induce a morphism on the associated K-spaces $(Y, \tilde{B}) \longrightarrow (X, \tilde{A})$, thus making $A \longmapsto \mathrm{spec}_K(A)$ a contravariant functor from affine K-algebras to K-spaces.

(5.3) K-schemes and prevarieties. By a K-scheme we shall understand a K-space $(X, \mathcal{O}_X)$ such that X has a finite covering by open sets U such that $(U, \mathcal{O}_X|U)$ is an affine K-scheme. Note that X is thus a noetherian space. If $(X, \mathcal{O}_X)$ is reduced, i.e. if, for each $x \in X$, the local ring $\mathcal{O}_{X,x}$ has no nilpotent elements $\neq 0$, then we call $(X, \mathcal{O}_X)$ a prevariety. In case $X = \mathrm{spec}_K(A)$ is affine then X is a prevariety if and only if A is reduced, in which case we call $\mathrm{spec}_K(A)$ an affine variety.

CAUTION. (1) A K-scheme is not a scheme in the usual sense. This would be the case if, in place of $\mathrm{spec}_K(A) = \max(A)$ we had used all of $\mathrm{spec}(A)$ (in the affine case). With this modification the definition of

K-scheme above corresponds to the notion of a "scheme of finite type over K" (or over spec(K)).

(2) Our notion of prevariety is essentially the same as that of Mumford (Chapter I) except that we have not required X to be irreducible.

Consider the affine K-scheme $\operatorname{spec}_K(K)$, consisting of one point with structure sheaf K. A morphism $\operatorname{spec}_K(K) \longrightarrow X$ just picks a point $x \in X$ together with compatible K-algebra homomorphisms $\mathcal{O}_X(U) \longrightarrow K$ for all neighborhoods U of x. The latter correspond to a K-algebra homomorphism $\mathcal{O}_x \longrightarrow K$, and there is only one such: $f \longmapsto f(x)$. Thus x determines the morphism, i.e. we can identity $\operatorname{Mor}_{K\text{-sch.}}(\operatorname{spec}_K(K), X)$ with X (as sets).

(5.4) THEOREM. Let $X = \operatorname{spec}_K(A)$ be an affine K-scheme and let Y be any K-scheme. The natural map $A \longrightarrow \tilde{A}(X)$ is an isomorphism, and the map

$$\operatorname{Mor}_{K\text{-sch.}}(Y, X) \longrightarrow \operatorname{Mor}_{K\text{-alg.}}(A, \mathcal{O}_Y(Y))$$

is bijective. In particular $A \longmapsto \operatorname{spec}_K(A)$ is a contravariant equivalence from the category of affine K-algebras to the category of affine K-schemes.

For this equivalence, see [M, Ch. II, §§1-2].

(5 5) Quasi-coherent modules [M, Ch. III, §§1-2]. Let A be an affine K-algebra. If M is an A-module then the

sheaf $\tilde{M}$ on $\mathrm{spec}_K(A)$ associated with the presheaf $U \mapsto A[S(U)^{-1}] \otimes_A M$ is a sheaf of $\tilde{A}$-modules, or, simply, an $\tilde{A}$-module. Moreover $M \mapsto \tilde{M}$ is an exact functor from A-modules to $\tilde{A}$-modules.

If Y is a K-scheme we say that an $\mathcal{O}_Y$-module (or sheaf of $\mathcal{O}_Y$-modules) F is quasi-coherent if Y can be covered by affine K-schemes $U = \mathrm{spec}_K(A)$ on which $F|U$ is isomorphic to some $\tilde{M}$ as above. If the U's can be chosen so that each M is a finitely generated (resp., free) A-module then we say F is coherent (resp., locally free).

If F is coherent then it follows easily from (AG. 3. 5) that

$$\mathrm{supp}(F) = \{y \in Y \mid F_y \neq 0\}$$

is closed. Moreover (AG. 3. 5) implies that, for F coherent, $\{y \in Y \mid F_y$ is a free $\mathcal{O}_y$-module$\}$ is open.

THEOREM. Let $X = \mathrm{spec}_K(A)$ be an affine K-scheme, and let $f \in A$. For any A-module M the natural map $M_f \to \tilde{M}(X_f)$ is an isomorphism. In particular

$$(\mathrm{spec}_K(A_f), \tilde{A}_f) \to (X_f, \tilde{A}|X_f)$$

is an isomorphism of K-schemes. Moreover $M \mapsto \tilde{M}$ is an equivalence from the category of A-modules to the category of quasi-coherent $\tilde{A}$-modules. $\tilde{M}$ is coherent if and only if M is finitely generated. In this case $\tilde{M}$ is locally free if and only if M is a projective A-module.

(5.6) Closed immersions [M, Ch. II, §5]. A morphism $\alpha : Y \longrightarrow X$ of K-schemes is called a closed immersion if α maps Y homeomorphically onto a closed subspace of X and if the local homomorphisms $\mathcal{O}_{X,\alpha(y)} \longrightarrow \mathcal{O}_{Y,y}$ are surjective for each $y \in Y$.

If $\mathcal{J}$ is a quasi-coherent sheaf of ideals in $\mathcal{O}_X$, and if $Y = \text{supp}(\mathcal{O}_X/\mathcal{J})$ then Y is closed and $\mathcal{O}_X/\mathcal{J}$ is the "extension by zeros" of a sheaf $\mathcal{O}_Y$ on X for which there is a natural closed immersion $(Y, \mathcal{O}_Y) \longrightarrow (X, \mathcal{O}_X)$. We then call Y the closed subscheme of X defined by $\mathcal{J}$.

In case $X = \text{spec}_K(A)$ is affine every such $\mathcal{J}$ is of the form $\tilde{I}$ for some ideal I in A, and Y is just the affine subscheme

$$\text{spec}_K(A/I) \hookrightarrow \text{spec}_K(A) \quad .$$

THEOREM. The map $I \longmapsto \text{spec}_K(A/I)$ is a bijection from the ideals of A to the set of closed subschemes of $\text{spec}_K(A)$. In particular every closed subscheme is affine.

An open immersion is a morphism isomorphic to one of the form $(U, \mathcal{O}_X|U) \longrightarrow (X, \mathcal{O}_X)$ where X is a K-scheme and U is an open subset. We call $(U, \mathcal{O}_X|U)$ an open subscheme of $(X, \mathcal{O}_X)$. A closed subscheme of an open subscheme is called a locally closed subscheme.

§6. PRODUCTS; VARIETIES

(6.1) Products exist [M, Ch. I, §6]. Let X and Y be K-schemes. The product $X \times Y$ is characterized by the property that morphisms from a K-scheme Z to $X \times Y$ are pairs of morphisms to the two factors. Applying this to $Z = \mathrm{spec}_K(K)$ we find that the underlying set of $X \times Y$ is the usual cartesian product. From (AG.5.4) it follows immediately that the product of affine K-schemes $\mathrm{spec}_K(A)$ and $\mathrm{spec}_K(B)$ exists and equals

$$\mathrm{spec}_K(A \otimes_K B) .$$

This is because $\otimes_K$ is the coproduct in the category of affine K-algebras.

More generally:

THEOREM. The product $X \times Y$ exists and the two projections are open maps. If $U \subset X$ and $V \subset Y$ are open subschemes then $U \times V \longrightarrow X \times Y$ is an open immersion.

From this theorem and the description of the product in the affine case it is easy to show that the local ring of $X \times Y$ at (x, y) is the localization of $\mathcal{O}_x \otimes_K \mathcal{O}_y$ at $\underline{m}_x \otimes \mathcal{O}_y + \mathcal{O}_x \otimes \underline{m}_y$.

(6.2) Varieties. Let X be a K-scheme. The pair $(1_X, 1_X)$ defines a diagonal morphism $d : X \longrightarrow X \times X$, and one says X is separated if d is a closed immersion.

A separated prevariety is called an (algebraic) variety.

For example:

(a) An affine variety is a variety.

(b) A locally closed sub prevariety of a variety is a variety.

(c) A product of two varieties is a variety.

Let $\alpha, \beta : Y \longrightarrow X$ be two morphisms of K-schemes, and let

$$\Gamma_{\alpha,\beta} = \{y \in Y \mid \alpha(y) = \beta(y)\} .$$

The pair (α, β) defines a morphism $\gamma : Y \longrightarrow X \times X$ and $\Gamma_{\alpha,\beta} = \gamma^{-1}(d(X))$, clearly. Hence, if X is separated then $\Gamma_{\alpha,\beta}$ is closed. In particular, if α and β coincide on a dense set then they coincide at all points.

Applying the above remarks to $\alpha \circ pr_Y, pr_X : Y \times X \longrightarrow X$ we see also that the graph of α is closed if X is separated.

(6.3) Regular functions and subvarieties. Let $(X, \mathcal{O}_X)$ be an algebraic variety. If U is open in X we shall write

$$K[U] \text{ in place of } \mathcal{O}_X(U) .$$

The elements f of $K[U]$ can be identified with K-valued functions on U, sometimes called regular functions. Moreover $res^U_V : K[U] \longrightarrow K[V]$ then corresponds to restriction of functions. For $x \in U$ the map $f \longmapsto f(x) = e_x(f)$ is the composite of $K[U] \longrightarrow \mathcal{O}_x$ with the map of $\mathcal{O}_x$ to its residue class field $K(x) = K$.

If U is open in X then $(U, \mathcal{O}_X|U)$ is a variety, called an open subvariety of X. In case U is affine we have $U = \mathrm{spec}_K(K[U])$.

If Y is a closed subspace of X then there is a unique reduced subscheme $(Y, \mathcal{O}_Y)$ of X. $\mathcal{O}_Y$ is the sheaf associated to the presheaf $(U \cap Y) \longmapsto K[U]/I_U(Y)$, where $I_U(Y)$ is the ideal of all functions on U vanishing on $Y \cap U$. (Thus, in case U is affine, $Y \cap U$ is just $\mathrm{spec}_K(K[U]/I_U(Y))$.) In this way we can canonically regard a closed subspace Y of X as a closed subvariety.

A locally closed subvariety is then just a closed subvariety of an open subvariety.

Let $\alpha : Y \longrightarrow X$ be a morphism of varieties. Then α is a continuous function and, whenever $U \subset X$ and $V \subset Y$ are open and $\alpha(V) \subset U$, there is a comorphism

$$\alpha_V^U : K[U] \longrightarrow K[V]$$

such that

$$\alpha_V^U(f)(y) = f(\alpha(y)), \quad \text{or}$$

$$\alpha_V^U(f) = f \circ \alpha$$

for $f \in K[U]$ and $y \in V$. Since we are dealing here with rings of functions it follows that α (as a map of spaces) determines the sheaf homomorphisms α_V^U. We shall denote the latter simply by α_0 (for all U and V) and call α_0 the comorphism(s) of α.

Note that, for any set function $\alpha : Y \longrightarrow X$, the comorphisms α_0 can be defined as above on the rings of all K-valued functions. The condition that α be a morphism of varieties then can be reformulated as follows: (i) α is continuous, and (ii) if $U \subset X$ and $V \subset Y$ are open and if $\alpha(V) \subset U$ then $\alpha_0 K[U] \subset K[V]$.

(6.4) The local rings on a variety. Consider the local ring $\mathcal{O}_x$ of a point x on a variety V. It reflects the "local properties" of V near x. For example, by passing to a neighborhood of x we may assume $V = \mathrm{spec}_K(A)$, an affine variety. Then $\mathcal{O}_x$ is the local ring of A at the maximal ideal $\underline{m} = \ker(e_x)$, and it follows from properties of localization that the prime ideals of $\mathcal{O}_x$ correspond bijectively to those of A contained in $\underline{m}$, i.e. to the irreducible subvarieties of V passing through x. We see thus that $\dim_x V$ (in the sense of (AG.1.4)) is the Krull dimension of $\mathcal{O}_x$.

Note further that the irreducible components of V containing x correspond to the minimal primes of $\mathcal{O}_x$. Thus x lies on a unique irreducible component if and only if $\mathcal{O}_x$ is an integral domain.

§7. PROJECTIVE AND COMPLETE VARIETIES

(7.1) The affine spaces V and K^n. Let V be a finite dimensional vector space (over K). Then the symmetric algebra $A = S_K(V^*)$ on the dual of V is the (graded) algebra of "polynomial functions" on V, generated by the linear functions V^* in degree one. The universal property of the symmetric algebra implies that

$$\mathrm{Hom}_{K\text{-alg}}(S_K(V^*), K) = \mathrm{Hom}_{K\text{-mod}}(V^*, K) = (V^*)^* = V .$$

In this way we can identify V with the points of the affine variety $\mathrm{spec}_K(A)$.

In case $V = K^n$ we have $A = K[T_1, \ldots, T_n]$, the polynomial ring in n variables, where $T_i(t) = t_i$ for $t = (t_1, \ldots, t_n) \in K^n$.

(7.2) <u>The projective spaces $\underline{P}(V)$ and $\mathbb{P}_n$</u> [M, Ch. I, §5]. The set of lines in V can be given the structure of a variety, denoted $\underline{P}(V)$, and called the projective space on V. We also write $\mathbb{P}_n = \underline{P}(K^{n+1})$.

It is convenient to describe the set $\underline{P}(V)$ as the set of equivalence classes, $[x]$, of non-zero vectors $x \in V$, where $[x] = [y]$ means $y = tx$ for some $t \in K^*$. Let $\pi : V - \{0\} \longrightarrow \underline{P}(V)$ denote the projection, $\pi(x) = [x]$. We topologize $\underline{P}(V)$ so that π is continuous and open, where $V - \{0\}$ is viewed as an open subvariety of V. Thus $U \subset \underline{P}(V)$ is open if and only if $\pi^{-1}(U)$ is open.

Let $A = S_K(V^*)$ as above, and let S be the multiplicative set of all homogeneous elements $\neq 0$ in A. Then $A[S^{-1}]$ is still a graded ring whose degree zero term is

$$L = \left\{ f/g \,\middle|\, \begin{array}{l} f \text{ and } g \text{ are homogeneous of the same} \\ \text{degree in } A \text{ and } g \neq 0 \end{array} \right\} .$$

If $[x] \in \underline{P}(V)$ we shall write

$$\mathcal{O}_{[x]} = \{f/g \in L \mid g(x) \neq 0\} .$$

First note that the condition $g(x) \neq 0$ depends only on $[x]$, for if g is of degree d we have $g(tx) = t^d g(x)$ for $t \in K^*$. This shows further that $f(x)/g(x)$ depends only on $[x]$ because f also has degree d. Thus a given $f/g \in L$ can be viewed as a function on the set of $[x] \in \underline{P}(V)$ for which $g(x) \neq 0$. Moreover $\mathcal{O}_{[x]}$ is the local ring of all such functions defined at $[x]$.

If U is open in $\underline{P}(V)$ we put

$$\mathcal{O}_{\underline{P}(V)}(U) = \bigcap_{[x] \in U} \mathcal{O}_{[x]}$$

and define restriction maps to be inclusions whenever $U' \subset U$. This is a sheaf on $\underline{P}(V)$, and $(\underline{P}(V), \mathcal{O}_{\underline{P}(V)})$ is the algebraic variety promised above.

Suppose $V = K^{n+1}$ so that $A = K[T_0, T_1, \ldots, T_n]$. Here we have $T_i(t) = t_i$ for $t = (t_0, \ldots, t_n) \in K^{n+1}$. Even though T_i is not a function on $\mathbb{P}_n = \underline{P}(K^{n+1})$ the set $\mathbb{P}_{n,T_i} = \{[t] \in \mathbb{P}_n \mid T_i(t) \neq 0\}$ still makes sense. Moreover there is a bijection $\mathbb{P}_{n,T_i} \longrightarrow K^n$ sending $[t_0, \ldots, t_n]$ to $(\frac{t_0}{t_i}, \ldots, \frac{\hat{t}_i}{t_i}, \ldots, \frac{t_n}{t_i}) = (s_1, \ldots, s_n)$. It is easily shown that this is an isomorphism from the open subvariety

$\mathbb{P}_{n,T_i}$ of $\mathbb{P}_n$ to the affine space K^n. Since the $\mathbb{P}_{n,T_i}$ $(0 \leqq i \leqq n)$ cover $\mathbb{P}_n$ this shows why $\mathbb{P}_n$ is at least a prevariety.

Consider the open set U in K^{n+1} of all $(t_0, \ldots, t_n)$ such that $t_0 \neq 0$. Then we have an isomorphism of varieties

$$K^* \times K^n \longrightarrow U$$

$$(s_0, s_1, \ldots, s_n) \longmapsto s_0 \cdot (1, s_1, \ldots, s_n) .$$

The composition of this with $U \longrightarrow \mathbb{P}_n$ is just projection on the factor K^n followed by the inverse of the isomorphism $\mathbb{P}_{n,T_0} \longrightarrow K^n$ constructed above. In this way we see that $V - \{0\} \longrightarrow \underline{P}(V)$ looks, locally, like a projection from a cartesian product as above.

(7.3) Projective varieties. A projective variety is one isomorphic to a closed subvariety of a projective space. A quasi-projective variety is an open subvariety of a projective variety. Since affine spaces are open subvarieties of projective spaces it follows that all affine varieties are quasi-projective.

Products of projective varieties are projective. To see this it suffices to show that each $\mathbb{P}_n \times \mathbb{P}_m$ is projective. For this, in turn, one has the explicit closed immersion

$$\mathbb{P}_n \times \mathbb{P}_m \longrightarrow \mathbb{P}_{(n+1)(m+1)-1} = \mathbb{P}_{nm+n+m}$$

defined by:

$$([x_i], [y_j]) \longmapsto ([x_i y_j]) .$$

(7.4) Complete varieties [M, Ch. I, §9]. A variety V is complete if, for any variety X, the projection $pr_X : X \times V \longrightarrow X$ is a closed map. (In the category of Hausdorff topological spaces the analogous property characterizes compact spaces. Thus "complete" for varieties is the analogue of "compact" for topological spaces.)

It follows immediately from the definition that a closed subvariety of a complete variety is complete, and that a product of complete varieties is complete.

Let $\alpha : V \longrightarrow X$ be a morphism of varieties with V complete. Then the graph $\Gamma_\alpha \subset V \times X$ is closed, so its projection into X, which is $\alpha(V)$, is closed in X. If α is surjective then it follows directly from the definition that X is also complete. Applying this to $\alpha(V)$ we conclude that the image of a morphism from a complete variety is closed and complete.

The affine line K is an open but not closed subset of the projective line $\mathbb{P}_1$, so K is not complete. The only other closed subsets of K are the finite ones, so a connected complete subvariety of K consists of a single point.

If V is a connected complete variety then

$K[V] = K$, i.e. every regular function f on V is constant. This follows from the last paragraph because $f(V)$ is a connected complete subvariety of K.

Combining the observations above we conclude easily that a morphism from a connected complete variety into an affine variety must be constant. For the image, being closed, is affine as well as complete. But an affine variety with only constant regular functions is a point.

That complete varieties exist in abundance follows from the:

THEOREM. Projective varieties are complete.

§8. RATIONAL FUNCTIONS; DOMINANT MORPHISMS

(8.1) Rational functions. Let V be an algebraic variety. The open dense sets U in V form an inverse system, under inclusion, so their rings of functions, $K[U]$, form an inductive system. The inductive limit

$$K(V) = \operatorname*{ind.lim.}_{\substack{U \text{ open} \\ \text{dense in } V}} K[U]$$

is called the ring of rational functions on V. The following properties are easily established.

(a) If U is open dense in V then $K[U] \longrightarrow K(V)$ is injective; we shall regard it as an inclusion. Moreover $K(U) = K(V)$.

(b) If $f \in K(V)$ we say f is regular at x if

$f \in K[U]$ for some neighborhood U of x (which is open dense). The set of all such x is then a dense open set U_0 called the domain of definition of f. U_0 is the largest dense open set for which $f \in K[U_0]$.

(c) Suppose V is irreducible. Then each dense open U is irreducible also. If $f \in K[U]$ is not zero then $U_f = \{x \in U \mid f(x) \neq 0\}$ is non-empty and open, hence dense (by irreducibility), and $1/f \in K[U_f]$. It follows that $K(V)$ is a field, called the <u>function field</u> of V.

(d) In general, let $V_1, \ldots, V_n$ be the irreducible components of V. It follows from (AG.1.2) that there is a dense open U such that the $U_i = U \cap V_i$ $(1 \leqq i \leqq n)$ are open in V and pairwise disjoint. It follows, using (a) and (c) above, that

$$K(V) = K(U) = \prod K(U_i) = \prod K(V_i) \quad ,$$

the product of the function fields of the irreducible components of V.

(e) If $V = \mathrm{spec}_K(A)$ is affine, where $A = K[V]$, then $K(V)$ is just the full ring of fractions of A.

(8.2) <u>Dominant morphisms</u>. The ring $K(V)$ of rational functions on V is not functorial. For if $\alpha : V \longrightarrow W$ is a morphism of varieties, and if U is open dense in W, then $\alpha^{-1}(U)$ need not be dense in V. But if this is always true, and if $\overline{\alpha(V)} = W$, we say α is <u>dominant</u>. Such an α induces an <u>injective</u> comorphism $\alpha_0 : K(W) \longrightarrow K(V)$.

If V, and therefore also W, are irreducible then this makes $K(V)$ a field extension of $K(W)$. We then say that α is <u>separable</u> if this extension is separable. Similarly we call α <u>purely inseparable</u> if $K(V)$ is a purely inseparable algebraic extension, and α is said to be <u>birational</u> if $K(V) = \alpha_0 K(W)$.

The local rings of V and W can be viewed as subrings of $K(V)$ and of $K(W)$, respectively, and α_0 induces an injection $\alpha_0 : \mathcal{O}_x \longrightarrow \mathcal{O}_{\alpha(x)}$ for $x \in V$. Identifying $K(W)$ with $\alpha_0 K(W)$ we see that the sheaf morphism corresponding to α is just induced by the inclusions of local rings in $K(V)$.

In general, if V is not irreducible but $\overline{\alpha(V)} = W$, then it is easy to see that $\alpha : V \longrightarrow W$ is dominant if and only if, for each irreducible component V' of V, $\overline{\alpha(V')} = W'$ is an irreducible component of W. We then say that α is separable (purely inseparable, birational, ...) if, for each such V', the induced morphism $V' \longrightarrow W'$ (which is dominant) has the corresponding property.

If V' is an irreducible component of V then $\overline{\alpha(V')} = W'$ is an irreducible subvariety of W, and it will be an irreducible component of W provided it contains a non-empty open set in W. Since V' contains such an open set in V this remark shows that: <u>If</u> α <u>is surjective and open then</u> α <u>is dominant</u>.

§9. DIMENSION [M, Ch. I, §7]

(9.1) <u>The dimension of a variety</u> V. We have the combinatorial dimension of V, denoted dim V, introduced in (AG.1.4). It is the supremum of the dimensions of the irreducible components of V. In case V is irreducible we have the function field K(V), and the basic fact is that, in this case,

$$\dim V = \text{tr.deg.}_K K(V) .$$

(9.2) <u>Hypersurfaces</u>. Let V be an irreducible variety and let $f \in K[V]$ be a non-constant function whose set $Z(f) = \{x \in V \mid f(x) = 0\}$ of zeros is not empty. Then the dimension of each irreducible component of Z(f) is dim V - 1.

(9.3) <u>Products</u>. The dimension of $V \times W$ is dim V + dim W.

§10. IMAGE AND FIBRES OF A MORPHISM [M, Ch. I, §8]

(10.1) <u>The basic theorem</u>. Let $\alpha : X \longrightarrow Y$ be a morphism of varieties. The <u>fibre</u> of α over $y \in Y$ is the subvariety $\alpha^{-1}(\{y\})$ of X. To study the non-empty fibres there is no harm in shrinking Y to the closure of the <u>image</u>, $\alpha(X)$, i.e. we may as well assume $\alpha(X)$ is dense in Y. If X (and Y) are irreducible this means that α is dominant.

THEOREM. <u>Let</u> $\alpha : X \longrightarrow Y$ <u>be a dominant morphism of</u>

irreducible varieties, and put $r = \dim X - \dim Y$. *Let* W *be an irreducible closed subvariety of* Y *and let* Z *be an irreducible component of* $\alpha^{-1}(W)$.

(1) *If* Z *dominates* W *then* $\dim Z \geqq \dim W + r$. *In particular, if* $W = \{y\}$, *then* $\dim Z \geqq r$.

(2) *There is an open dense* $U \subset Y$ *(depending only on* α) *such that*

(i) $U \subset \alpha(X)$, *and*

(ii) *If* $Z \cap \alpha^{-1}(U) \neq \phi$ *then*

$$\dim Z = \dim W + r \quad .$$

In particular, if $W = \{y\} \subset U$ *then* $\dim Z = r$.

(10.2) COROLLARY (Chevalley). *Let* $\alpha : X \longrightarrow Y$ *be any morphism of varieties. Then the image of any constructible set is constructible. In particular* $\alpha(X)$ *contains a dense open subset of* $\overline{\alpha(X)}$.

The last assertion follows from the first using (AG.1.3). The proof of the first assertion can be reduced easily to the case of a dominant morphism of irreducible varieties. Then it is deduced, by induction on $\dim Y$, from part (2)(i) of the theorem.

(10.3) COROLLARY. *Let* $\alpha : X \longrightarrow Y$ *be a morphism of varieties. If* $x \in X$ *let* $e(x)$ *be the maximum dimension of an irreducible component, containing* x, *of the fibre of*

α through x (i.e. of $\alpha^{-1}(\alpha(x))$). Then $x \mapsto e(x)$ is upper semi-continuous, i.e. the sets $\{x \in X \mid e(x) \geqq n\}$ are closed for each integer n.

§11. k-STRUCTURES ON K-SCHEMES

This and the following two sections contain the basic notions required here for the treatment of rationality questions. Recall that k denotes a subfield of the algebraically closed field K.

(11.1) k-structures on vector spaces. A k-structure on a (not necessarily finite dimensional) vector space V (over K) is a k-module $V_k \subset V$ such that the homomorphism $K \otimes_k V_k \longrightarrow V$, induced by the inclusion, is an isomorphism. The surjectivity means that V_k spans V (over K), and the injectivity means that elements of V_k linearly independent over k are also linearly independent over K. The elements of V_k are said to be rational over k.

If U is a subspace of V we put $U_k = U \cap V_k$, and we say U is defined (or rational) over k if U_k is a k-structure on U. This is equivalent to U_k spanning U.

If W = V/U we write W_k for the projection of V_k into W, and we say W is defined over k if this is a k-structure on W. This happens if and only if U is defined over k, or if and only if elements of W_k linearly independent over k are linearly independent over K.

Let $f : V \longrightarrow W$ be a K-linear map of vector spaces with k-structures. We say that f is <u>defined over</u> k, or that f is a k-<u>morphism</u> if $f(V_k) \subset W_k$. The k-morphisms from V to W form a k-submodule

$$\mathrm{Hom}_K(V, W)_k \subset \mathrm{Hom}_K(V, W) ,$$

and this is even a k-structure provided that W is finite dimensional. In particular, when $W = K$, we have a k-structure on the dual V^* of V.

Similarly $V_k \otimes_k W_k$ is a k-structure on $V \otimes_K W$, and there are natural k-structures on the exterior and symmetric algebras of V.

(11.2) k-<u>structures on</u> K-<u>algebras</u>. A k-structure on a K-algebra A is a k-structure A_k which is a k-subalgebra.

If J is an ideal in A then J is defined over k if and only if $J_k (= J \cap A_k)$ generates J as an ideal. This is easily seen.

If S is a multiplicative set in A_k then $A_k[S^{-1}]$ is easily seen to be a k-structure on $A[S^{-1}]$.

If B is another K-algebra with k-structure then we write

$$\mathrm{Mor}_{K\text{-alg}}(A, B)_k$$

for the K-algebra homomorphisms defined over k. The

map $f \mapsto 1_K \otimes f$ is a bijection from $\mathrm{Mor}_{k\text{-alg}}(A_k, B_k)$ to this set.

(11. 3) k-<u>structures on</u> K-<u>schemes</u>. A k-<u>structure</u> on a K-scheme $(X, \mathcal{O}_X)$ consists of

(1) a k-topology $k\text{-top}(X) \subset \mathrm{top}(X)$,

and

(2) a k-structure on $\mathcal{O}_X(U)$ for each k-open U, such that the restriction homomorphisms are defined over k.

(Condition (2) just says that the restriction of $\mathcal{O}_X$ to k-top(X) is a sheaf of K-algebras-with-k-structures.) It is further required that, on k-open affine subschemes, the induced k-structure be of the following type:

A k-structure on an affine K-scheme $X = \mathrm{spec}_K(A)$ is one defined by a k-structure A_k on A as follows: A set is k-<u>closed</u> if it is of the form supp(A/J) for some ideal J defined over k. For example, if $f \in A_k$ then X_f is k-open, and any k-open set is covered by a finite number of these. Moreover $A_f = \tilde{A}(X_f)$ has the k-structure $(A_k)_f$ (see (11. 2)).

If U is k-open we can cover U by X_{f_i}'s for a family of $f_i \in A_k$. Moreover $X_{f_i} \cap X_{f_j} = X_{f_i f_j}$. By the sheaf axiom we have an exact sequence

$$\tilde{A}(U) \longrightarrow \prod_i \tilde{A}(X_{f_i}) \underset{\beta}{\overset{\alpha}{\rightrightarrows}} \prod_{i,j} \tilde{A}(X_{f_i f_j}) .$$

Therefore $\tilde{A}(U)$ acquires a natural k-structure as the kernel of

$$\prod_i A_{f_i} \xrightarrow{\alpha-\beta} \prod A_{f_i f_j} ,$$

which is a k-morphism of vector spaces with k-structures.

It is not difficult to check that this k-structure on $\widetilde{A}(U)$ is well defined, and that the above construction satisfies the requirements of (1) and (2) above.

Note that we recover A_k as the k-structure on $\widetilde{A}(X)$.

Let $\alpha : X \longrightarrow Y$ be a morphism of K-schemes with k-structures. We say α is <u>defined over</u> k or that α is a k-<u>morphism</u> if (i) α is continuous relative to the k-topologies, and (ii) if $U \subset Y$ and $V \subset X$ are k-open such that $\alpha(V) \subset U$ then $\alpha_V^U : \mathcal{O}_Y(U) \longrightarrow \mathcal{O}_X(V)$ is defined over k. The set of morphisms defined over k will be denoted

$$\mathrm{Mor}(X, Y)_k .$$

A homomorphism $\alpha_0 : B \longrightarrow A$ of K-algebras with k-structures induces a morphism $\alpha : \mathrm{spec}_K(A) \longrightarrow \mathrm{spec}_K(B)$ and it is clear that α is defined over k if and only if α_0 is defined over k. Thus the category of affine K-schemes with k-structures, and k-morphisms, is contravariantly equivalent to the category of affine K-algebras with k-structures, and k-morphisms, and the latter is clearly equivalent to the category of affine k-algebras.

(11.4) Subschemes defined over k. Let $(X, \mathcal{O}_X)$ be a K-scheme with k-structure. If $U \subset X$ is k-open then $(U, \mathcal{O}_X|U)$ has an induced k-structure.

Suppose $(Z, \mathcal{O}_Z)$ is a closed subscheme of X. We say it is defined over k if (i) Z is k-closed, and (ii) the sheaf $\mathcal{J}$ of ideals such that $\mathcal{O}_X/\mathcal{J}$ is the extension by zeros of $\mathcal{O}_Z$ is defined over k, i.e. $\mathcal{J}(U) \subset \mathcal{O}_X(U)$ is defined over k for all k-open U. Condition (ii) is equivalent to the condition that, for all k-open affine U, the kernel $(\mathcal{J}(U))$ of the epimorphism of affine rings, $\mathcal{O}_X(U) \longrightarrow \mathcal{O}_Z(U \cap Z)$, is defined over k. Thus we see that $(Z, \mathcal{O}_Z)$ acquires a unique k-structure such that the closed immersion $Z \longrightarrow X$ is defined over k.

It further follows easily that $(Z, \mathcal{O}_Z)$ is defined over k if and only if, for some covering of X by k-open affine U's, $(Z \cap U, \mathcal{O}_Z | Z \cap U)$ is defined over k in $(U, \mathcal{O}_X | U)$ for each U.

§12. k-STRUCTURES ON VARIETIES

(12.1) Affine k-varieties. A variety V with a k-structure will be called a k-variety. Let $V = \mathrm{spec}_K(A)$ be an affine k-variety with k-structure defined by $A_k = k[V]$ in $A = K[V]$.

Let $Z = \mathrm{spec}_K(A/J)$ be a closed subvariety of V, where J is the ideal of all functions vanishing on Z. Then we have an exact sequence

$$0 \longrightarrow J_k \longrightarrow k[V] \longrightarrow k[Z] \longrightarrow 0,$$

where $J_k = J \cap k[V]$ and where $k[Z]$ is the restriction to Z of $k[V]$. Thus $k[Z]$ is a reduced affine k-algebra, and we denote its full ring of fractions by $k(Z)$. We have $K \otimes_k k[Z] = K[V]/J_k \cdot K[V]$ so that the kernel of the epimorphism $K \otimes_k k[Z] \longrightarrow K[Z]$ is $J/J_k \cdot K[V]$.

Now Z is k-closed when it is the set of zeros of some ideal defined over k. It follows that

$$Z \text{ is k-closed} \Longleftrightarrow J = \sqrt{J_k \cdot K[V]} \ .$$

In this case then the kernel above is the nil radical of $K \otimes_k k[Z]$.

We conclude therefore that the following conditions on a k-closed Z are equivalent:

(a) Z is defined (as a subvariety) over k, i.e. $J = J_k \cdot K[V]$.

(b) $k[Z]$ and K are linearly disjoint over k in $K[Z]$.

(c) $K \otimes_k k[Z]$ is reduced.

(d) $K \otimes_k k(Z)$ is reduced.

The equivalence of (c) and (d) follows from (AG. 3. 3) because $K \otimes_k k(Z)$ is a ring of fractions of $K \otimes_k k[Z]$ with respect to a multiplicative set of non-divisors of zero.

We can look at these conditions also from the following point of view. Suppose we are given a reduced affine k-algebra B_k. Then B_k is a k-structure on

$B = K \otimes_k B_k$ and hence defines one on the affine K-scheme $Z = \mathrm{spec}_K(B)$. Z is a variety if and only if B is reduced. Thus we can think of k-closed subsets of V as the underlying spaces of closed subschemes of V which are defined over k, but not necessarily as subvarieties defined over k.

Suppose $\mathrm{char}(k) = p > 0$. Then the zeros of $f \in A$ and of f^p coincide. If $f \in k^{1/p}[V]$ then $f^p \in k[V]$. Thus any $k^{1/p}$-closed set is also k-closed. It follows that the k-topology coincides with the $k^{p^{-\infty}}$-topology.

(12.2) Subvarieties defined over k. Let V be any (not necessarily affine) k-variety, and let Z be a k-closed subvariety. If U is k-open in V we write $k[Z \cap U]$ for the restriction to $Z \cap U$ of $k[U]$. Passing to the inductive limit over k-open U for which $Z \cap U$ is dense in Z we obtain the ring $k(Z)$ of "rational functions on Z defined over k." In case V is affine this notation is consistent with that introduced in (12.1) above (cf. (AG. 8.1)). It follows from (AG. 11.4) and (12.1) that Z is defined over k if and only if $K \otimes_k k(Z)$ is reduced.

Now $k(Z)$ is the product of a finite number of finitely generated field extensions of k. Using the results of (AG. 2.2) we therefore conclude that the following conditions are equivalent:

(a) Z is defined over k.

(b) $K \otimes_k k(Z)$ is reduced.

(c) $k^{p^{-\infty}} \otimes_k k(Z)$ is reduced.

(d) Each factor of $k(Z)$ is a separable field extension of k.

In particular we see that:

<u>A</u> k-<u>closed subvariety is defined over</u> $k^{p^{-\infty}}$, <u>and hence over</u> k <u>if</u> k <u>is perfect</u>.

(12.3) <u>Irreducible components are defined over</u> k_s. For consider the irreducible components of a k-variety V. To show that each one is defined over k_s there is no loss in assuming that $k = k_s$. It suffices further to check this on a covering of V by k-open affine subvarieties, so we may assume V is affine. Then we must show that, if $P_1, \ldots, P_n$ are the minimal primes of $k[V]$, each $P_i \cdot K[V]$ is still a prime ideal. Since k is separably closed it follows from (AG. 2.1) that $K[V]/(P_i \cdot K[V])(= K \otimes_k (k[V]/P_i))$ has a unique minimal prime, so it remains to be shown that $K \otimes_k (k[V]/P_i)$ is reduced.

We have $k[V] \subset \prod (k[V]/P_i)$, because $k[V]$ is reduced, and both of these rings have the same full ring of fractions, $k(V)$. Since $K \otimes_k k(V) = K(V)$ is reduced it follows, as claimed, that each $K \otimes_k (k[V]/P_i)$ is reduced.

§13. SEPARABLE POINTS

(13.1) <u>The functor of points</u>. Let V be a k-variety. For any affine K-algebra B we shall write

$$V(B) = \mathrm{Mor}_{K\text{-sch.}}(\mathrm{spec}_K(B),\ V) \ .$$

If B has a k-structure B_k we also write $V(B_k) = V(B)_k$, the set of morphisms as above which are defined over k.

If $V = \mathrm{spec}_K(A)$ is affine then

$$V(B) = \mathrm{Mor}_{K\text{-alg.}}(A,\ B) = \mathrm{Mor}_{k\text{-alg}}(A_k,\ B) \ ,$$

and $V(B_k) = \mathrm{Mor}_{k\text{-alg}}(A_k,\ B_k)$. From these descriptions it is clear that one can extend the definitions to any K-algebra B, not necessarily affine. (For example B might be a large field extension of K.) In this way we obtain a functor $B_k \longmapsto V(B_k)$ from k-algebras to sets. It is called the functor of points of the k-variety V.

$V(B_k)$ is also functorial in V. If $\alpha : V \longrightarrow W$ is a k-morphism of k-varieties then α induces a map $V(B_k) \longrightarrow W(B_k)$.

In the special case $B = K$ we have $V(K) = \mathrm{Mor}_{K\text{-sch.}}(\mathrm{spec}_K(K),\ V)$, which we can, and will, canonically identify with the points of V. Moreover, for any subfield k' of K containing k we have $V(k') \subset V$. These are the k'-rational points of V. In particular we have $V(k) \subset V(k_s) \subset V(\bar{k}) \subset V$. The points of $V(k_s)$ are called separable points.

If W is any locally closed subvariety of V, not necessarily defined over k, we shall permit ourselves to write $W(k')$ for the k'-rational points of V which lie in W.

EXAMPLES. If $V = K^n = \text{spec}_K(K[t_1, \ldots, t_n])$ with the standard k-structure, given by $k[t_1, \ldots, t_n]$, then $V(k) = k^n$.

If V is a vector space with k-structure V_k then $\underline{P}(V)$ acquires a k-structure so that $\underline{P}(V)(k)$ is the image of $V_k - \{0\}$ under the canonical projection $V - \{0\} \longrightarrow \underline{P}(V)$.

We remark, finally, that the definitions above apply without change to any K-scheme V (resp. K-scheme with k-structure).

(13.2) THEOREM. *Let $\alpha : V \longrightarrow W$ be a k-morphism of k-varieties which is dominant and separable. Then there is an open dense set $W_0 \subset W$ such that $W_0 \subset \alpha(V)$ and such that, for each $w \in W_0(k_s)$, the fibre $\alpha^{-1}(w)$ has a dense set of separable points.*

We shall carry out the proof in several steps.

(a) There is clearly no loss in assuming that $k = k_s$.

(b) This done, it follows from (AG.12.3) that the irreducible components of a k-variety are defined over k.

(c) There is no harm in replacing W by a dense k-open set W', and V by $\alpha^{-1}(W')$. Thus we can easily reduce to the case when W is irreducible and affine. Then cover V by irreducible k-open affines V_i. This is possible, using (b). If W_{0i} answers the requirements of the theorem for $\alpha_i : V_i \longrightarrow W$ then $W_0 = \bigcap W_{0i}$ will work for α. Hence we may assume that V and W are irreducible and affine. Furthermore, with the aid of (AG. 10. 1) we can, after shrinking W, assume that α is surjective and that all irreducible components of all fibres have the same dimension.

(d) α is induced by the comorphism $k[W] \longrightarrow k[V]$ which we can regard as an inclusion. Since $K(V)$ is separable over $K(W)$, by hypothesis, and since K is linearly disjoint, over k, from $k(W)$ and from $k(V)$, it follows that $k(V)$ is separable over $k(W)$. Hence we can apply the (separable) normalization lemma (AG. 3. 7) to the affine $k(W)$-algebra $k(W) \otimes_{k[W]} k[V]$. This permits us to consider the latter as a finite integral extension of some polynomial ring $k(W)[t_1, \ldots, t_n]$ over whose field of fractions $k(V)$ is (finite and) separable. Since $k[V]$ has a finite number of generators we can find a "common denominator" $f \neq 0$ in $k[W]$ for each of the t_i as well as for the coefficients of the integral equations of the generators of $k[V]$ over the polynomial ring. Then if, using (c), we replace $k[W]$ by $k[W]_f = k[W_f]$, and V by $V_f = \alpha^{-1}(W_f)$, we can already write $k[V]$ as a finite integral extension of the polynomial ring $k[W][t_1, \ldots, t_n] = k[W \times K^n]$. Thus we have reduced our problem to the case where α admits a factorization

$$V \xrightarrow{\beta} W \times K^n \xrightarrow{\pi} W .$$

Here π is the coordinate projection, and β is a finite integral morphism such that $k(V)$ is separable over $k(W \times K^n)$.

(e) We claim that there is a dense open set $U_0 \subset W \times K^n$ such that $\beta_0 : V_0 = \beta^{-1}(U_0) \longrightarrow U_0$ has the following property: Each fibre of β_0 over a separable point consists entirely of separable points.

Write $A = k[W \times K^n]$ and say $k[V] = A[b_1, \ldots, b_m]$. Let $P_i(b_i) = 0$ be the minimal polynomial equation of b_i over the field of fractions, $k(W \times K^n)$, of A. Since P_i is a separable polynomial its derivative, P_i', does not vanish at b_i.

The P_i all have coefficients in A_g for some $g \neq 0$ in A. Put $b = \prod_i P_i'(b_i) (\neq 0)$. Since $k[V]_g$ is integral over A_g it follows from (AG. 3. 6) that there is a non-zero multiple h of b in A_g. Then $k[V]_{gh}$ is integral over A_{gh}, and each residue class field of the former is generated by roots of polynomials which are separable over the corresponding residue class field of A_{gh}. Thus $U_0 = (W \times K^n)_{gh}$ has the property described above.

(f) We conclude the proof now by showing that $W_0 = \pi(U_0)$ satisfies the requirements of the theorem. Since π is an open map W_0 is open in W. We must show, for $w \in W(k)$ (recall $k = k_s$), that $\alpha^{-1}(w)$ has a dense set of separable points.

Since the irreducible components of $\alpha^{-1}(w)$ are equidimensional, and since β is a closed surjective map, it follows that $\beta : \alpha^{-1}(w) \longrightarrow \beta(\alpha^{-1}(w)) = \pi^{-1}(w)$ is dominant. Clearly $\pi^{-1}(w)$ is a subvariety defined over k and k-isomorphic to K^n. Therefore β maps each irreducible component, X, of $\alpha^{-1}(w)$ onto $\pi^{-1}(w)$. Let X' denote the closure of the set of separable points in X. It follows from (d) that $\beta(X')$ contains all separable points in $U_0 \cap \pi^{-1}(w)$, which is a dense open set in (the irreducible variety) $\pi^{-1}(w)$. Since β is closed it follows that $\beta(X') = \pi^{-1}(w)$. Therefore, since β is finite, $\dim X' = \dim \pi^{-1}(w) = \dim X$. But X is irreducible so $X' = X$. Q. E. D.

(13. 3) COROLLARY. Let V be a k-variety. Then $V(k_s)$ is dense in V.

We just apply the theorem to the projection of V onto a point.

§14. GALOIS CRITERIA FOR RATIONALITY

The Galois group $Gal(k_s/k)$ of k_s over k will be denoted by Γ.

(14. 1) Galois actions on vector spaces. Let V be a vector space with k-structure V_k. Then Γ operates on $V_{k_s} = k_s \otimes_k V_k$ through the first factor, and it is clear that V_k is the set $V_{k_s}^{\Gamma}$ of fixed points under Γ. If W is another vector space with a k-structure, then Γ operates on

$$\mathrm{Hom}_K(V, W)_{k_s} = \mathrm{Hom}_{k_s}(V_{k_s}, W_{k_s})$$

by

$$({}^\sigma f)(v) = \sigma(f(\sigma^{-1} v)) \quad .$$

Here $\sigma \in \Gamma$, $f : V \longrightarrow W$ is defined over k_s, and $v \in V_{k_s}$. It is easily seen that the following conditions on such an f are equivalent:

(i) f is defined over k.

(ii) $f : V_{k_s} \longrightarrow W_{k_s}$ is Γ-equivariant.

(iii) $f \in \mathrm{Hom}(V, W)_{k_s}^{\Gamma}$.

(14.2) <u>The k- structure defined by a Galois action.</u> Consider a vector space V with a k_s-structure V_{k_s} on which Γ operates semi-linearly. I. e.

$$\sigma(ax) = \sigma(a)\sigma(x) \qquad (a \in k_s, \ x \in V_{k_s}) \quad .$$

Suppose further that the stability group of each $x \in V_{k_s}$ is an open subgroup (of finite index) in Γ. Then we claim that

$$V_k = V_{k_s}^{\Gamma}$$

<u>is a k-structure on</u> V.

Certainly V_k is a k-subspace, and the natural map $k_s \otimes_k V_k \longrightarrow V_{k_s}$ is Γ-equivariant. Its kernel is therefore a Γ-invariant k_s-subspace having zero intersection with $1 \otimes V_k$. Therefore the proposition above implies that the map is a monomorphism.

It remains to show that V_k spans V_{k_s}. Let $x \in V_{k_s}$ and Γ_x be the stability group of x. It contains a normal open subgroup Γ' of Γ. The fixed point set k' of Γ' in k_s is a Galois extension of finite degree of k. Let

$$\Gamma'' = \Gamma/\Gamma' = \{\sigma_1, \dots, \sigma_n\} \cong \mathrm{Gal}(k'/k)$$

and let $a_1, \dots, a_n$ be a k-basis of k'. The elements $y_i = \Sigma_j \sigma_j(a_i x)$ clearly belong to V_k. Since the elements of Γ' are linearly independent over k', the matrix $(\sigma_j(a_i))$ is invertible, say with inverse (b_{rs}). Then

$$\sum_i b_{ih} y_i = \sum_i b_{ih} \sum_j \sigma_j(a_i)\sigma_j(x) =$$

$$= \sum_j (\sum_i \sigma_j(a_i) b_{ih})\sigma_j(x) = \sum_j \delta_{jh}\sigma_j(x) = \sigma_h(x) .$$

Some σ_h is the identity, so x is indeed a linear combination of fixed elements.

PROPOSITION. <u>Let</u> W <u>be a subspace of a vector space</u> V <u>with</u> k-<u>structure</u>. <u>Then</u> W <u>is defined over</u> k <u>if and only if</u> (i) W <u>is defined over</u> k_s, <u>and</u> (ii) W_{k_s} <u>is</u> Γ-<u>stable</u>.

PROOF. The "only if" is clear, and the "if" follows if we prove that the subspace W' spanned by W_k coincides with W. In any case we can pass to V/W' and the subspace W/W' and so reduce to the case $W_k = 0$. We claim

$W = 0$. Choose a k-basis (e_i) for V and, if $W \neq 0$, choose a $w \neq 0$ in W_{k_s} so that w is a linear combination of the least possible number of e_i's. After renumbering the e_i's and multiplying w by an element of k_s^* we can write $w = e_1 + a_2 e_2 + \dots$ with each coefficient in k_s, but $a_2 \notin k$. Then there is a $\sigma \in \Gamma$ such that $\sigma(a_2) \neq a_2$, so $w - \sigma w \in W_{k_s}$ is non-zero and is a linear combination of fewer of the e_i's; contradiction.

(14.3) <u>Galois actions on</u> k-<u>varieties</u>. Let V be a k-variety. We know from (AG.13.3) that $V(k_s)$ is dense in V. We shall introduce now an action of Γ on $V(k_s)$. It will leave $U(k_s)$ stable for all k-open U, so it suffices to describe the action when V is affine. Then we can match $V(k_s)$ with $\mathrm{Mor}_{k_s\text{-alg}}(k_s[V], k_s)$ so that $x \in V(k_s)$ corresponds to the algebra homomorphism e_x. If $\sigma \in \Gamma$ then $\sigma(x)$ is defined by

$$e_{\sigma(x)} = \sigma \circ e_x \circ \sigma^{-1} .$$

Here the left hand σ operates on k_s and the right hand one on $k_s[V] = k_s \otimes_k k[V]$. If we denote the latter action by $f \mapsto {}^{\sigma}f$ for $f \in k_s[V]$ then the equation above reads

$$f(\sigma(x)) = \sigma({}^{\sigma^{-1}}f)(x), \quad \text{or}$$

$$({}^{\sigma}f)(x) = \sigma(f(\sigma^{-1}x)) .$$

Writing $V(f)$ for the variety of zeros of f we see that σ maps the separable points of $V(f)$ to those of $V({}^{\sigma}f)$. The same applies to $V(J)$ for any ideal J in $k_s[V]$. In this way we can define the *conjugate variety* ${}^{\sigma}W$ of any closed subvariety W of V defined over k_s. Such a definition is allowable because of the density of separable points. In the affine case ${}^{\sigma}W$ is just the variety obtained by applying σ to the coefficients of equations defining W over k_s.

Let $\alpha : V \longrightarrow W$ be a morphism of k-varieties, and assume α is defined over k_s. Then, for $\sigma \in \Gamma$, we define a k_s-morphism ${}^{\sigma}\alpha : V \longrightarrow W$ as follows:

$$ {}^{\sigma}\alpha(x) = \sigma(\alpha(\sigma^{-1}x)) \qquad (x \in V(k_s)) . $$

By density of separable points there is at most one k_s-morphism with this property. To see that there is one it suffices to exhibit, for k-open $V' \subset V$ and $W' \subset W$ such that $\alpha V' \subset W'$, the comorphism $({}^{\sigma}\alpha)_0 : k_s[W'] \longrightarrow k_s[V']$. It is defined by the commutativity of

$$ \begin{array}{ccc} k_s[V'] & \xleftarrow{\ ({}^{\sigma}\alpha)_0\ } & k_s[W'] \\ \Big\downarrow{\scriptstyle \sigma} & & \Big\downarrow{\scriptstyle \sigma} \\ k_s[V'] & \xleftarrow[\ \alpha_0\ ]{} & k_s[W'] \end{array} , $$

i.e. $({}^{\sigma}\alpha)_0 = \sigma^{-1} \circ \alpha_0 \circ \sigma$. Thus, for $f \in k_s[W']$, $({}^{\sigma}\alpha)_0(f) = \sigma^{-1}(\alpha_0({}^{\sigma}f))$. Thus Γ acts on $\mathrm{Mor}(V, W)_{k_s}$.

The following conditions on α are easily seen to be equivalent:

(i) α is defined over k;

(ii) $\alpha : V(k_s) \longrightarrow W(k_s)$ is Γ-equivariant;

(iii) $\alpha \in \mathrm{Mor}(V, W)_{k_s}^{\Gamma}$.

(14.4) THEOREM. Let V be a k-variety and let Z be a closed subvariety. The following conditions are equivalent:

(1) Z is defined over k.

(2) Z is defined over k_s and $Z(k_s)$ is Γ-stable.

(3) There is a subset $E \subset Z \cap V(k_s)$ such that E is Γ-stable and dense in Z.

PROOF. (1) $\Longrightarrow$ (2) is clear, and (2) $\Longrightarrow$ (3) follows from the density of $Z(k_s)$ (AG.13.3).

(3) $\Longrightarrow$ (1): By covering V with k-open affine varieties, we can reduce to the case when V is affine. Then $J = \bigcap_{x \in E} \underline{m}_x = I(\bar{E}) = I(Z)$ is the ideal of functions vanishing on Z. Since $E \subset V(k_s)$ it follows that J is defined (as a subspace of $K[V]$) over k_s. If $\sigma \in \Gamma$, then

$$^{\sigma}J_{k_s} = \bigcap_{x \in E} {}^{\sigma}\underline{m}_{x, k_s} = \bigcap_{x \in E} \underline{m}_{\sigma(x), k_s} = \bigcap_{x \in E} \underline{m}_{x, k_s} = J_{k_s} ,$$

the latter because E is Γ-stable. Hence, by (14.1), J is defined over k, as claimed.

(14.5) COROLLARY. Let $\alpha : V \longrightarrow W$ be a k-morphism of k-varieties. Then $\overline{\alpha(V)}$ is defined over k.

PROOF. Since $V(k_s)$ is dense in V (AG. 13. 3), $\overline{\alpha(V(k_s))}$ is dense in $\overline{\alpha(V)}$, so that we may apply criterion (3) to it.

(14. 6) COROLLARY. Let (Z_i) be a family of subvarieties of V defined over k, and let Z be the closure of $\bigcup_i Z_i$. Then Z is defined over k.

PROOF. Apply criterion (3) to $E = \bigcup_i Z_i(k_s)$.

(14. 7) COROLLARY. Let $\alpha : V \longrightarrow W$ be a k-morphism of k-varieties which is dominant and separable. Then there is a dense open set W_0 in W such that every fibre of α over a k-rational point of W_0 is defined over k.

PROOF. Let W_0 be as in (AG. 13. 2). If $w \in W_0(k)$ then the set E of separable points in $\alpha^{-1}(w)$ is Γ-stable. Moreover (AG. 13. 2) implies that E is dense in $\alpha^{-1}(w)$, so the corollary follows from (14. 4), criterion (3).

§15. DERIVATIONS AND DIFFERENTIALS (Cf. [EGA, Ch. 0, §20].)

This section contains the algebra which is preliminary to the discussion of tangent spaces, to follow in (AG. 16).

(15. 1) $\Omega_{A/k}$. We shall work with k-algebras, even though most of the discussion applies when k is a commutative ring, not necessarily a field.

Since a k-algebra A is commutative we can

regard an A-module M as a bimodule, so that $ax = xa$ for $x \in M$ and $a \in A$. With this convention a k-derivation from A to M is a k-linear map $X : A \longrightarrow M$ such that

$$X(ab) = (Xa)b + a(Xb) \qquad (a,\ b \in A)\ .$$

Since $X(ab) = aX(b)$ for $a \in k$ we can take $b = 1$ to conclude that $Xa = 0$ for $a \in k$.

The set

$$\mathrm{Der}_k(A,\ M)$$

of all such k-derivations is an A-module which is functorial in M.

There is a universal k-derivation

$$d(= d_{A/k}) : A \longrightarrow \Omega(= \Omega_{A/k})$$

obtained by taking Ω to be the A-module defined by generators, $da\ (a \in A)$, and relations, $d(ab) = (da)b + a(db) \quad (a,\ b \in A)$ and $dc = 0 (c \in k)$. Its universality is expressed by the natural isomorphism

$$\mathrm{Hom}_{A\text{-mod}}(\Omega,\ M) \longrightarrow \mathrm{Der}_k(A,\ M)$$

sending f to $f \circ d$.

(There is a well known construction of Ω which we won't need: Let J be the kernel of $A \otimes_k A \longrightarrow A$, $a \otimes b \longmapsto ab$. Then $a \otimes 1 - 1 \otimes a \longrightarrow da$ induces an isomorphism $J/J^2 \longrightarrow \Omega$.)

If $f : A \longrightarrow B$ is a k-algebra homomorphism, it induces a semi-linear map $df : \Omega_A \longrightarrow \Omega_B$ sending $d_A a$ to $d_B f(a)$. (We drop k from the notation when k is fixed by the discussion.) This corresponds to the map

$$\mathrm{Der}_k(B, M) \longrightarrow \mathrm{Der}_k(A, M)$$

defined by:

$$X \longmapsto X \circ f \quad ,$$

for each B-module (and hence also A-module) M. In this way Ω_A is functorial in A.

(15.2) Polynomial rings. If $A = k[T_1, \ldots, T_n]$ is a polynomial ring, then Ω is a free A-module with basis $dT_1, \ldots, dT_n$. Moreover $d : A \longrightarrow \Omega$ is given by

$$df = \Sigma \frac{\partial f}{\partial T_i} dT_i$$

for $f \in A$. These assertions translate the fact that a derivation $X : A \longrightarrow M$ is determined by the XT_i, which can be arbitrarily prescribed.

(15.3) Residue class rings. Let $A' = A/J$ for some ideal J, and let M be an A'-module (or A-module annihilated by J). Then, since $JM = 0$, we have

$$\begin{aligned} \mathrm{Der}_k(A, M) &= \mathrm{Hom}_{A\text{-mod}}(\Omega_A, M) \\ &= \mathrm{Hom}_{A'\text{-mod}}(\Omega_A / J\Omega_A, M) \end{aligned}$$

We can identify $\mathrm{Der}_k(A', M)$ with the k-derivations $A \longrightarrow M$ which kill J, i.e.

$$\mathrm{Der}_k(A', M) = \mathrm{Hom}_{A'\text{-mod}}(\Omega_A / A \cdot d_A J,\ M) \ .$$

Thus $\Omega_{A'}$ is Ω_A modulo the A-module generated by all df $(f \in J)$. It even suffices to vary the f's over a set of generators of J.

For example, suppose $A = k[T_1, \ldots, T_n]$ is a polynomial ring, so that $A' = k[t_1, \ldots, t_n]$ (t_i = image of T_i). Then if $f_1, \ldots, f_m$ generate J we conclude from above that $\Omega_{A'}$ is defined by generators dt_i $(1 \leqq i \leqq n)$ and relations

$$\sum_i \left(\frac{\partial f_j}{\partial T_i}\right)(t)dt_i = 0 \qquad (1 \leqq j \leqq m) \ .$$

Here $g(t)$ denotes the image in A' of a polynomial $g(T) = g(T_1, \ldots, T_n)$ in A.

(15.4) PROPOSITION. Suppose above that $A = k \oplus J$, i.e. that k maps onto $A' = A/J$. Then d_A induces an isomorphism of A'-modules

$$J/J^2 \longrightarrow \Omega_A / J \cdot \Omega_A \ .$$

PROOF. It suffices to show that these modules have the same homomorphisms into any A'-module M, i.e. that $\mathrm{Der}_k(A, M) \cong \mathrm{Hom}_{A'\text{-mod}}(J/J^2, M)$. If $X : A \longrightarrow M$ is a k-derivation then $X(k) = 0$ so, since $A = k \oplus J$, X is determined by $X|J$. Since $JM = 0$ we must have $X(J^2) = 0$, so X is determined by a homomorphism $h : J/J^2 \longrightarrow M$. Conversely, given such an h, it induces $J \longrightarrow J/J^2 \longrightarrow M$, and hence an $X : A \longrightarrow M$ so that $X(k) = 0$. A routine calculation shows that X is a k-derivation.

(15.5) Localization. Let S be a multiplicative set in A. Then $\Omega_{A[S^{-1}]} = \Omega_A[S^{-1}]$, and we have

$$d(\frac{a}{s}) = \frac{(da)s - a(ds)}{s^2} \qquad (a \in A,\ s \in S) .$$

In particular, it follows that, if M is an $A[S^{-1}]$-module, i.e. an A-module on which the elements of S act invertibly, then

$$\mathrm{Der}_k(A, M) = \mathrm{Der}_k(A[S^{-1}], M) .$$

For example, if M is a module over one of the local rings A_P of A then $\mathrm{Der}_k(A, M) = \mathrm{Der}_k(A_P, M)$.

Here is another important consequence of the localizability of Ω: Suppose V is a K-scheme. Then there is a coherent sheaf $\Omega_{V/K}$ of $\mathcal{O}_V$-modules such that, on any affine open subscheme $U = \mathrm{spec}_K(A)$, the sheaf $\Omega_{U/K} = \Omega_{V/K}|U$ is the sheaf $\tilde{\Omega}_{A/K}$ corresponding to $\Omega_{A/K}$. If $x \in U$ then the stalk Ω_x of $\Omega_{V/K}$ is therefore just the localization of $\Omega_{A/K}$ at the local ring $\mathcal{O}_x$ of A, or, alternatively, $\Omega_{\mathcal{O}_x/K}$.

(15.6) Separable field extensions (see (AG.2.3)). Suppose

A is a finitely generated field extension of k of transcendence degree n. Then

$$\dim_A \Omega_A \geqq n$$

with equality if and only if A is separable over k. In this case $a_1, \ldots, a_n \in A$ are a separating transcendence basis of A over k if and only if $da_1, \ldots, da_n$ are an A-basis of Ω_A.

If B is a finitely generated field extension of A which is separable over k then it follows from the exact sequence

$$0 \longrightarrow \mathrm{Der}_A(B, B) \longrightarrow \mathrm{Der}_k(B, B) \longrightarrow \mathrm{Der}_k(A, B) ,$$

by counting B-dimensions, that B is separable over $A \Longleftrightarrow \mathrm{Der}_k(B, B) \longrightarrow \mathrm{Der}_k(A, B)$ is surjective $\Longleftrightarrow B \otimes_A \Omega_A \longrightarrow \Omega_B$ is injective.

(15.7) <u>Tensor products.</u> Suppose $A = A_1 \otimes_k A_2$, and write $\Omega_i = \Omega_{A_i}$. Then

$$\Omega_A \cong (\Omega_1 \otimes_k A_2) \oplus (A_1 \otimes_k \Omega_2) .$$

Equivalently, if M is any A-module, we have

$$\mathrm{Der}_k(A, M) \cong \mathrm{Der}_k(A_1, M) \oplus \mathrm{Der}_k(A_2, M) .$$

The map from left to right is induced by the homomorphisms $A_i \longrightarrow A$. For the inverse we must produce a k-derivation

$X : A \longrightarrow M$ from a given pair of them $X_i : A_i \longrightarrow M$. The formula is:

$$X(a_1 \otimes a_2) = (X_1 a_1 \otimes a_2) + (a_1 \otimes X_2 a_2) .$$

(15.8) Base change. For any base change $k \longrightarrow k'$ we have a natural isomorphism

$$k' \otimes_k \Omega_{A/k} \longrightarrow \Omega_{k' \otimes_k A/k'} .$$

(15.9) The tangent bundle lemma. We consider k-algebras A and D where D is of the form $D = B \oplus M$ with B a subalgebra and M an ideal of square zero. If $f : A \longrightarrow B$ is an algebra homomorphism we write M_f for the resulting A-module M with A operating via f.

The projection $D \longrightarrow B = D/M$ induces a map

$$\mathrm{Hom}_{k\text{-alg}}(A,\ D) \xrightarrow{p} \mathrm{Hom}_{k\text{-alg}}(A,\ B) .$$

We assert that, for f as above, there is a canonical bijection

$$\mathrm{Der}_k(A,\ M_f) \longrightarrow p^{-1}(f) .$$

In fact, any element of $p^{-1}(f)$ can be written uniquely in the form $f + X$, for some k-linear map $X : A \longrightarrow M$, with the understanding that $(f+X)(a) = f(a) + X(a) \in D = B \oplus M$. The assertion above can then be translated: $f + X$ is multiplicative if and only if X is a derivation. To see this take $a, b \in A$. Then

$$(f(a)+X(a))(f(b)+X(b)) = f(a)f(b)+X(a)f(b)+f(a)X(b)+X(a)X(b)$$
$$= f(ab) + (X(a)f(b) + f(a)X(b)) \quad ,$$

because f is multiplicative and $M^2 = 0$.

§16. TANGENT SPACES

(16.1) The Zariski tangent space. Let x be a point on a variety (or even a K-scheme) V. Recall that $K(x) = \mathcal{O}_x/\underline{m}_x$ denotes the residue field of the local ring of x. It coincides with K, but the notation refers, more precisely, to its $\mathcal{O}_x$-module structure.

The tangent space of V at x is

$$T(V)_x = \mathrm{Der}_K(\mathcal{O}_x, K(x)) \quad .$$

It follows from (AG.15.4) that this is canonically isomorphic to

$$\mathrm{Hom}_{K\text{-mod}}(\underline{m}_x/\underline{m}_x^2, K) \quad .$$

If $f \in \mathcal{O}_x$ write $(df)_x$ for the image modulo $\underline{m}_x^2$ of $f - f(x)$. Then the "tangent vector" $X \in T(V)_x$ corresponding to $h : \underline{m}_x/\underline{m}_x^2 \longrightarrow K(x)$ is defined by $Xf = h((df)_x)$.

Suppose V has a k-structure and $x \in V(k)$. Then $\mathcal{O}_x$ has a natural k-structure $\mathcal{O}_{x,k}$, whose residue class field k(x) is a k-structure on K(x). Thus we obtain a k-structure $\mathrm{Der}_k(\mathcal{O}_{x,k}, k(x))$ on $T(V)_x$. As above this k-structure is isomorphic to

$$\mathrm{Hom}_{k\text{-mod}}(\underline{m}_{x,k}/\underline{m}^2_{x,k}, k) .$$

Let $\alpha : V \longrightarrow W$ be a morphism of varieties (or of K-schemes). Then we have the comorphism

$$\alpha_0 : \mathcal{O}_{\alpha(x)} \longrightarrow \mathcal{O}_x .$$

Viewing K(x) thus as an $\mathcal{O}_{\alpha(x)}$-module it coincides with $K(\alpha(x))$. Therefore we have a natural map

$$\mathrm{Der}_K(\mathcal{O}_x, K(x)) \longrightarrow \mathrm{Der}_K(\mathcal{O}_{\alpha(x)}, K(\alpha(x)))$$

which we denote by

$$(d\alpha)_x : T(V)_x \longrightarrow T(W)_{\alpha(x)} .$$

Explicitly, if $X \in T(V)_x$ and if $f \in \mathcal{O}_{\alpha(x)}$, then

$$(d\alpha)_x(X)(f) = X(\alpha_0(f)) .$$

In case α is a k-morphism relative to k-structures on V and W and if $x \in V(k)$, then $\alpha(x) \in W(k)$ and it is easy to see that $(d\alpha)_x$ is defined over k, relative to the k-structure described above on the tangent spaces.

The differential, $(d\alpha)_x$, behaves functorially in the following sense:

$$(d1_V)_x = 1_{T(V)_x} .$$

If $\beta : W \longrightarrow Z$ then

$$d(\beta \circ \alpha)_x = (d\beta)_{\alpha(x)} \circ (d\alpha)_x \quad \text{(chain rule)} .$$

Suppose $V = V_1 \times V_2$ is a <u>product</u> and that $x = (x_1, x_2)$. Define $\alpha_i : V_i \longrightarrow V$ $(i = 1, 2)$ by $\alpha_1(u) = (u, u_2)$ and $\alpha_2(y) = (x_1, y)$. We claim that

$$(d\alpha_1)_{x_1} + (d\alpha_2)_{x_2} : T(V_1)_{x_1} \oplus T(V_2)_{x_2} \longrightarrow T(V)_x$$

is an isomorphism. Since this is a local matter we can assume the V_i to be affine, say $V_i = \operatorname{spec}_K(A_i)$. Then $V = \operatorname{spec}_K(A)$ where $A = A_1 \otimes_K A_2$. It follows from (AG.15.5) that we can compute the tangent spaces as $T(V)_x = \operatorname{Der}_K(A, K(x))$ and $T(V_i)_{x_i} = \operatorname{Der}_K(A_i, K(x_i))$. As an A-module we have $K(x) = K(x_1) \otimes_K K(x_2)$, (both sides being isomorphic to K). Hence it follows from (AG.15.7) that $T(V)_x = T(V_1)_{x_1} \oplus T(V_2)_{x_2}$, and it is easily checked that this identification admits the description given above.

(16.2) <u>The tangent bundle</u>. At each point of a K-scheme V we have a tangent space. We shall now construct the <u>tangent bundle</u>, T(V), which fits all of these vector spaces into a coherent family parametrized by V.

Write $K[\delta] = K \oplus K\delta$ for the <u>dual numbers</u>, the algebra with one generator, δ, and one relation, $\delta^2 = 0$. We have the inclusion i and projection p,

$$K[\delta] \underset{i}{\overset{p}{\rightleftarrows}} K ,$$

defined by $p(\delta) = 0$. As a set we define T(V) to be

$V(K[\delta])$, the points of V in $K[\delta]$ (see (AG. 13.1)). It therefore comes equipped with maps

$$\begin{array}{ccc} T(V) & = & V(K[\delta]) \\ {\scriptstyle p_V}\downarrow\uparrow{\scriptstyle i_V} & & \downarrow\uparrow \\ V & & V(K) \end{array}$$

induced by p and i above. Moreover $T(V)$ is functorial: If $\alpha : V \longrightarrow W$ is a morphism of varieties we have a commutative square

$$\begin{array}{ccc} T(V) & \xrightarrow{T(\alpha)} & T(W) \\ {\scriptstyle p_V}\downarrow & & \downarrow{\scriptstyle p_W} \\ V & \xrightarrow{\alpha} & W \end{array}$$

It also commutes if we replace the p's by i's.

Recall that

$$V(K[\delta]) = \mathrm{Mor}_{K\text{-sch}}(\mathrm{spec}_K(K[\delta]),\ V) \ .$$

It is clear that the scheme $\mathrm{spec}_K(K[\delta])$ consists of a single point, with local ring $K[\delta]$. Hence a point of $V(K[\delta])$ corresponds to a point $x \in V$ and a comorphism $\mathcal{O}_x \longrightarrow K[\delta]$. The latter can be written in the form $e_x + \delta X$ for some K-linear map $X : \mathcal{O}_x \longrightarrow K$. This sends $f \in \mathcal{O}_x$ to $f(x) + \delta X(f)$ in $K[\delta]$. According to (AG. 15.9) the X's so obtained vary precisely over $\mathrm{Der}_K(\mathcal{O}_x,\ K(x)) = T(V)_x$.

We shall denote the element $e_x + \delta X$ also by

$$e_x^{\delta X} ,$$

and view it both as a homomorphism $\mathcal{O}_x \longrightarrow K[\delta]$ and as a point of $T(V)$. From the latter point of view we see that the projection p_V is given by

$$p_V : e_x^{\delta X} \longmapsto x .$$

(Moreover i_V sends x to $e_x = e_x^{\delta 0}$.) Thus we can reformulate the conclusion above as follows: <u>There is a natural bijection</u>

$$T(V)_x \longrightarrow p_V^{-1}(x)$$

<u>given by</u>

$$X \longmapsto e_x^{\delta X}$$

Suppose $\alpha : V \longrightarrow W$ is a morphism. Then $T(\alpha)(e_x^{\delta X}) = e_x^{\delta X} \circ \alpha_0$, where $\alpha_0 : \mathcal{O}_{\alpha(x)} \longrightarrow \mathcal{O}_x$. Expanding the right side we obtain $(e_x + \delta X) \circ \alpha_0 =$ $= e_x \circ \alpha_0 + \delta X \circ \alpha_0 = e_{\alpha(x)} + \delta(d\alpha)_x X$. Thus

$$T(\alpha)(e_x^{\delta X}) = e_{\alpha(x)}^{\delta(d\alpha)_x X}$$

In other words, the map that $T(\alpha)$ induces on the fibre over x corresponds to the differential $(d\alpha)_x$.

(16.3) $T(V)$ <u>"is" a</u> K-<u>scheme</u>. To give $T(V)$ the structure of a K-scheme it suffices to do so when V is affine and to verify that the construction in that case is suitably functorial. Before doing this we recall some properties of symmetric algebras.

Let M be a module over a (commutative) ring A. The symmetric algebra, $S_A(M)$, is the largest commutative quotient of the tensor algebra of M. Both of these A-algebras are graded, with A in degree zero, and M in degree one. The universal property of the symmetric algebra is expressed by the identification

$$\mathrm{Hom}_{A\text{-alg.}}(S_A(M), B) = \mathrm{Hom}_{A\text{-mod}}(M, B)$$

for all (commutative) A-algebras B. In other words, a module homomorphism $M \longrightarrow B$ extends uniquely to an A-algebra homomorphism $S_A(M) \longrightarrow B$.

The following facts are easily verified:

(a) If M is free with basis $t_1, \ldots, t_n$, then $S_A(M) = A[t_1, \ldots, t_n]$, the polynomial ring.

(b) $S_A(M \oplus N) = S_A(M) \otimes_A S_A(N)$.

(c) If $A \longrightarrow A'$ is any base change then $S_{A'}(A' \otimes_A M) = A' \otimes_A S_A(M)$.

Now let $V = \mathrm{spec}_K(A)$ be an affine K-scheme, and put $\Omega = \Omega_{A/K}$, the A-module of K-differentials (see (AG.15.1)). We propose to construct a bijection

$$\varphi : T(V) \longrightarrow \mathrm{spec}_K(S_A(\Omega)) \quad ,$$

which is functorial in A, and so that p_V and i_V on the left correspond, on the right, to the inclusion $A \longrightarrow S_A(\Omega)$ and the projection $S_A(\Omega) \longrightarrow A$ sending Ω to 0, respectively. Moreover, if V has a k-structure given by $A_k \subset A$ then φ will be compatible with the k-structure on the right given by $S_{A_k}(\Omega_k)$, where $\Omega_k = \Omega_{A_k/k}$ (see (AG.15.8) and (c) above).

We define the K-algebra homomorphism

$$\varphi(e_x^{\delta X}) : S_A(\Omega) \longrightarrow K$$

as follows: Viewing $e_x : A \longrightarrow K(x)$ as a base change, it induces

$$e_x : S_A(\Omega) \longrightarrow S_K(\Omega(x)) \quad ,$$

where $\Omega(x) = K(x) \otimes_A \Omega$. We define $\varphi(e_x^{\delta X})$ to be the composite of this with some

$$h : S_K(\Omega(x)) \longrightarrow K$$

to be explained now. We have

$$\mathrm{Hom}_{K\text{-alg}}(S_K(\Omega(x)), K) = \mathrm{Hom}_{K\text{-mod}}(\Omega(x), K) \quad .$$

If Ω_x is the localization of Ω at $\mathcal{O}_x$ then $\Omega(x) = K(x) \otimes_A \Omega = K(x) \otimes_{\mathcal{O}_x} \Omega_x = \Omega_x / \underline{m}_x \Omega_x$. Moreover, with the aid of (AG.15.5) and (AG.15.3) we see that

$$\mathrm{Hom}_{K\text{-mod}}(\Omega(x), K) = \mathrm{Der}_K(\mathcal{O}_x, K(x)) = T(V)_x \quad .$$

Combining these identifications, we can now choose $h \in \mathrm{Hom}_{K\text{-alg}}(S_K(\Omega(x)), K)$ to correspond to $X \in T(V)_x$.

The properties of φ claimed above are all easily verified, in particular, the fact that φ is bijective.

Suppose now that V is a variety. It does not then follow from the construction above that $T(V)$ is a variety, because $S_A(\Omega)$ may not be reduced. However, if Ω is free then (see (a) above) $S_A(\Omega)$ is a polynomial ring over A, so $T(V)$ is a variety of the form $V \times K^n$ for some n. More generally, then, we conclude that:

If V is a variety and if Ω is locally free then $T(V)$ is a variety locally isomorphic to the product of V with an affine space.

§17. SIMPLE POINTS

(17.1) A point x on a variety V is said to be *simple on* V if $\mathcal{O}_x$ is a regular local ring (see (AG. 3. 9)). If all points of V are simple we say that V is *smooth*.

In the next theorem, Ω_x denotes the module of differentials $\Omega_{\mathcal{O}_x/K}$ (cf. (AG. 15. 5)).

THEOREM. *The following conditions are equivalent:*

(1) x *is simple on* V.

(2) $\dim_K T(V)_x = \dim_x V$.

(3) x *lies on a unique irreducible component of* V, *and* Ω_x *is a free* $\mathcal{O}_x$*-module*.

Using (AG. 15. 4) we see that

$$T(V)_x = \mathrm{Der}_K(\mathcal{O}_x, K(x))$$

$$= \mathrm{Hom}_{K\text{-mod}}(\Omega_x/\underline{m}_x\Omega_x, K)$$

and

$$\Omega_x/\underline{m}_x\Omega_x \cong \underline{m}_x/\underline{m}_x^2 \ .$$

Moreover (see (AG. 3. 9)) we have

$$\dim_K(\underline{m}_x/\underline{m}_x^2) \geqq \dim \mathcal{O}_x (= \dim_x V)$$

with equality if and only if $\mathcal{O}_x$ is regular. These remarks already show the equivalence of (1) and (2).

The point x lies on a unique irreducible component if and only if $\mathcal{O}_x$ is an integral domain. Since regular local rings are integral domains it suffices, for the rest of the proof, to assume V is irreducible. If not, pass to an irreducible open neighborhood of x.

Let S be a minimal set of generators of Ω_x as an $\mathcal{O}_x$-module. It follows from (AG. 3. 2) that card $S = \dim_K(\Omega_x/\underline{m}_x\Omega_x)$, and Ω_x is free if and only if S is a basis. The latter is equivalent to $1 \otimes S$ being a basis over $K(V)$, the field of fractions of $\mathcal{O}_x$, of $K(V) \otimes_{\mathcal{O}_x} \Omega_x$. Since $1 \otimes S$ spans the latter we conclude that Ω_x is $\mathcal{O}_x$-free if and only if card $S = \dim_{K(V)}(K(V) \otimes_{\mathcal{O}_x} \Omega_x)$.

From the fact that $\Omega_x/\underline{m}_x\Omega_x \cong \underline{m}_x/\underline{m}_x^2$ we see that

$$\text{card } S = \dim T(V)_x \geqq \dim_x V \ .$$

On the other hand it follows from (AG. 15. 5) and (AG. 15. 6), using the separability of $K(V)$ over K, that $K(V) \otimes_{\mathcal{O}_x} \Omega_x = \Omega_{K(V)/K}$, and

$$\dim_{K(V)} \Omega_{K(V)/K} = \text{tr. deg.}_K K(V) = \dim_x V \ .$$

Combining these remarks we have:
Ω_x is $\mathcal{O}_x$-free $\Longleftrightarrow$ card $S = \dim_x V \Longleftrightarrow \dim_K T(V)_x = \dim_x V$. This proves (2) $\Longleftrightarrow$ (3), thus concluding the proof of the theorem.

(17. 2) COROLLARY. _Let_ V _be a variety._ _The set_ U _of simple points on_ V _is an open dense subvariety whose irreducible and connected components coincide._

It follows from (AG. 1. 2) that the set U_0 of points of V lying on a unique irreducible component is open and dense, and the irreducible and connected components of U_0 coincide. Since $U \subset U_0$ we can therefore reduce to the case when V is irreducible. If Ω is the coherent sheaf of differentials on V (see (AG. 15. 5)) then it follows from criterion (3) above that $U = \{x \in V | \Omega_x$ is a free $\mathcal{O}_x$-module$\}$. To show this is open dense we can assume V is affine, say $\text{spec}_K(A)$, and that Ω is the A-module $\Omega_{A/K}$. In this case it follows from (AG. 3. 5) that $U' = \{x \in \text{spec}(A) | \Omega_x$ is a free A_x-module$\}$ is open in spec(A). Taking for x the zero prime ideal, in which case A_x is a field, we see that U' is not empty. Since spec(A) is irreducible, U' is dense, and hence likewise for $U = U' \cap \mathrm{spec}_K(A)$.

(17.3) THEOREM. The following conditions on a morphism $\alpha : V \longrightarrow W$ of varieties are equivalent:

(1) α is (dominant and) separable.

(2) There is a dense open subvariety V_0 of V such that $(d\alpha)_x$ is surjective for all $x \in V_0$.

(3) In each irreducible component of V there is a simple point x (of V) such that $\alpha(x)$ is simple on W and such that $(d\alpha)_x$ is surjective.

Suppose $V' \subset V$ and $W' \subset W$ are dense open subvarieties such that α induces a morphism $\alpha' : V' \longrightarrow W'$. Then clearly the theorem for α will follow once we prove it for α', thanks to the density of simple points. In this way one can easily reduce to the case where V and W are each irreducible, affine, and smooth. The latter condition implies that the modules $\Omega_V = \Omega_{K[V]/K}$ and $\Omega_W = \Omega_{K[W]/K}$ are locally free. By shrinking V and W still further we can assume they are (globally) free.

The comorphism $\alpha_0 : K[W] \longrightarrow K[V]$ induces $\Omega_W \longrightarrow \Omega_V$, and $(d\alpha)_x$ then corresponds to the induced homomorphism from

$$\mathrm{Hom}_{K[V]\text{-mod}}(\Omega_V, K(x))$$

to

$$\mathrm{Hom}_{K[V]\text{-mod}}(K[V] \otimes_{K[W]} \Omega_W, K(x)) .$$

Write $d : M \longrightarrow N$ for the homomorphism $K[V] \otimes_{K[W]} \Omega_W \longrightarrow \Omega_V$. The modules M and N are free of ranks dim W and dim V, respectively, and d is represented by a matrix (f_{ij}) over $K[V]$. The description of $(d\alpha)_x$ above shows that it is represented by the matrix $(f_{ji}(x))$ over K. Thus $(d\alpha)_x$ is surjective if and only if the rank of $(f_{ji}(x))$ is dim W. The set of such x is therefore open, and it is non-empty if and only if (f_{ji}) has rank dim W as a matrix over K(V). The latter, in turn, is equivalent to the injectivity of $\Omega_W \longrightarrow \Omega_V$. This is equivalent to (i) the injectivity of α_0 (i.e. the dominance of α), and (ii) the surjectivity of $\mathrm{Der}_K(K(V), K(V)) \longrightarrow \mathrm{Der}_K(K(W), K(V))$. The last condition means that K-derivations of K(W) into K(V) extend to K(V), and this condition (see (AG. 15. 6)) characterizes separability of K(V) over K(W).

(17.4) COROLLARY. <u>If</u> $\alpha_i : V_i \longrightarrow W_i$ $(i = 1, 2)$ <u>are two separable morphisms then</u> $\alpha_1 \times \alpha_2 : V_1 \times V_2 \longrightarrow W_1 \times W_2$ <u>is separable</u>.

This follows easily from criterion (2).

§18. NORMAL VARIETIES

This section contains the main results needed in Chapter II, §6 for the construction of homogeneous spaces.

(18.1) DEFINITION. A point x on a variety V is said to

be normal on V if the local ring $\mathcal{O}_x$ is normal, i.e. if $\mathcal{O}_x$ is an integral domain integrally closed in its field of fractions. In particular such an x lies on a unique irreducible component of V, i.e. it has an irreducible open neighborhood. Consequently most questions involving normality can be easily reduced to the case of irreducible varieties.

If every point of V is normal on V then V is called a normal variety.

As an example, every simple point of V is normal on V (i.e. a regular local ring is normal). It follows (see (AG.17.2)) that the set of normal points on V contains a dense open set; in fact, it is itself open.

Moreover, a product of two normal varieties is normal [Fond., Ch. V, I, Prop. 3].

(18.2) Normalization. Let V be an irreducible algebraic variety, and let L be a finite (algebraic) extension of K(V). Then there is a normal irreducible variety V' and a surjective morphism $\alpha : V' \longrightarrow V$ with finite fibres, and a K(V)-algebra isomorphism $K(V') \longrightarrow L$. Moreover these data are essentially unique. We usually identify K(V') with L, and call $\alpha : V' \longrightarrow V$ the normalization of V in L. It is determined by the following property: If U is open affine in V, then $U' = \alpha^{-1}(U)$ is $\mathrm{spec}_K(K[U]')$, where $K[U]'$ is the integral closure of $K[U]$ in L, and α is induced by $K[U] \subset K[U]' = K[U']$. If $L = K(V)$ we just call $\alpha : V' \longrightarrow V$ the normalization of V.

Note that a normalization of an affine variety is affine. Moreover, a normalization of a projective (resp., complete) variety is projective (resp., complete). For projectiveness see [M, Ch. III, §8, Thm. 4]. For completeness, we must show that $V' \times X \longrightarrow X$ is closed for all X, knowing the analogous assertion for V. It clearly suffices to verify that $V' \times X \longrightarrow V \times X$ is closed. This is a local property which need only be verified when V and X are affine, in which case it follows from the fact (see (AG. 3. 6)) that $\mathrm{spec}_K(B) \longrightarrow \mathrm{spec}_K(A)$ is surjective and closed whenever $A \subset B$ is a finite integral extension.

The next theorem is taken from [Class., exp. 5, no. 2], on Zariski's Main Theorem.

THEOREM. Let $\alpha : V \longrightarrow W$ be a dominant morphism of irreducible normal varieties. Assume the fibres of α have finite constant cardinality n. Then α is the normalization of W in $K(V)$, and n is the separable degree of $K(V)$ over $K(W)$. In particular, if α is birational then α is an isomorphism, and if α is bijective then $K(V)$ is purely inseparable over $K(W)$.

Using this theorem the following result can be deduced [Class., exp. 8, Prop. 1].

PROPOSITION. Let $\alpha : V \longrightarrow W$ be a dominant morphism of irreducible varieties, and suppose that $f \in K[V]$ is constant along the fibres of α. Then f is purely inseparable over $K(W)$.

(18.3) PROPOSITION. Let $\alpha : V \longrightarrow W$ be a bijective morphism of varieties and assume that W is normal.

(1) If W is complete then V is complete.

(2) If V is affine then W is affine.

It is clearly enough to consider the case when W is irreducible. Then V must also be irreducible, because each irreducible component of V dominates W, and α is bijective.

Suppose W' is open in W, and set $V' = \alpha^{-1}(W')$. We claim that the inclusion $\alpha_0 K[W'] \subset K[V'] \cap \alpha_0 K(W)$, is an equality. Since $\alpha' : V' \longrightarrow W'$ inherits all of our hypotheses it suffices to treat the case $W' = W$. So suppose $f \in K[V]$ and that $f = \alpha_0 h$ for some $h \in K(W)$. We must show that $h \in K[W]$, i.e. that h is everywhere defined on W. We use the following Lemma [Class., exp. 8, Lemme 1]:

LEMMA. Let x be a normal point on an irreducible variety W, and suppose $h \in K(W)$ is not defined at x. Then there is a $y \in W$ at which $1/h$ is defined and vanishes.

Returning to the argument above, if h is not defined at $x \in W$ then choose y as in the Lemma. Writing $y = \alpha(z)$ we see that $1/f = \alpha_0(1/h)$ is defined and vanishes at $z \in V$, contrary to the assumption that $f \in K[V]$. Thus we have shown that

$$\alpha_0 K[W'] = K[V'] \cap \alpha_0 K(W) \quad ,$$

for all open W' in W, where $V' = \alpha^{-1}(W')$.

The Proposition of (18.2) implies that $K(V)$ is purely inseparable over $\alpha_0 K(W)$. This, together with the result just proved, implies that $K[V']$ is integral over $\alpha_0 K[W']$. Therefore, if $\beta : \tilde{W} \longrightarrow W$ is the normalization of W in $K(V)$, it follows that β factors as $\tilde{W} \xrightarrow{\gamma} V \xrightarrow{\alpha} W$, and γ is surjective.

Now if W is complete then, by (18.2), $\tilde{W}$ is complete, so it follows that V is also complete.

Next suppose V is affine. Since $\alpha_0 K[W]$ contains $K[V]^{p^n}$ for some n ($p = \mathrm{char}(K)$) it follows easily that $K[W]$ is an affine K-algebra. Therefore we have a morphism $\delta : W \longrightarrow \mathrm{spec}_K(K[W])$, and we claim δ is an isomorphism. Since W is normal so also is $\mathrm{spec}_K(K[W])$. Hence, by (18.2), it suffices to see that δ is birational. But this follows easily from the fact, proved above, that $\alpha_0 K[W]$ contains $K[V] \cap \alpha_0 K(W)$, and the fact that, since V is affine, $K(V)$ is the field of fractions of $K[V]$.

(18.4) PROPOSITION [Fond., Ch. V, V, Prop. 3]. _Let_ $\alpha : V \longrightarrow W$ _be a dominant morphism of irreducible varieties, and put_ $r = \dim V - \dim W$. _Let_ x _be a point of_ V _such that_ $y = \alpha(x)$ _is normal on_ W. _Suppose_ further that each irreducible component passing through x of the fibre of α over y has dimension r. Then if U is a neighborhood of x in V, $\alpha(U)$ is a neighborhood of y in W.

COROLLARY. Let $\alpha : V \longrightarrow W$ be a dominant morphism of varieties, where W is normal. Assume the dimensions of the irreducible components of the fibres of α are constant. Then α is an open map.

(18.5) Algebraic curves (cf. [M, Ch. III, §8, Cor. to Prop. 1, and Thm. 5]). An algebraic curve is an algebraic variety of dimension 1. In the discussion to follow we shall assume that all algebraic varieties are irreducible.

(a) An algebraic curve is smooth if and only if it is normal.

(b) Let L be a finitely generated field extension of K of transcendence degree 1. Then there is an essentially unique complete smooth curve C whose function field is isomorphic (as K-algebra) to L. Moreover C is a projective variety.

(c) If V is any smooth algebraic curve then the dominant morphisms $\alpha : V \longrightarrow C$ correspond bijectively to the K-algebra homomorphisms $\alpha_0 : K(C) \longrightarrow K(V)$. If α_0 is an isomorphism then α is an open immersion.

If we apply (b) to $K(V)$ and (c) to the identity map of $K(V)$ we obtain:

(d) A smooth curve V is an open subset of a

unique complete smooth curve $\overline{V}$.

Another corollary of (c) is:

(e) If C is a complete smooth curve then the anti-homomorphism

$$\mathrm{Aut}_{\mathrm{alg.\,var.}}(C) \longrightarrow \mathrm{Aut}_{K\text{-alg.}}(K(C))$$

is bijective.

Finally, we record:

(f) Let $\alpha : V \longrightarrow W$ be a morphism from a smooth curve V into a complete variety W. Then α extends to a morphism $\overline{\alpha} : \overline{V} \longrightarrow W$.

To see this we can first replace W by $\overline{\alpha(V)}$ and thus assume α is dominant. Forgetting the trivial case when W is a point we may then assume W is a (complete) curve. Let $\pi : \tilde{W} \longrightarrow W$ be its normalization (in $K(W)$). Then (see (18.2) and (a) above) $\tilde{W}$ is a complete smooth curve. Since V is smooth (hence normal), α factors through π via $\beta : V \longrightarrow \tilde{W}$. According to (c), the co-morphism $\beta_0 : K(\tilde{W}) \longrightarrow K(V) = K(\overline{V})$ is induced by a morphism $\overline{\beta} : \overline{V} \longrightarrow \tilde{W}$. Now $\pi \circ \overline{\beta} = \overline{\alpha}$ is the desired extension of α.

REFERENCES

[N. B.] N. Bourbaki, (a) Algèbre, Chapitre 5, Corps commutatifs (1959), (b) Algèbre commutative, Hermann, éd. Paris.

[C. -C.] Séminaire Cartan-Chevalley, Géométrie algébrique, Paris (1955/56).

[Class.] Séminaire C. Chevalley, Classification des groupes de Lie algébriques, Paris (1956-58).

[Fond.] C. Chevalley, Fondements de la géométrie algébrique, Paris (1958).

[EGA] A. Grothendieck et J. Dieudonné, Eléments de géométrie algébrique, Publ. IHES.

[M] D. Mumford, Introduction to algebraic geometry, Harvard notes.

[Z. -S.] O. Zariski and P. Samuel, Commutative algebra, van Nostrand, Princeton (1958).

CHAPTER I

GENERAL NOTIONS ASSOCIATED WITH ALGEBRAIC GROUPS

§1. THE NOTION OF AN ALGEBRAIC GROUP

(1.1) Algebraic groups. An algebraic group is an algebraic variety G together with:

(id) an element $e \in G$;

(mult) a morphism $\mu : G \times G \longrightarrow G$,

denoted $(x, y) \longmapsto xy$;

(inv) a morphism $i : G \longrightarrow G$,

denoted $x \longmapsto x^{-1}$,

with respect to which (the set) G is a group. We call G a k-group if G is a k-variety and if μ and i are defined over k (see (AG.12)). It follows then that $e \in G(k)$, because $\{e\}$ is the image of the k-morphism $\alpha \circ \delta$, where $\delta(x) = (x, x)$ and $\alpha(x, y) = xy^{-1}$ (see (AG.14.5)).

A morphism of algebraic groups is a morphism of varieties which is also a homomorphism of groups. The expression "$\alpha : G \longrightarrow G'$ is a k-morphism of k-groups" means G and G' are k-groups and α is a morphism defined over k.

(1.2) <u>The connected component</u> of e in an algebraic group G will be denoted

$$G^0$$

PROPOSITION. <u>Let</u> G <u>be an algebraic group.</u>

(a) G <u>is smooth (as a variety).</u>

(b) G^0 <u>is a normal subgroup of finite index in</u> G <u>whose cosets are the connected, as well as irreducible, components of</u> G. <u>If</u> G <u>is defined over</u> k, <u>so is</u> G^0.

(c) <u>Every closed subgroup of finite index contains</u> G^0.

PROOF. (a) G is "homogeneous," i.e. it has (as a variety) a transitive group of automorphisms. (Namely, the translations $x \longmapsto xy$.) Since G has some simple points (AG.17.2) it follows that all points are simple. Moreover it now follows from (AG.17.2) that the irreducible and connected components of G coincide.

(b) If $x \in G^0$ then $x^{-1}G^0$ is a connected component of G containing e, and hence equal to G^0. Thus $x^{-1}G^0 = G^0$ for all $x \in G^0$. It follows that $G^0 = (G^0)^{-1}$ and $G^0G^0 = G^0$, so G^0 is a group. Its cosets (say left) are each connected components of G, clearly, so they must be finite in number (the space G is noetherian). Finally, if $y \in G$ then yG^0y^{-1} is a connected component of G containing e, and hence equal to G^0. Thus G^0

is normal in G. Let G be defined over k. Then G^0 and its cosets are defined over k_s (AG.12.3). They are permuted by the Galois group Γ of k_s over k, acting as in (AG.14.3). Since $e \in G(k)$ (1.1), it follows that $G^0(k_s)$ is stable under Γ, hence G^0 is defined over k (AG.14.4).

(c) If H is a closed subgroup of finite index in G, then the complement of H, being a finite union of the non identity left cosets, is also closed. Thus H is open and closed so it must contain G^0.

The proposition implies that the notions "connected" and "irreducible" coincide for algebraic groups. The term "connected" is preferred because the word "irreducible" has a different use in the representation theory of G.

(1.3) PROPOSITION. Let G be a k-group and let H be a not necessarily closed subgroup. Let U and V be dense open sets in G.

(a) $U \cdot V = G$.

(b) $\bar{H}$ is a subgroup of G. If $H \subset G(k_s)$ and if H is stable under $Gal(k_s/k)$, then $\bar{H}$ is defined over k.

(c) If H is constructible, then $H = \bar{H}$.

PROOF. (a) Given $x \in G$, the dense open sets U and xV^{-1} have a common point, say $u = xv^{-1}$, so $x = uv \in U \cdot V$.

(b) Since $x \mapsto x^{-1}$ is a homeomorphism we have $\bar{H}^{-1} = \overline{H^{-1}} = \bar{H}$. If $x \in H$ then $x\bar{H} = \overline{xH} = \bar{H}$, so $H\bar{H} = \bar{H}$. If $y \in \bar{H}$ then $Hy \subset \bar{H}$ so $\bar{H}y = \overline{Hy} \subset \bar{H}$. Thus $\bar{H}\bar{H} = \bar{H}$, so $\overline{H}$ is a group.

The assertions concerning rationality over k follow from (AG.14.4).

(c) If H is constructible then it follows from (AG.10.2) that H contains a dense open subset of $\overline{H}$. By part (b) $\overline{H}$ is a closed subgroup, so part (a) implies $\overline{H} = H \cdot H = H$.

(1.4) COROLLARY. Let G' be a k-group and $\alpha : G \longrightarrow G'$ a morphism.

(a) $\alpha(G)$ is a closed subgroup of G; and it is defined over k if α is defined over k.

(b) $\alpha(G^0) = \alpha(G)^0$.

(c) $\dim G = \dim \ker(\alpha) + \dim \alpha(G)$.

PROOF. (a) According to (AG.10.2) the subgroup $\alpha(G)$ is constructible, so (1.3)(c) implies that it is closed. Moreover (AG.14.5) implies that it is defined over k if α is so.

(b) By part (a), $\alpha(G^0)$ is closed. Since it is also connected and of finite index in $\alpha(G)$ it follows from (1.2)(c) that $\alpha(G^0) = \alpha(G)^0$.

(c) It follows from (AG.10.1) that for all x in some dense open set in $\alpha(G)$, $\dim G - \dim \alpha(G) = \dim \alpha^{-1}(x)$. But $\dim \alpha^{-1}(x) = \dim \ker(\alpha)$ for all x, clearly.

(1.5) Affine groups. Let $G = \mathrm{spec}_K(A)$ be an affine algebraic group, $A = K[G]$. We shall translate the elements of structure of G in terms of A.

$$e \in G: \qquad e : A \longrightarrow K, \; e(f) = f(e) \;.$$

(The latter homomorphism, evaluation at e, was formerly denoted "e_e.")

$$\mu : G \times G \longrightarrow G : \mu_0 : A \longrightarrow A \otimes_K A \;.$$

If $\mu_0 f = \Sigma g_i \otimes h_i$ then $f(xy) = \Sigma g_i(x) h_i(y)$.
Next we have the inverse.

$$i : G \longrightarrow G: \qquad i_0 : A \longrightarrow A \;.$$

$$(i_0 f)(x) = f(x^{-1}) \;.$$

In order to formulate the group axioms we introduce

$$p : G \longrightarrow G \quad : \quad p_0 : A \longrightarrow A$$

$$x \longmapsto e \qquad (p_0 f)(x) = f(e) \;.$$

Now the group axioms are expressed by the commutativity of the following diagrams:

$$\text{(Ass)} \quad \begin{array}{ccc} G \times G \times G & \xrightarrow{\mu \times 1} & G \times G \\ {\scriptstyle 1 \times \mu}\downarrow & & \downarrow{\scriptstyle \mu} \\ G \times G & \xrightarrow[\mu]{} & G \end{array} \qquad \begin{array}{ccc} A \otimes A \otimes A & \xleftarrow{\mu_0 \otimes 1} & A \otimes A \\ {\scriptstyle 1 \otimes \mu_0}\uparrow & & \uparrow{\scriptstyle \mu_0} \\ A \otimes A & \xleftarrow[\mu_0]{} & A \end{array}$$

(Id)

$$
\begin{array}{ccc}
G & \xrightarrow{(p,\ 1)} & G \times G \\
{\scriptstyle (1,\ p)}\downarrow & \searrow^{1} & \downarrow{\scriptstyle \mu} \\
G \times G & \xrightarrow[\mu]{} & G
\end{array}
\qquad
\begin{array}{ccc}
A & \xleftarrow{(p_0,\ 1)} & A \otimes A \\
{\scriptstyle (1,\ p_0)}\uparrow & \searrow^{1} & \uparrow{\scriptstyle \mu_0} \\
A \otimes A & \xleftarrow[\mu_0]{} & A
\end{array}
$$

(Inv)

$$
\begin{array}{ccc}
G & \xrightarrow{(i,\ 1)} & G \times G \\
{\scriptstyle (1,\ i)}\downarrow & \searrow^{p} & \downarrow{\scriptstyle \mu} \\
G \times G & \xrightarrow[\mu]{} & G
\end{array}
\qquad
\begin{array}{ccc}
A & \xleftarrow{(i_0,\ 1)} & A \otimes A \\
{\scriptstyle (1,\ i_0)}\uparrow & \nwarrow^{p_0} & \uparrow{\scriptstyle \mu_0} \\
A \otimes A & \xleftarrow[\mu_0]{} & A
\end{array}
$$

Note that p_0 is just the composite of the augmentation $e : A \longrightarrow K$ with the inclusion $K \subset A$. Thus, in terms of A, G is determined by the data (A, e, μ_0, i_0) subject to the above three axioms.

The data (A, e, μ_0) subject to (Ass) and (Id) are sometimes called an associative Hopf algebra with identity and μ_0 is referred to as its diagonal map.

If C is any K-algebra we can describe the group structure on

$$G(C) = \mathrm{Hom}_{K\text{-alg.}}(A,\ C)$$

as follows: If $x, y \in G(C)$ then the product in $G(C)$ of x and y is the composite:

$$A \xrightarrow{\mu_0} A \otimes A \xrightarrow{x \otimes y} C \otimes C \xrightarrow{m} C \ ,$$

where m is the multiplication in C $(m(a \otimes b) = ab)$. If

$C \longrightarrow C'$ is an algebra homomorphism then $G(C) \longrightarrow G(C')$ is a group homomorphism. Quite generally, for any (not necessarily affine) algebraic group its functor of points, $C \longmapsto G(C)$, is a group valued functor.

(1.6) EXAMPLES.

(1) The <u>additive group</u> $\mathbb{G}_a$. Its affine ring is $k[\mathbb{G}_a] = k[T]$, a polynomial ring in one variable; $\mu_0(T) = (T \otimes 1) + (1 \otimes T)$; $i_0(T) = -T$; $e(T) = 0$.

(2) <u>The general linear group</u> $\mathbb{GL}_n$. The affine ring is

$$k[\mathbb{GL}_n] = k[T_{11}, T_{12}, \ldots, T_{nn}, D^{-1}] ,$$

where $D = \det(T_{ij})$. Thus $\mathbb{GL}_n$ is the principal open set $(K^{n^2})_D$, in affine n^2-space. We have

$$e(T_{ij}) = \delta_{ij}$$

$$\mu_0(T_{ij}) = \Sigma_h T_{ih} \otimes T_{hj}$$

and

$$i_0(T_{ij}) = (-1)^{i+j} D^{-1} \det(T_{rs})_{r \neq j,\, s \neq i} .$$

(3) <u>The multiplicative group</u> $\mathbb{GL}_1$ is sometimes denoted $\mathbb{G}_m$ in the literature. As a special case of the above formulas we have

$$k[\mathbb{GL}_1] = k[T, T^{-1}]$$

$$e(T) = 1,\ \mu_0(T) = T \otimes T;\ i_0(T) = T^{-1} .$$

(4) The special linear group, $\mathbb{SL}_n$, is the kernel of the morphism

$$\det : \mathbb{GL}_n \longrightarrow \mathbb{GL}_1 .$$

Thus $k[\mathbb{SL}_n] = k[T_{11}, T_{12}, \ldots, T_{nn}]/(\det(T_{ij}) - 1)$. The maps μ_0 and i_0 are induced, on passing to the quotient, by those of $k[\mathbb{GL}_n]$. The same remark applies to any closed subgroup of $\mathbb{GL}_n$, such as the following examples.

(5) The group of upper triangular matrices

$$\mathbb{T}_n = \{g \in \mathbb{GL}_n \mid g_{ij} = 0 \text{ for } j < i\}$$

and the upper triangular unipotent group

$$\mathbb{U}_n = \{g \in \mathbb{T}_n \mid g_{ii} = 1 \ (1 \leqq i \leqq n)\} .$$

$\mathbb{T}_n$ is the semi-direct product of $\mathbb{U}$ and of the diagonal group

$$\mathbb{D}_n = \{g \in \mathbb{GL}_n \mid g_{ij} = 0 \text{ for } i \neq j\} .$$

(6) The symplectic group

$$\mathbb{S}p_{2n} = \{g \in \mathbb{GL}_{2n} \mid {}^t g J g = J\}$$

where ${}^t g$ denotes the transpose of g and

$$J = \begin{pmatrix} O & I_n \\ -I_n & O \end{pmatrix} .$$

(7) If S is a non-singular symmetric n by n matrix then

$$O(S) = \{g \in \mathbb{GL}_n \mid {}^t gSg = S\}$$

is called the <u>orthogonal group</u> of S.

(8) Let V be a finite dimensional vector space, and let $S_K(V^*)$ be the symmetric algebra of its dual space. Then we can identify V with the affine variety $\operatorname{spec}_K(S_K(V^*))$. Indeed, for any K-algebra B we have $\operatorname{Hom}_{K\text{-alg}}(S_K(V^*), B) = \operatorname{Hom}_{K\text{-mod}}(V^*, B) = B \otimes_K V$. In case $B = K$ this gives the bijection $V \longrightarrow \operatorname{spec}_K(S_K(V^*))$ making V a variety, and it shows that the points of V in B are just

$$V(B) = B \otimes_K V \quad ,$$

the B-module obtained by base change $K \longrightarrow B$. We can make V an algebraic group using the addition $V \times V \longrightarrow V$, and this is compatible with the natural addition in $B \otimes_K V$.

If V has a k-structure V_k as vector space, then it has a corresponding k-structure as variety given by $S_k(V_k^*)$ in $S_K(V^*)$. In case B is a k-algebra we then obtain, just as above, $V(B) = B \otimes_k V_k$.

The vector space $E = \operatorname{End}_{K\text{-mod}}(V)$ can also be made into a variety, and we then have $E(B) = B \otimes_K E = B \otimes_K \operatorname{End}_{K\text{-mod}}(V) = \operatorname{End}_{B\text{-mod}}(B \otimes V) = \operatorname{End}_{B\text{-mod}}(V(B))$. In this way the natural action of E on V extends naturally to the functor of points.

Relative to any basis for V, the determinant, det, is a polynomial with integer coefficients in the matrix coordinates of E. Thus if V has a k-structure then $E_k = \mathrm{End}_{k\text{-mod}}(V_k)$ is a k-structure on E, and we see that $\det \in S_K(E^*)$ is defined over k. The principal k-open set $E_{\det} = \{g \in E \mid \det(g) \neq 0\}$ is denoted

$$GL(V) \text{ or } GL_V .$$

It inherits a multiplication from E making it a group. Since the inverse of a matrix is a polynomial in the matrix coefficients and $\det^{-1}$ it follows that GL_V is an algebraic group. Moreover, if B is any K-algebra we have

$$GL_V(B) = \{g \in E(B) \mid \det(g) \text{ is invertible}\}$$

where we identify $E(B)$ with B-module endomorphisms of the free B-module $V(B)$. Thus

$$GL_V(B) = \mathrm{Aut}_{B\text{-mod}}(B \otimes_K V) .$$

A closed subgroup of GL_V is called a <u>linear algebraic group</u>. A morphism $\alpha : G \longrightarrow GL_V$ of algebraic groups is called a <u>rational (linear) representation</u> of G. If G is a k-group we say α is defined over k, or that α is k-rational, if it is a k-morphism with respect to the k-structure on GL_V induced as above by one given on V. Relative to a k-rational basis of V, this just means that the corresponding matrix coefficients $\alpha(g)_{ij}$ are k-rational functions $G \longrightarrow K$. Since these functions are all of the form $g \longmapsto h(\alpha(g)(v))$ with $v \in V_k$ and $h \in V_k^*$ it follows that $\alpha : G \longrightarrow GL_V$ is a k-rational representation if and only if the corresponding map $G \times V \longrightarrow V$ is a k-morphism of varieties.

A representation $\alpha : G \longrightarrow GL_V$ will be called immersive if it induces an isomorphism of G with the closed subgroup $\alpha(G)$ of GL_V, in other words, if it is a closed immersion.

(9) The multiplicative group of an algebra. Let Λ be a finite dimensional associative (not necessarily commutative) K-algebra, and let N be the norm, $N_{\Lambda/K} : \Lambda \longrightarrow K$ (the determinant of the regular representation). Viewing Λ as an affine space, we see that the group $\mathbb{GL}_1(\Lambda)$ of invertible elements in Λ is the principal open set defined by N. Hence $\mathbb{GL}_1(\Lambda)$ is an affine algebraic group which is a "rational variety." The latter means that $\mathbb{GL}_1(\Lambda)$ is irreducible and that its function field, $K(\mathbb{GL}_1(\Lambda))$, is a field of rational functions (in $\dim_K \Lambda$ variables).

If Λ has a k-structure given by a k-subalgebra Λ_k then the norm N is defined over k, and $\mathbb{GL}_1(\Lambda)$ becomes a k-group (see (AG.12.4)). In this case $k(\mathbb{GL}_1(\Lambda))$ is already a purely transcendental extension of k, i.e. $\mathbb{GL}_1(\Lambda)$ is "k-rational." For any k-algebra k' the points, $\mathbb{GL}_1(\Lambda)(k')$, form the multiplicative group

$\mathbb{GL}_1(\Lambda(k'))$ of $\Lambda(k') = \Lambda_k \otimes_k k'$.

(1.7) Actions of groups on varieties. An algebraic transformation space is a triple (G, V, α) where G is an algebraic group, V is a variety, and $\alpha : G \times V \longrightarrow V$, $(g, x) \longmapsto gx = \alpha(g, x)$, is a morphism satisfying

$$ex = x \text{ and } g(hx) = (gh)x$$

for all $x \in V$ and all $g, h \in G$. We sometimes refer to this situation by saying that "G acts morphically on the variety V." If G and V are given with k-structures we say G acts "k-morphically" if α is defined over k. Because of the notation gx or $g \cdot x$ or $g(x)$, a symbol for α is superfluous, and is usually omitted.

For subsets M and N of V we have the transporter

$$\mathrm{Tran}_G(M, N) = \{g \in G \mid gM \subset N\} ,$$

sometimes also denoted $\mathrm{Tr}_G(M, N)$. One calls

$$N_G(M) = \mathrm{Tran}_G(M, M)$$

the normalizer of M in G. For example

$$G_x = N_G(\{x\})$$

is the stability group or the isotropy group of $x \in V$, and

$$G(x) = \{gx \mid g \in G\}$$

is called the <u>orbit</u> of x. The set

$$Z_G(M) = G^M = \bigcap_{x\in M} G_x$$

is called the <u>centralizer</u> of M in G.

PROPOSITION. *Let G be a k-group acting k-morphically on a k-variety V, and let M and N be subsets of V.*

(a) *We have* $\mathrm{Tran}_G(M, N) \subset \mathrm{Tran}_G(\overline{M}, \overline{N})$, *with equality if N is closed.*

(b) *If N is k-closed and if* $M \subset V(k)$, *then* $\mathrm{Tran}_G(M, N)$ *is k-closed.*

(c) *If* $M \subset V(k)$ *then* $Z_G(\overline{M}) = Z_G(M)$ *and* $N_G(\overline{M})$ *are k-closed.*

PROOF. (a) If $gM \subset N$ then $g\overline{M} = \overline{gM} \subset \overline{N}$. If $N = \overline{N}$ then $g\overline{M} \subset \overline{N}$ implies $gM \subset N$.

(b) Define $\alpha_x : G \longrightarrow V$, $\alpha_x(g) = gx$ for $x \in V$. Then if $x \in V(k)$, α_x is defined over k, so $\alpha_x^{-1}(N) = \mathrm{Tran}_G(\{x\}, N)$ is k-closed. Since $M \subset V(k)$ it follows that $\mathrm{Tran}_G(M, N) = \bigcap_{x\in M} \alpha_x^{-1}(N)$ is k-closed.

(c) The fixed points in V of any $g \in G$ are closed (because varieties are separated) so it follows that $Z_G(M) = Z_G(\overline{M})$. Part (b) implies G_x is k-closed for $x \in V(k)$, so $Z_G(M) = \bigcap_{x\in M} G_x$ is k-closed.

Moreover $N_G(\overline{M}) = \mathrm{Tran}_G(\overline{M}, \overline{M}) = \mathrm{Tran}_G(M, \overline{M})$ (part (a)), and the latter is k-closed by part (b).

REMARKS. (1) It is not true in part (b) that $\mathrm{Tran}_G(M, N)$ need be defined over k even if N is defined over k and

$M \subset V(k)$.

(2) The proposition applies notably to the action of G on itself by inner automorphisms.

(1.8) Closed orbit lemma. The following simple result is a basic technical tool for the theory of algebraic groups.

PROPOSITION. *Let G be an algebraic group acting morphically on a non-empty variety V. Then each orbit is a smooth variety which is open in its closure in V. Its boundary is a union of orbits of strictly lower dimension. In particular, the orbits of minimal dimension are closed.*

PROOF. Let $M = G(x)$ be the orbit of $x \in V$. Since M is the image of the morphism $g \mapsto gx$ it follows from (AG.10.2) that M contains a dense open set in $\overline{M}$. Now G operates transitively on M, and it evidently leaves $\overline{M}$ stable. Since M contains an $\overline{M}$-neighborhood of one of its points it follows from homogeneity that M is open in $\overline{M}$. Hence $\overline{M} - M$ is closed and of lower dimension, as well as being G-stable. Finally, the smoothness of M follows from homogeneity.

COROLLARY. *Closed orbits exist.*

(1.9) Translations. Let G be an affine k-group acting k-morphically on an affine k-variety V, via $a : G \times V \longrightarrow V$. Thus a is defined by the comorphism

$$\alpha_0 : k[V] \longrightarrow k[G] \otimes_k k[V]$$

of affine rings over k.

If $g \in G$ we denote by λ_g the comorphism of $x \mapsto g^{-1}x$. Then

$$f \mapsto \lambda_g f, \ (\lambda_g f)(x) = f(g^{-1}x) \quad ,$$

is a linear automorphism of $K[V]$ which we call *left translation* of functions by g. The reason for the inverse is to make $g \mapsto \lambda_g$ a homomorphism: $\lambda_g \cdot \lambda_h = \lambda_{gh}$.

PROPOSITION. *Let* F *be any finite dimensional vector subspace of* $K[V]$. *Then there is a finite dimensional subspace* E *which* (i) *contains* F, (ii) *is defined over* k, *and* (iii) *is stable under left translation by* G. *Moreover a necessary and sufficient condition that* F *be invariant under left translation is that*

$$\alpha_0 F \subset K[G] \otimes_K F \ .$$

PROOF. We begin with the first assertion. By enlarging F we may assume F is defined over k. We may further assume that F is spanned by a single function $f \in k[V]$, for the general case will then follow by taking the sum of the E's obtained for each element of a k-basis of F.

Write $\alpha_0 f = \Sigma_{i=1}^n f_i \otimes h_i \in k[G] \otimes_k k[V]$, so that n is minimal. Then for $g \in G$ we have $(\lambda_g f)(x) = f(g^{-1}x) = \Sigma f_i(g^{-1})h_i(x)$, so that $\lambda_g f = \Sigma f_i(g^{-1})h_i$. There exists therefore a finite dimensional subspace of $k[V]$, defined over k, containing all $\lambda_g f (g \in G)$. The intersection of all such subspaces of $K[V]$ clearly satisfies the three required conditions.

To prove the last assertion, let F be a subspace of $K[V]$ and let $\{f_i\} \cup \{h_j\}$ be a basis for $K[V]$ such that $\{f_i\}$ spans F. If $f \in F$ and $g \in G$ we have $\lambda_g f = \Sigma\, r_i(g^{-1})f_i + \Sigma\, s_j(g^{-1})h_j$, where $\alpha_0 f = \Sigma\, r_i \otimes f_i + \Sigma\, s_j \otimes h_j$. Hence $\lambda_g f \in F \Longleftrightarrow s_j(g^{-1}) = 0$ for all j. Varying $g \in G$ and $f \in F$ we see that $\lambda_g F \subset F$ for all $g \in G \Longleftrightarrow \alpha_0 F \subset K[G] \otimes_K F$. Q. E. D.

Consider the special case where $V = G$ and G acts on itself by both left and right translation. More precisely we let $(g, h) \in G \times G$ act on $x \in G$ by $x \longmapsto gxh^{-1}$. In this way we obtain two actions of G on functions $f \in K[G]$:

<u>left translation</u>: $(\lambda_g f)(x) = f(g^{-1}x)$

<u>right translation</u>: $(\rho_g f)(x) = f(xg)$.

They are both homomorphisms of G:

$$\lambda_{gh} = \lambda_g \lambda_h, \quad \rho_{gh} = \rho_g \rho_h \quad ;$$

and they commute:

$$\lambda_g \rho_h = \rho_h \lambda_g \quad \text{for all } g, h \in G \ .$$

Applying the proposition above we obtain the

COROLLARY. <u>Every finite dimensional subspace</u> F <u>of</u>

K[G] is contained in a finite dimensional subspace E defined over k which is stable under both left and right translation by G.

(1.10) PROPOSITION. Let G be an affine k-group. Then G is k-isomorphic to a closed subgroup, defined over k, of some $\mathbb{GL}_n$.

PROOF. Write $k[G] = k[f_1, \ldots, f_n]$. Using (1.9) we can even do this so that $f_1, \ldots, f_n$ is a basis for a subspace E of K[G] stable under right translation, i.e. so that $\mu_0 E \subset E \otimes_K K[G]$ (see (1.9)). Thus, for each i, we have

$$\mu_0 f_i = \sum_j f_j \otimes m_{ji}$$

for some $m_{ji} \in k[G]$. If $g \in G$ then $(\rho_g f_i)(x) = f_i(xg) = \Sigma f_i(x) m_{ji}(g)$, i.e.

$$\rho_g f_i = \Sigma_j m_{ji}(g) f_i \quad .$$

It follows that

$$\alpha : G \longrightarrow \mathbb{GL}_n, \; \alpha(g) = (m_{ji}(g))$$

is a morphism of algebraic groups, and it is evidently defined over k, because the m_{ji} are. Indeed, the co-morphism

$$\alpha_0 : k[\mathbb{GL}_n] = k[T_{11}, \ldots, T_{nn}, D^{-1}] \longrightarrow k[G]$$

is defined by $\alpha_0(T_{ji}) = m_{ji}$. Since $f_i(x) = f_i(ex) = \Sigma_j f_j(e)m_{ji}(x)$ we have $f_i = \Sigma_j f_j(e)m_{ji} \in im(\alpha_0)$ for each i. Hence α_0 is surjective, so α is a closed immersion. We know from (1.4) that $G' = \alpha(G)$ is defined over k, so α induces the desired k-isomorphism $G \longrightarrow G'$.

REMARK. It follows easily from an argument like the one above that, if E is any finite dimensional right invariant subspace of K[G], the homomorphism $\alpha : G \longrightarrow GL(E)$ induced by right translation is a rational representation of G.

(1.11) Actions of groups on groups; semi-direct products. Let G and H be k-groups, and let $\alpha : G \times H \longrightarrow H$ be an action of G on H. (This means that elements of G act as group automorphisms of H.) The basic example of this occurs when G and H are subgroups of a larger group in which G normalizes H, and the action is induced by conjugation: $\alpha(g, h) = ghg^{-1}$. In fact this is essentially the most general case, as we see now by constructing the semi-direct product

$$H \cdot G ,$$

as follows: as a variety it is $H \times G$, and the multiplication is defined by

$$(h_1, g_1)(h_2, g_2) = (h_1\alpha(g_1, h_2), g_1g_2) .$$

It is easy to check that this makes $H\cdot G$ a group. For example

$$(h, g)^{-1} = (\alpha(g^{-1}, h)^{-1}, g^{-1})$$

Moreover we have the exact sequence of morphisms

$$1 \longrightarrow H \xrightarrow{i} H\cdot G \xrightarrow{p} G \longrightarrow 1 ,$$

and a section $s : G \longrightarrow H\cdot G$ of p, defined by

$$i(h) = (h, e), \quad p(h, g) = g, \quad s(g) = (e, g)$$

If α is defined over k then it is clear that $H\cdot G$ has a natural k-structure so that i, p, and s are k-morphisms. The morphism i is an isomorphism of H with a normal subgroup of $H\cdot G$, and α is induced, via s, by conjugation of iH by sG:

$$(e, g)(h, e)(e, g)^{-1} = (\alpha(g, h), e) .$$

Suppose G' is an algebraic group and G and H are closed subgroups with H normalized by G. Then we shall say G' is the <u>semi-direct product of the subgroups</u> G and H if the multiplication map

$$H \times G \longrightarrow G', \ (h, g) \longmapsto hg$$

is an isomorphism of varieties. Then $\alpha(g, h) = ghg^{-1}$ defines an action of G on H so that G' is isomorphic to the group $H\cdot G$ constructed above.

§2. GROUP CLOSURE; SOLVABLE AND NILPOTENT GROUPS

(2.1) Group closure. Let M be a subset of a k-group G. We write

$$\mathcal{A}(M)$$

for the intersection of all closed subgroups of G containing M; thus $\mathcal{A}(M)$ is one of them, the smallest one. From (1.3)(b) we have:

(a) *If M is a subgroup of G then $\mathcal{A}(M) = \bar{M}$.*

Put $N = M \cup \{e\} \cup M^{-1}$ and let N_m denote the image of the product map $\alpha_m : N \times \ldots \times N \longrightarrow G$. Then $H = \bigcup_m N_m$ is the subgroup generated by M, so (a) implies that $\mathcal{A}(M) = \bar{H}$.

If M is a subvariety defined over k then so also is N. Since each α_m is a morphism defined over k it follows from (AG.14.5) that each $\bar{N}_m$ is defined over k. Now (AG.14.6) further implies that $\mathcal{A}(M) = \bar{H}$, being the closure of $\bigcup_m \bar{N}_m$, is also defined over k. Thus we have proved:

(b) *If M is a subvariety defined over k then $\mathcal{A}(M)$ is defined over k.*

Next we treat products:

(c) *If M_i is a subset of an algebraic group $G_i (i = 1, 2)$ then $\mathcal{A}(M_1 \times M_2) = \mathcal{A}(M_1) \times \mathcal{A}(M_2)$.*

The right-hand side is a closed subgroup containing $M_1 \times M_2$, and hence contains the left-hand side.

On the other hand $\mathcal{A}(M_1 \times M_2)$ contains $M_1 \times \{e\}$ and hence also $\mathcal{A}(M_1 \times \{e\})$, which is clearly equal to $\mathcal{A}(M_1) \times \{e\}$. Similarly it contains $\{e\} \times \mathcal{A}(M_2)$, and hence also the right-hand side.

(d) Let M and N be subsets of G such that N normalizes (resp. centralizes) M. Then $\mathcal{A}(N)$ normalizes (resp., centralizes) $\mathcal{A}(M)$.

Let $C(X)$ denote the normalizer (resp. centralizer) of a subset X of G. By hypothesis $N \subset C(M)$, and evidently $C(M) \subset C(\mathcal{A}(M))$. It follows from (1.7) that $C(\mathcal{A}(M))$ is closed, and hence $\mathcal{A}(N) \subset C(\mathcal{A}(M))$.

(e) If M and N are subgroups of G then the commutator groups (M, N) and $(\bar{M}, \bar{N})$ have the same closure.

Let $c : G \times G \longrightarrow G$, $c(x, y) = xyx^{-1}y^{-1}$. Since $M \times N$ is dense in $\bar{M} \times \bar{N}$ the same is true of $c(M \times N)$ in $c(\bar{M} \times \bar{N})$, so $\mathcal{A}(c(M \times N)) = \mathcal{A}(c(\bar{M} \times \bar{N}))$. But it follows from part (a) that these groups are the closures of (M, N) and of $(\bar{M}, \bar{N})$, respectively.

(f) If $\alpha : G \longrightarrow G'$ is a morphism of algebraic groups then

$$\alpha(\mathcal{A}(M)) = \mathcal{A}(\alpha(M)) .$$

$\alpha(\mathcal{A}(M))$ contains $\alpha(M)$ and, according to (1.4), it is closed. Hence it contains $\mathcal{A}(\alpha(M))$. On the other hand $\alpha^{-1}\mathcal{A}(\alpha(M))$ is closed (α is continuous) and contains M, so it contains $\mathcal{A}(M)$. Applying α we obtain

$\mathcal{A}(\alpha(M)) \supset \alpha(\alpha^{-1}\mathcal{A}(\alpha(M))) \supset \alpha(\mathcal{A}(M))$, thus reversing the inclusion proved above.

(2.2) PROPOSITION. Let $f_i : V_i \longrightarrow G (i \in I)$ be a family of k-morphisms from irreducible k-varieties V_i into a k-group G, and assume $e \in f_i V_i = W_i$ for each $i \in I$. Put $M = \cup W_i (i \in I)$. Then $\mathcal{A}(M)$ is a connected subgroup of G defined over k. Moreover, there is a finite sequence $(\alpha(1), \ldots, \alpha(n))$ in I such that $\mathcal{A}(M) = W_{\alpha(1)}^{e_1} \ldots W_{\alpha(n)}^{e_n}$, where each $e_i = \pm 1$.

PROOF. By enlarging I if necessary we can assume the morphisms $x \longmapsto f_i(x)^{-1}$ are also among the f_i's. If $\alpha = (\alpha(1), \ldots, \alpha(n))$ is a finite sequence in I put $W_\alpha = W_{\alpha(1)} \ldots W_{\alpha(n)}$. The set W_α is the image of the k-morphism,

$$V_{\alpha(1)} \times \ldots \times V_{\alpha(n)} \xrightarrow{f_{\alpha(1)} \times \ldots \times f_{\alpha(n)}} G \times \ldots \times G \xrightarrow{\text{mult.}} G \; ;$$

it follows therefore from the hypotheses that W_α is constructible, and that $\overline{W}_\alpha$ is an irreducible k-variety (see (AG.10.2)). As a consequence, for dimension reasons, there is an α such that $\overline{W}_\alpha$ is maximal.

If β and γ are two finite sequences, then

$$(1) \qquad \overline{W}_\beta \cdot \overline{W}_\gamma \subset \overline{W}_{(\beta, \gamma)} \; .$$

In fact, for $x \in W_\gamma$, the map $y \longmapsto y \cdot x$ sends W_β into $W_{(\beta,\gamma)}$, hence $\overline{W}_\beta$ into $\overline{W}_{(\beta,\gamma)}$, whence $\overline{W}_\beta \cdot W_\gamma \subset \overline{W}_{(\beta,\gamma)}$.

As a consequence, $x \cdot \overline{W}_\gamma \subset \overline{W}_{(\beta,\gamma)}$ for every $x \in \overline{W}_\beta$, from which (1) follows. Since $\overline{W}_\alpha$ is maximal, this yields in particular, for any β:

$$\overline{W}_\alpha \subset \overline{W}_\alpha \cdot \overline{W}_\beta \subset \overline{W}_{(\alpha,\beta)} = \overline{W}_\alpha \ .$$

Thus, $\overline{W}_\alpha$ is stable under products, and, taking β such that $W_\beta = W_\alpha^{-1}$, we also see that $\overline{W}_\alpha = \overline{W}_\alpha^{-1}$. Therefore, $\overline{W}_\alpha$ is a closed subgroup containing W_β for all β. Then, clearly, $W_\alpha = \mathcal{A}(M)$.

REMARK. The proof shows that the n in the statement of the proposition can be taken to be $\leqq 2 \cdot \dim G$.

(2.3) Group closure of a commutator group.

COROLLARY. *Let G' be a k-group and let G and H be closed subgroups defined over k, with G connected. Then the commutator group (G, H) is a closed connected subgroup defined over k.*

PROOF. If $h \in H$, define $f_h : G \longrightarrow G'$ by $f_h(g) = (g, h) = ghg^{-1}h^{-1}$. These are morphisms of the connected variety G into G', which all map e onto e, so (2.2) implies that the group generated by all $f_h(G)(h \in H)$, which is just (G, H), is closed.

It follows that $(G, H) = \mathcal{A}(M)$ where M is the image of the commutator map $G \times H \longrightarrow G'$. The latter is a k-morphism, so $\overline{M}$ is defined over k, and (2.1)(b) implies that $\mathcal{A}(\overline{M})$, which equals $\mathcal{A}(M)$, is defined over k.

If neither G nor H is connected then (G, H) need not be closed. One need only consider an infinite group generated by two finite subgroups G and H (for example the modular group $SL_2(\mathbb{Z})/\{\pm 1\}$ in $\mathbb{P}\mathbb{G}\mathbb{L}_2$). However this cannot happen if G or H is normal.

PROPOSITION. Let G be a k-group and let H and N be closed subgroups defined over k such that N is normalized by H. Then (H, N) is a closed subgroup of G defined over k and normal in HN.

COROLLARY. The smallest normal subgroup of G containing H is a closed subgroup defined over k.

For, since (H, G) is normal in G, that subgroup is H(H, G), which is closed.

PROOF (of the Proposition). There is no loss in assuming that G = HN. Once we show that (H, N) is closed the fact that it is defined over k follows just as in the proof of the first corollary above. That corollary further implies that (H^0, N) and (H, N^0) are closed and connected. Hence so also is the group L generated by them together with all of their conjugates in G.

We shall now invoke the theorem of Baer in the appendix at the end of §2. We have first that (H, N) is normal, so that L, the least normal subgroup containing (H^0, N) and (H, N^0), is contained in (H, N). Since L is closed it suffices to show that L has finite index in

(H, N); the latter will then be a finite union of cosets of L.

Pass to the group $G' = G/L$, and denote the image in G' of a subgroup $M \subset G$ by M'. Then H' and N' are such that $H^{0}{}'$ centralizes N' and $N^{0}{}'$ centralizes H' (by definition of L). Hence the set of commutators of elements of H' with elements of N' is a quotient of the finite set $(H'/H^{0}{}') \times (N'/N^{0}{}')$. Now the desired finiteness of (H', N') follows from Baer's theorem (appendix).

(2.4) Solvable and nilpotent groups. Let G be an abstract group. The derived series (D^nG) $(n \geqq 0)$, and the descending central series (C^nG) $(n \geqq 0)$, are defined inductively by:

$$D^0G = G, \quad D^{n+1}G = (D^nG, D^nG), \quad (n \geqq 0)$$

$$C^0G = G, \quad C^{n+1}G = (G, C^nG), \quad (n \geqq 0) \ .$$

We sometimes write $D^{\infty}G = \bigcap D^nG$ and $C^{\infty}G = \bigcap C^nG$. These are all characteristic subgroups (i.e. stable under all automorphisms) of G, evidently. One says that G is solvable (resp., nilpotent) if, for some n, we have $D^nG = \{e\}$ (resp., $C^nG = \{e\}$).

Now suppose G is an algebraic group. Then it would be natural to introduce notions of "algebraic solvability" and "nilpotence" for G, using the series $\mathcal{a}(D^nG)$ and $\mathcal{a}(C^nG)$, respectively. However, it follows from the results of (2.3) that the groups D^nG and C^nG are closed, so these notions coincide with the "abstract" group notions of solvability and nilpotence.

PROPOSITION. *Let* G *be an algebraic group, and let* M *and* N *be not necessarily closed subgroups such that* M *normalizes* N. *Then* $\overline{M}$ *normalizes* $\overline{N}$ *and* $\overline{(M, N)} = (\overline{M}, \overline{N})$.

PROOF. It is clear that $\overline{M}$ normalizes $\overline{N}$ (cf. (1.7)). Part (e) of (2.1) says (M, N) and $(\overline{M}, \overline{N})$ have the same closure, and (2.3) says $(\overline{M}, \overline{N})$ is closed (because $\overline{N}$ is normal in $\overline{M}\overline{N}$).

By a simple induction on n this implies:

COROLLARY 1. *For all* $n \geqq 0$ *we have*

$$\overline{D^n(M)} = D^n(\overline{M}) \text{ and } \overline{C^n(M)} = C^n(\overline{M}) \quad .$$

In particular, if M *is closed, then so also are the groups in its derived and descending central series.*

COROLLARY 2. *If* N *is a normal subgroup of* M *such that* M/N *is abelian (resp., nilpotent, resp. solvable) then the same is true of* $\overline{M}/\overline{N}$.

COROLLARY 3. *The following conditions on a* k-*group* G *are equivalent:*

(1) G *is solvable.*

(2) *There is a chain* $G = G_0 \supset G_1 \supset \dots \supset G_n = \{e\}$ *of closed subgroups defined over* k *such that* $(G_i, G_i) \subset G_{i+1}$ $(0 \leqq i < n)$.

PROOF. (2) $\Longrightarrow D^iG \subset G_i$ so G is solvable. Taking $G_i = D^iG$ we see that (1) $\Longrightarrow$ (2) by applying Corollary 1, plus (2.3) to get the G_i defined over k.

COROLLARY 4. The following conditions on a k-group G are equivalent:

(1) G is nilpotent.

(2) There is a chain $G = G_0 \supset G_1 \supset \dots \supset G_n = \{e\}$ of closed subgroups defined over k such that $(G, G_i) \subset G_{i+1} (0 \leqq i < n)$.

PROOF. (2) $\Longrightarrow C^iG \subset G_i$ so G is nilpotent. Conversely if G is nilpotent then Corollary 1 and (2.3) imply that the C^iG satisfy the conditions in (2).

APPENDIX. We present here a proof, due to Rosenlicht, of the following result of Baer. (See M. Rosenlicht, Proc. A.M.S. 13 (1962), 99-101.)

PROPOSITION. Let H and N be subgroups of a group G such that H normalizes N. Then the commutator group (H, N) is normal in HN. If the set of commutators

$$\{hnh^{-1}n^{-1} \mid h \in H, n \in N\}$$

is finite then (H, N) is finite.

We begin with a special case:

If $Z(G)$ has finite index in G then (G, G) is finite.

It suffices to show that any product of commutators

of elements of G can be written as such a product with at most n^3 factors, n being the index of the center of G. Noting that there are at most n^2 distinct commutators, and that in any product of commutators any two factors may be brought together by replacing the intermediate factors by conjugates, also commutators, it suffices to show that the (n+1)th power of a commutator is the product of n commutators. But if $a, b \in G$, then $(aba^{-1}b^{-1})^n$ is central, so

$$(aba^{-1}b^{-1})^{n+1} = b^{-1}(aba^{-1}b^{-1})^n b(aba^{-1}b^{-1}) \ ,$$

which may be written

$$b^{-1}((aba^{-1}b^{-1})^{n-1}(ab^2a^{-1}b^{-2}))b \ ,$$

a product of n commutators.

We proceed to prove the general result. It is worth remarking that if one is only interested in the case where both H and N are normal, the trickiest points below collapse to trivialities.

Assume, as we may, that $G = HN$, and consider the set S of all commutators of conjugates of elements of H by elements of N. Any conjugate of an element of H is of the form nhn^{-1}, with $n \in N$, $h \in H$, so each element of S is of the form

$$(nhn^{-1})n_1(nhn^{-1})^{-1}n_1^{-1} = (hnh^{-1}n^{-1})^{-1}(h(n_1n)h^{-1}(n_1n)^{-1}) \ ,$$

with $n_1 \in N$, which shows that S is a finite subset of

(H, N). But S clearly generates (H, N) and each inner automorphism of G permutes the elements of S. We deduce that (H, N) is normal in G, and also that there exists a normal subgroup G_0 of G of finite index that centralizes S, hence also (H, N). Now $G_0 \cap (H, N)$ is a central subgroup of (H, N) of finite index, so $((H, N), (H, N))$ is finite. Since the latter subgroup is normal in G, we may divide by it to suppose that (H, N) is commutative.

We now claim that the subgroup $(H, (H, N))$ of (H, N) is normal in G. Conjugation by elements of H clearly leaves it invariant, so we must show that if $n \in N$, $h \in H$, $m \in (H, N)$, then $n(hmh^{-1}m^{-1})n^{-1} \in (H, (H, N))$. But the latter element can also be written

$$hn(n^{-1}h^{-1}nh)mh^{-1}m^{-1}n^{-1},$$

which, by the commutativity of (H, N), is equal to

$$hnm(n^{-1}h^{-1}nh)h^{-1}m^{-1}n^{-1} = h(nmn^{-1})h^{-1}(nmn^{-1})^{-1} \in (H, (H, N)).$$

Note also that any commutator of H and (H, N) is one of H and N, so there are only a finite number of such and they all commute. Furthermore, if we square any such commutator, say $hmh^{-1}m^{-1}$, we get $(hmh^{-1}m^{-1})^2 = (hmh^{-1})^2m^{-2} = hm^2h^{-1}m^{-2}$, which is also a commutator. Thus $(H, (H, N))$ is finite. Dividing G by this subgroup, we see that we may suppose that H centralizes (H, N).

To finish the proof, recall that (H, N) is commutative and generated by a finite number of commutators $hnh^{-1}n^{-1}$, and note that here too the square of such a commutator is also a commutator:

$$(hnh^{-1}n^{-1})^2 = (hnh^{-1}n^{-1})(nh^{-1}n^{-1}h) = hnh^{-2}n^{-1}h = h^2nh^{-2}n^{-1} .$$

Thus (H, N) is finite.

§3. THE LIE ALGEBRA OF AN ALGEBRAIC GROUP

(3.1) Restricted Lie algebras. Let p denote the characteristic exponent of $k(p = \mathrm{char}(k)$ if $\mathrm{char}(k) > 0$, and $p = 1$ if $\mathrm{char}(k) = 0)$. A restricted Lie algebra over k is a Lie algebra g together with a "p-operation," $X \longmapsto X^{[p]}$, such that:

If $p = 1$ then $X^{[p]} = X$ and if $p > 1$ the p-operation satisfies

(i) $\mathrm{ad}(X^{[p]}) = \mathrm{ad}(X)^p \quad (X \in \underline{g})$

(ii) $(tX)^{[p]} = t^p X^{[p]} \quad (t \in k,\ X \in \underline{g})$

(iii) $(X+Y)^{[p]} = X^{[p]} + Y^{[p]} + \sum_{i=1}^{p-1} i^{-1} s_i(X, Y)$, where $s_i(X, Y)$ is the coefficient of t^i in $\mathrm{ad}(tX + Y)^{p-1}(X)\cdot(X, Y \in \underline{g})$.

Here, as usual, we write

$$\mathrm{ad}(X)(Y) = [X, Y] .$$

We shall have no occasion to use formula (iii) except in the special case (iii') If $[X, Y] = 0$ then $(X+Y)^{[p]} = X^{[p]} + Y^{[p]}$.

For a general discussion of restricted Lie algebras, and, in particular, of the following examples, the reader can consult Jacobson, pp. 185 ff. in [10].

EXAMPLES. (1) An associative k-algebra A gives rise to a restricted Lie algebra with underlying k-module A, where

$$[X, Y] = XY - YX, \quad X^{[p]} = X^p \ .$$

(2) In case $A = \mathrm{End}_k(E)$, where E is a vector space over k, we write $\underline{gl}(E)$ for the corresponding restricted Lie algebra.

(3) Suppose E itself is a not necessarily associative k-algebra. Then

$$\mathrm{Der}_k(E, E) = \{X \in \underline{gl}(E) \mid X(f\cdot g) = (Xf)\cdot g + f\cdot(Xg) \text{ for all } f, g \in E\}$$

is a restricted Lie subalgebra of $\underline{gl}(E)$.

Let F be a set of k-automorphisms of E. Then

$$L = \{X \in \mathrm{Der}_k(E, E) \mid Xs = sX, \quad (s \in F)\}$$

is a restricted Lie subalgebra of $\mathrm{Der}_k(E, E)$.

(4) Let $\underline{g}$ be a restricted Lie algebra, and let $\underline{h}$ and S be a subalgebra and subset, respectively, of $\underline{g}$. Then

$$\underline{h}^S = \{X \in \underline{h} \mid [X, Y] = 0 \text{ for all } Y \in S\}$$

is a restricted Lie subalgebra of $\underline{h}$, called the centralizer of S in $\underline{h}$.

(3.2) Derivatives of products. Let G be an algebraic group, let $\alpha_i : V_i \longrightarrow G$ be a morphism of varieties, and let $v_i \in V_i$ be a point such that $\alpha_i(v_i) = e$ $(1 \leqq i \leqq n)$. Put

$$v = (v_1, \ldots, v_n) \in V = V_1 \times \ldots \times V_n$$

and define $\alpha : V \longrightarrow G$ to be the product map

$$\alpha(x_1, \ldots, x_n) = \alpha_1(x_1) \ldots \alpha_n(x_n) .$$

Define $\beta_i : V_i \longrightarrow V$ by

$$\beta_i(x) = (v_1, \ldots, v_{i-1}, x, v_{i+1}, \ldots, v_n) .$$

Since $\alpha_i(v_i) = e$, we have $\alpha_i = \alpha \circ \beta_i$ $(1 \leqq i \leqq n)$. By (AG.16.1) there is a canonical isomorphism

$$T(V)_v \cong T(V_1)_{v_1} \oplus \ldots \oplus T(V_n)_{v_n} ,$$

so that

$$(d\alpha)_v(X_1, \ldots, X_n) = \Sigma_i (d\alpha \circ d\beta_i)_{v_i} X_i = \Sigma_i (d\alpha_i)_{v_i} X_i .$$

Applying this to $\mu : G \times G \longrightarrow G$ we obtain

$$T(G \times G)_{(e, e)} = T(G)_e \oplus T(G)_e ,$$

and

$$(d\mu)_{(e, e)}(X, Y) = X + Y .$$

(The $\alpha_i (i = 1, 2)$ both correspond, in this case, to the identity morphism $G \longrightarrow G$.) Next consider the composite

$$G \xrightarrow{(id,\, i)} G \times G \xrightarrow{\mu} G$$

sending x to $xx^{-1} = e$. Its derivative is zero, clearly, so we have

$$\begin{aligned} 0 &= d(\mu \circ (id, i))_e(X) \\ &= (d\mu)_{(e,e)}(d(id, i)_e X) \\ &= (d\mu)_{(e,e)}(X, (di)_e X) \\ &= X + (di)_e X \ . \end{aligned}$$

Thus

$$(di)_e X = -X \ .$$

(3.3) <u>The Lie algebra of an algebraic group.</u> Let $\alpha : G \longrightarrow G'$ be a k-morphism of affine k-groups, and let $\alpha_0 : A' \longrightarrow A$ be its comorphism. We shall write

$$L(\alpha) : L(G) \longrightarrow L(G')$$

in place of

$$(d\alpha)_e : T(G)_e \longrightarrow T(G')_e \ .$$

We further introduce the set

$$Lie(G) = \{D \in Der_K(A, A) \mid D\lambda_g = \lambda_g D \text{ for all } g \in G\}$$

of all <u>left invariant derivations</u> of A. According to (3.1), examples (3) and (4), Lie(G) <u>is a restricted Lie algebra</u> with operations

$$[D_1, D_2] = D_1 \circ D_2 - D_2 \circ D_1; \; D^{[p]} = D \circ D \circ \ldots \circ D \text{ (p factors)} .$$

We shall see that

$$\mathrm{Lie}(G)_k = \mathrm{Der}_k(A_k, A_k) \cap \mathrm{Lie}(G) = \{D \in \mathrm{Lie}(G) \mid DA_k \subset A_k\}$$

is a k-structure on Lie(G). If $D \in \mathrm{Lie}(G)$ then $e \circ D \in \mathrm{Der}_K(A, K(e)) = L(G)$, and

$$e \circ : \mathrm{Lie}(G) \longrightarrow L(G)$$

is a linear map sending $\mathrm{Lie}(G)_k$ into $L(G)_k$, clearly.

PROPOSITION. $\mathrm{Lie}(G)_k$ <u>is a</u> k-<u>structure on</u> Lie(G), <u>and</u> $e \circ : \mathrm{Lie}(G) \longrightarrow L(G)$ <u>is a linear isomorphism defined over</u> k. <u>The map</u> $L(\alpha) : L(G) \longrightarrow L(G')$ <u>is a homomorphism of restricted Lie algebras</u>.

In the second assertion, and in the sequel, it is understood that L(G) is given a structure of restricted Lie algebra, to be called the <u>Lie algebra of</u> G, by means of $e \circ$.

COROLLARY. $\mathrm{Lie}(G) = \mathrm{Lie}(G^0)$ <u>and</u> $\dim_K \mathrm{Lie}(G) = \dim G$.

The proposition will be proved below in (3.4). It expresses the fact that "a left invariant vector field on G is uniquely determined (via left translation) by its value at e, which may be any tangent vector at e."

We shall henceforth view $G \mapsto L(G) = T(G)_e$ as a functor from (affine) algebraic groups to restricted Lie algebras. The Lie algebras of groups G, H, M, N, ... will frequently be denoted by the corresponding letters $\underline{g}$, $\underline{h}$, $\underline{m}$, $\underline{n}$, ... (in the absence of Gothic typewriters). For example we would write $L(\alpha) : \underline{g} \longrightarrow \underline{g}'$ above, and we shall sometimes put $d\alpha$ in place of $L(\alpha)$, i.e. of $(d\alpha)_e$.

EXAMPLES. (1) Let $G = \mathbb{G}_a$, the additive group, so that $K[G] = K[T]$, a polynomial ring. If $D \in \text{Lie}(G)$ then D is determined completely by $f(T) = DT$. Left invariance requires that, for all $x \in G(= K)$ we have $\lambda_{-x} DT = f(T+x)$ equal to $D(\lambda_{-x}(T)) = D(T+x) = DT + Dx = f(T)$. But $f(T+x) = f(T)$ for all x means that f is constant, so Lie(G) consists of all K-multiples of $D = d/dT$. Since $D^{[p]}T^n = n(n-1) \ldots (n-(p-1))T^{n-p}$ (or zero if $n < p$) it follows that, if $\text{char}(k) > 0$, the p-operation is zero in $\text{Lie}(\mathbb{G}_a)$ (because the product of p consecutive integers is divisible by p).

(2) Consider $G = \mathbb{GL}_1$, so that $K[G] = K[T, T^{-1}]$. If $D \in \text{Lie}(G)$, then D is determined by the Laurent polynomial $DT = f(T)$. This time left invariance requires that, for all $x \in G(= K^*)$ we have $f(xT) = xf(T)$. It is easy to see that this implies $f(T) = aT$ for some $a \in K$. It follows that $D^{[p]}T = a^pT$ in this case. Thus Lie(G) is isomorphic to the one dimensional Lie algebra K with

p-operation $a \mapsto a^p$. If $\mathrm{char}(k) > 0$, therefore, the p-operations distinguish the Lie algebras of the additive and multiplicative groups.

(3.4) <u>Convolution</u>. In the course of proving the proposition in (3.3) we shall establish a formalism which permits us to introduce the Lie algebra structure directly in $L(G)$. We keep the notation

$$\alpha : G \longrightarrow G', \ \alpha_0 : A' \longrightarrow A \ ,$$

of (3.3). If V is a vector space over K we shall write

$$A(V) = \mathrm{Hom}_{K\text{-mod}}(A, V) \ ,$$

and similarly for $A'(V)$. If W is another vector space, we define a K-bilinear pairing

$$A(V) \times A(W) \longrightarrow A(V \otimes_K W)$$

$$(X, Y) \longmapsto X \cdot Y \ ,$$

where

$$X \cdot Y = (X \otimes Y) \circ \mu_0 \ .$$

EXAMPLE. *If* $g, h \in G$ *then*

$$e_g \cdot e_h = e_{gh} \quad (\text{in } A(K)) \ .$$

More generally, if B is any K-algebra, then $G(B)$, the group of points of G in B, corresponds (under the map $g \mapsto e_g$) to $\mathrm{Hom}_{K\text{-alg}}(A, B) \subset A(B)$, and the above formula becomes

$$e_{gh} = m \circ (e_g \cdot e_h)$$

where $m : B \otimes_K B \longrightarrow B \otimes_B B = B$ is the canonical map. We shall freely identify $K \otimes_K V$ and $V \otimes_K K$ with V.

LEMMA 1. *Let* U, V, *and* W *be vector spaces, and let* $X \in A(U)$, $Y \in A(V)$, *and* $Z \in A(W)$.

(a) $e \cdot X = X = X \cdot e$.

(b) $(X \cdot Y) \cdot Z = X \cdot (Y \cdot Z)$.

(c) $A(K)$ *is an associative* K-*algebra with identity* e, *and* $A(V)$ *is an* $A(K)$-*bimodule*. *The map* $g \longmapsto e_g$ *is a monomorphism from* G *to the group of invertible elements of* $A(K)$.

(d) *We have*

$$(X \cdot Y) \circ \alpha_0 = (X \circ \alpha_0) \cdot (Y \circ \alpha_0) \quad ,$$

where the product on the right is defined with respect to $\mu_0' : A' \longrightarrow A' \otimes_K A'$. *In particular* $\circ\, \alpha_0 : A(K) \longrightarrow A'(K)$ *is an algebra homomorphism inducing* $\alpha : G \longrightarrow G'$ *via the embedding defined in* (c).

(e) *If* U *and* V *have* k-*structures such that* X *and* Y *are defined over* k, *then* $X \cdot Y$ *is defined over* k.

PROOF. Let $f \in A$ and write $\mu_0 f = \Sigma_i f_i \otimes h_i$. Then

$$f(x) = f(ex) = \Sigma_i f_i(e) h_i(x) = f(xe) = \Sigma_i f_i(x) h_i(e) \quad .$$

Hence

$$f = \Sigma_i f_i(e)h_i = \Sigma_i f_i h_i(e) \quad .$$

(a) We have, since X is K-linear,

$$(e\cdot X)(f) = (e \otimes X)\mu_0 f = \Sigma f_i(e)X(h_i) = X(\Sigma f_i(e)h_i) = X(f) \quad .$$

Thus $e\cdot X = X$, and similarly $X\cdot e = X$.

(b) With $I : A \longrightarrow A$ standing for the identity map, the associativity of μ is expressed by

$$(I \otimes \mu_0) \circ \mu_0 = (\mu_0 \otimes I) \circ \mu_0$$

(or $I\cdot \mu_0 = \mu_0 \cdot I$ in the present notation). Now

$$(X \otimes Y \otimes Z) \circ (I \otimes \mu_0) \circ \mu_0 = (X \otimes ((Y \otimes Z) \circ \mu_0)) \circ \mu_0 = X\cdot (Y\cdot Z)$$

and, similarly,

$$(X \otimes Y \otimes Z) \circ (\mu_0 \otimes I) \circ \mu_0 = (X\cdot Y)\cdot Z \quad .$$

Part (c) is an immediate consequence of parts (a) and (b), together with the example above.

(d) The fact that $\circ a_0$ is a homomorphism is expressed by the equation

$$\mu_0 \circ a_0 = (a_0 \otimes a_0) \circ \mu_0' \quad .$$

Now

$$(X\cdot Y) \circ a_0 = (X \otimes Y) \circ \mu_0 \circ a_0 = (X \otimes Y) \circ (a_0 \otimes a_0) \circ \mu_0' = (X \circ a_0)\cdot (Y \circ a_0).$$

The remaining assertions of (d) are clear.

(e) follows from the formula $X \cdot Y = (X \otimes Y) \circ \mu_0$ and the fact that μ_0 is defined over k. This completes the proof of Lemma 1.

As above let $I \in A(A)$ denote the identity map. If $X \in A(K)$, we define <u>right convolution by</u> X,

$$*X = I \cdot X : A \longrightarrow A$$

and <u>left convolution by</u> X,

$$X* = X \cdot I : A \longrightarrow A \quad .$$

If $f \in A$ and $\mu_0 f = \Sigma f_i \otimes h_i$ then

$$f*X = \Sigma f_i \; X(h_i), \; X*f = \Sigma X(f_i) \; h_i \quad .$$

We have

$$(f*X)(g) = X(\lambda_{g^{-1}} f) \quad \text{and} \quad (X*f)(g) = X(\rho_g f) \quad .$$

The first equation follows because

$$(f*X)(g) = \Sigma f_i(g) X(h_i) = X(\Sigma f_i(g) h_i) = X(\lambda_{g^{-1}} f) \quad ,$$

and similarly for the second.

We shall now establish several formulas for these operations. Let $g \in G$, let $X, Y \in A(K)$, and let $\mu_0 f$ be as above.

(1) $$*e_g = \rho_g, \quad \text{and} \quad e_g* = \lambda_{g^{-1}} .$$

For $f*e_g = \Sigma f_i h_i(g) = \rho_g f$, and similarly for e_g*.

(2) $$X \circ (*Y) = X \cdot Y \quad \text{and} \quad X \circ (Y*) = Y \cdot X .$$

We have $X \circ (I \otimes Y) \circ \mu_0 = (X \otimes Y) \circ \mu_0$, and similarly $X \circ (Y \otimes I) \circ \mu_0 = (Y \otimes X) \circ \mu_0$. Using part (a) of Lemma 1 we thus obtain:

(3) $$e \circ (*X) = X = e \circ (X*) .$$

Combining (2) and (3) we find that

(4) $$e \circ ((*X) \circ (*Y)) = X \cdot Y .$$

A simple check shows that $(I \otimes X) \circ \mu_0 \circ (I \otimes Y) = ((I \otimes X) \circ \mu_0) \otimes Y$, so that $(*X) \circ (*Y) = (*Y) \circ Y$. The latter is $(I \cdot X) \cdot Y$ which, by part (b) of Lemma 1, equals $I \cdot (X \cdot Y)$. Thus,

(5) $$(*X) \circ (*Y) = *(X \cdot Y) .$$

Similar computations, starting from

$$(I \otimes X) \circ \mu_0 \circ (Y \otimes I) = Y \otimes ((I \otimes X) \circ \mu_0)$$
$$(Y \otimes I) \circ \mu_0 \circ (I \otimes X) = ((Y \otimes I) \circ \mu_0) \otimes X$$

show that

$$(*X) \circ (Y*) = Y \cdot (*X) = Y \cdot (I \cdot X), \text{ and } (Y*) \circ (*X) = (Y \cdot I) \cdot X ,$$

whence

$$(6) \qquad (*X) \circ (Y*) = (Y*) \circ (*X) \ .$$

LEMMA 2. The composite $X \mapsto e \circ (I \cdot X) = e \circ (*X)$ of the K-linear maps

$$A(K) \xleftarrow{I\cdot} A(A) \xrightarrow{e\circ} A(K)$$

is the identity. Moreover $I\cdot$ is a K-algebra monomorphism onto the K-algebra of elements in $A(A)$ commuting with all left translations $\lambda_g (g \in G)$. In particular $I\cdot$ maps $L(G)$ isomorphically onto $Lie(G)$. Finally, both $e\circ$ and $I\cdot$ preserve the property that an element is defined over k.

PROOF. The first assertion is just (3), and it implies that $I\cdot$ is an isomorphism onto its image, whose inverse is induced by $e\circ$. From (5) we see moreover that $e\circ$ is an algebra homomorphism. Formula (6) says that left and right convolutions commute. Hence all $*X$ (i.e. $m(I\cdot)$) commute with all $\lambda_{g^{-1}} = e_{g*}$ (see (1)). To show that $I\cdot$ maps $A(K)$ onto the set of left invariant elements of $A(A)$ it suffices to show that $e\circ$ is injective on left invariant elements. So let $D \in A(A)$ be left invariant and suppose $e \circ D = 0$. Then $(Df)(g) = (\lambda_{g^{-1}}(Df))(e) = (D(\lambda_{g^{-1}}f)) = (e \circ D)(\lambda_{g^{-1}}f) = 0$ for all g, so $Df = 0$ for all f.

We know that e carries derivations to derivations so it remains to check that $I\cdot$ does so also. If $X \in A(K)$

is a derivation $A \longrightarrow K(x)$ then $I \otimes X : A \otimes_K A \longrightarrow A \otimes_K K(x)$ is the derivation obtained by the base change $K \longrightarrow A$, so $*X = (I \otimes X) \circ \mu_0$ is also a derivation because μ_0 is an algebra homomorphism.

Finally it is clear that $e \circ$ preserves elements defined over k (because e is defined over k). That $I \cdot$ does also follows from part (e) of Lemma 1.

This completes the proof of Lemma 2.

LEMMA 3. $L(G)$ is a restricted Lie subalgebra of $A(K)$. That is, if $X, Y \in L(G)$, we have

$$[X, Y] = X \cdot Y - Y \cdot X, \quad X^{[p]} = X \cdot X \ldots X \text{ (p factors)} .$$

Since we have seen, in part (d) of Lemma 1, that $a_0 : A' \longrightarrow A$ induces an algebra homomorphism $\circ a_0 : A(K) \longrightarrow A'(K)$, it follows that its restriction, $L(a) : L(G) \longrightarrow L(G')$ is a restricted Lie algebra homomorphism. Hence we have established all the assertions of the proposition in (3.3).

(3.5) The adjoint representation. Let G be an affine k-group with Lie algebra $\underline{g}$. If $g \in G$ we have the inner automorphism

$$\mathrm{Int}(g) : G \longrightarrow G, \quad x \longmapsto {}^g x = gxg^{-1}$$

whose differential $L(\mathrm{Int}(g))$ we denote by

$$\mathrm{Ad}(g) : \underline{g} \longrightarrow \underline{g} .$$

This is a restricted Lie algebra homomorphism, and the functoriality of differentiation implies that

$$\mathrm{Ad} : G \longrightarrow GL(\underline{g})$$

is a homomorphism of groups. We claim that it is even a k-morphism of k-groups, the <u>adjoint representation</u> of G.

To see this we shall compute Ad in the tangent bundle (AG.16.2)

$$\begin{array}{ccc} T(G) & = & G(K[\delta]) \\ p\downarrow\uparrow s & & p\downarrow\uparrow s \\ G & = & G(K) \end{array}$$

Recall that $K[\delta]$ is the algebra of dual numbers $(\delta^2 = 0)$ and p and s are induced by $K[\delta] \longrightarrow K (\delta \longmapsto 0)$ and by $K \subset K[\delta]$, respectively.

A typical element of $T(G)$ is of the form (see (AG.16.2))

$$e_g^{\delta X} = e_g + \delta X \qquad (g \in G,\ X \in T(G)_g) \ .$$

It is the algebra homomorphism $K[G] \longrightarrow K[\delta]$ sending f to $f(g) + \delta X(f)$. According to (1.5) the group multiplication in $T(G)$ is given by

$$(e_g + \delta X)(e_h + \delta Y) = m \circ ((e_g + \delta X) \otimes (e_h + \delta Y)) \circ \mu_0$$

where $m : K[\delta] \otimes K[\delta] \longrightarrow K[\delta]$ is the multiplication in the k-algebra $K[\delta]$. Thus, with the notation $X \cdot Y = (X \otimes Y) \circ \mu_0$ introduced in (3.4), we have

$$\begin{aligned}&(e_g + \delta X)(e_h + \delta Y)\\ &= m \cdot (e_g \cdot e_h + (1 \otimes \delta) e_g \cdot Y + (\delta \otimes 1) X \cdot e_h + (\delta \otimes \delta) X \cdot Y)\\ &= e_{gh} + \delta(e_g \cdot Y + X \cdot e_h) \ ,\end{aligned}$$

or

$$e_g^{\delta X} e_h^{\delta Y} = e_{gh}^{\delta(e_g \cdot Y + X \cdot e_h)} \tag{1}$$

The map p sends $e_g^{\delta X}$ to g and s sends g to $e_g (= e_g^{\delta 0})$. Since the composite $p \circ s$ is the identity on G it follows that the group T(G) is the semi-direct product of sG with $\ker(p) = p^{-1}(e)$. Writing $e^{\delta X}$ in place of $e_e^{\delta X}$, it follows from (AG.16.2) that $X \mapsto e^{\delta X}$ is a bijection from $T(G)_e = \underline{g}$ to ker(p). Moreover it follows from (1) and Lemma 1 of (3.4) that it is a homomorphism of groups:

$$e^{\delta X} e^{\delta Y} = e^{\delta(X+Y)}$$

Thus we have a split group extension

$$0 \longrightarrow \underline{g} \xrightarrow{e^{\delta(\cdot)}} T(G) \xrightarrow{p} G \longrightarrow 1$$

with everything defined over k.

If $\mathrm{Int} : G \times G \longrightarrow G$ is the action of G on G by inner automorphisms then the commutative diagram

$$\begin{array}{ccc} G \times G & \xrightarrow{\text{Int}} & G \\ \downarrow & & \downarrow \\ T(G) \times T(G) & \xrightarrow{T(\text{Int})} & T(G) \end{array}$$

shows that $T(\text{Int}(g)) = \text{Int}(e_g)$. The restriction of $T(\text{Int}(g)) : T(G) \longrightarrow T(G)$ to $\underline{g} = \ker(p)$ is (see (AG.16.2)) just $d(\text{Int}(g)) = \text{Ad}(g)$. Explicitly, this says that $\text{Ad}(g)$ is defined by the formula

$$\text{(2)} \qquad \text{Int}(e_g)(e^{\delta X}) = e^{\delta\, \text{Ad}(g)X} \quad .$$

Viewing G and $\underline{g}$ as subgroups of $T(G)$, both defined over k, we see that Ad is just the action $T(\text{Int}) : G \times \underline{g} \longrightarrow \underline{g}$. In particular this action is a k-morphism. Since the action of G on $\underline{g}$ is linear it further follows (see example (8) of (1.6)) that $\text{Ad} : G \longrightarrow GL(\underline{g})$ is a morphism defined over k.

Finally, suppose $\alpha : G \longrightarrow G'$ is a morphism of algebraic groups. Then $T(\alpha) : T(G) \longrightarrow T(G')$ induces α on the subgroups $G \subset T(G)$ and $G' \subset T(G')$ so $\text{Int}(\alpha(g))(T(\alpha)(x)) = T(\alpha)(gxg^{-1}) = T(\alpha)(\text{Int}(g)(x))$, i.e.

$$\text{Int}(\alpha(g)) \circ T(\alpha) = T(\alpha) \circ \text{Int}(g) \quad .$$

Restricting to the Lie algebras this formula becomes

$$\text{(3)} \qquad \text{Ad}_{G'}(\alpha(g)) \circ (d\alpha) = (d\alpha) \circ \text{Ad}_G(g) \quad .$$

(3.6) <u>The Lie algebra of</u> GL(V) <u>is</u> <u>gl</u>(V). We view a finite dimensional vector space V as the variety $\operatorname{spec}_K(S_K(V^*))$. As such its points in a K-algebra B are

$$V(B) = \operatorname{Hom}_{K\text{-alg}}(S_K(V^*), B) = \operatorname{Hom}_{K\text{-mod}}(V^*, B) = B \otimes_K V.$$

Thus V(B) is the module obtained from V by the base change $K \longrightarrow B$. Moreover this module structure is natural in B and V in an obvious sense.

Applying this to $E = \operatorname{End}_{K\text{-mod}}(V)$, we have

$$E(B) = B \otimes_K E = \operatorname{End}_{B\text{-mod}}(V(B)) \quad .$$

Moreover this ring structure is easily seen to be natural in the following sense: The multiplication $\mu : E \times E \longrightarrow E$ in E as a variety extends to the functor of points, as $\mu(B) : E(B) \times E(B) \longrightarrow E(B)$, and this is just the natural multiplication in E(B) as B-module endomorphisms of V(B).

The same remark applies to the open subvariety $GL_V \subset E$. We can identify $GL_V(B)$ with the invertible elements of the algebra E(B), i.e. with the group $\operatorname{Aut}_{B\text{-mod}}(V(B))$.

Taking $B = K[\delta]$, the dual numbers, we can then obtain an isomorphism of the Lie algebra $L(GL_V)$ with the kernel of "kill δ": $GL_V(K[\delta]) \longrightarrow GL_V(K)$. This kernel is clearly the set of all $I + \delta X$ with $X \in \underline{gl}_V$, thus establishing a natural additive isomorphism $\underline{gl}_V \cong L(GL_V)$. Under this identification we then have, in view of the definition of Ad,

$$\mathrm{Ad}(g)(X) = g \circ X \circ g^{-1}$$

for $g \in GL_V$ and $X \in \underline{gl}_V$.

We further claim that the above identification of $L(GL_V)$ with $\underline{gl}_V$ is compatible with the respective restricted Lie algebra structures. To see this we shall make the identification explicit in the case of $\mathbb{GL}_n$.

Write $K[\mathbb{GL}_n] = K[T_{11}, T_{12}, \ldots, T_{nn}, D^{-1}]$ where, if T is the matrix (T_{ij}), we have $D = \det(T)$. Then $g \in \mathbb{GL}_n$ is identified with the matrix $(g_{ij}) = e_g(T) = (T_{ij}(g))$. Similarly an $X \in L(\mathbb{GL}_n)$ is identified with the matrix $(X_{ij}) = X(T) = (X(T_{ij})) \in \underline{gl}_n$.

The Lie algebra structure in $L(\mathbb{GL}_n)$ is deduced from the associative product $X \cdot Y = (X \otimes Y) \circ \mu_0$ (see (3.4)) and that in $\underline{gl}_n$ from the associative matrix multiplication. To see that these agree here we just compute:

$$(X \cdot Y)(T_{ij}) = (X \otimes Y)(\Sigma_h T_{ih} \otimes T_{hj}) = \Sigma X_{ih} Y_{hj} .$$

It is also convenient to note the following description of right translation and convolution:

$$\rho_g(T) = Tg, \quad T*X = TX ,$$

where the product in the right-hand sides is the matrix product. On the left the notation refers to

$$\rho_g(T) = (\rho_g(T_{ij})) \text{ and } T*X = (T_{ij}*X) ,$$

respectively. The two formulas follow from an obvious calculation.

(3.7) <u>The differential of</u> Ad <u>is</u> ad. Let $\alpha : G \longrightarrow G'$ be a morphism of algebraic groups. Then we have

$$\alpha(e^{\delta X}) = e^{\delta d\alpha(X)} , \qquad (X \in \underline{g}) ,$$

where the α on the left is identified with $T(\alpha) : T(G) \longrightarrow T(G')$, by abuse of notation.

Now suppose $G' = GL_V$, so that $\underline{g}' = \underline{gl}_V$. Then $T(GL_V)$ operates on $T(V)$ and we have

$$\alpha(e^{\delta X})(v) = e^{\delta d\alpha(X)}(v) \qquad (v \in V) .$$

Applying this to $\alpha = \mathrm{Ad} = \mathrm{Ad}_G$, we get

$$\mathrm{Ad}(e^{\delta X})(Y) = e^{\delta d\mathrm{Ad}(X)}(Y) \quad (X, Y \in \underline{g}) .$$

In recalling the definition of Ad we shall use a second copy, $K[\delta']$, of the dual numbers, in order to avoid confusion with that above. Namely, Ad is defined by the formula

$$\mathrm{Int}(e_g)(e^{\delta' Y}) = e^{\delta' \mathrm{Ad}(g)(Y)}$$

for $g \in G$ and $Y \in \underline{g}$. Apply this formula now to $e^{\delta X}$ in place of e_g to obtain

$$\mathrm{Int}(e^{\delta X})(e^{\delta' Y}) = e^{\delta' \mathrm{Ad}(e^{\delta X})(Y)} =$$
$$= e^{\delta' e^{\delta d\mathrm{Ad}(X)}(Y)} = e^{\delta'(Y + \delta d\mathrm{Ad}(X)(Y))} .$$

Expanding the initial term we have

$$e^{\delta X}e^{\delta' Y}e^{-\delta X} = (e+\delta X+\delta' Y+\delta\delta' X\cdot Y)(e^{-\delta X}) =$$

$$= e + \delta X + \delta' Y + \delta\delta' X\cdot Y - \delta X - \delta'\delta Y\cdot X =$$

$$= e + \delta'(Y+\delta(X\cdot Y - Y\cdot X)) .$$

Comparing this with the last term in the formula above we see that

$$dAd(X)(Y) = X\cdot Y - Y\cdot X = [X, Y] ,$$

i.e. that $dAd(X) = ad(X)$.

(3.8) Ker(Ad) <u>can be larger than</u> Z(G). Clearly one has $Z(G) \subset \ker(Ad)$. This is even an equality if $char(k) = 0$ or if G is semi-simple. The following example of Chevalley shows that the inclusion can be proper in general.

Assume $char(k) = p > 0$ and let $G = \{g(a, b) \mid a \in K^*, b \in K\}$ where

$$g(a, b) = \begin{pmatrix} a & 0 & 0 \\ 0 & a^p & b \\ 0 & 0 & 1 \end{pmatrix} .$$

Then $g(a, b)g(a', b') = g(aa', a^p b' + b)$, so that G is a closed subgroup of $\mathbb{GL}_3$. It is, as a group, the semi-direct product of the normal subgroup $H = \{g(1, b) \mid b \in K\} \cong \mathbb{G}_a$ with the group $\{g(a, 0) \mid a \in K^*\} \cong \mathbb{GL}_1$, the action of the latter on H

being given by the Frobenius homomorphism. In particular G is not commutative; indeed $Z(G) = \{e\}$. The elements of $T(G)$ can be written in the form $g(u+\delta v, r+\delta s)$ with $u \in K^*$ and $v, r, s \in K$. In particular the elements of $\underline{g}$ correspond to those of the form $g(1+\delta v, \delta s)$, and $Ad(g(a, b))$ operates on this by conjugation: $g(a, b)g(1+\delta v, \delta s)g(a, b)^{-1} = g(a+\delta av, \delta a^p s+b)g(a^{-1}, -a^{-p}b)$ $= g(1+\delta v, -(a+\delta av)^p a^{-p}b+\delta a^p s+b) = g(1+\delta v, \delta a^p s)$. Hence the action is trivial if and only if $a = 1$, so $\ker(Ad) = H$.

The bracket in $\underline{g}$ can be computed from the commutator of $g(1+\delta r, \delta s)$ with $g(1+\delta u, \delta v)$. We have

$$g(1+\delta r, \delta s)g(1+\delta u, \delta v) =$$
$$= g(1+\delta r+\delta u+\delta\delta ru, \quad (1+\delta r)^p \delta v+\delta s) =$$
$$= g(1+\delta r+\delta u+\delta\delta ru, \quad \delta v+\delta s) \quad .$$

Thus it is clear that these elements commute, so their bracket is trivial. Hence the Lie algebra $\underline{g}$ is abelian. This should be contrasted with the fact that $Z(G) = \{e\}$ and $(G, G) = H$ (cf. (3.12) below).

(3.9) Some differentiation formulas. Let G be an algebraic group with Lie algebra $\underline{g}$.

(1) If $a \in G$ then $g \mapsto ag^{-1}a^{-1}$ is the composite of $Int(a)$ with i, so its differential is $-Ad(a)$. Multiplying by the identity map we obtain the commutator map $c_a : g \mapsto (g, a) = gag^{-1}a^{-1}$, so $dc_a = Id - Ad(a)$. Following c_a by right multiplication by a, we get a

formula for the differential of $g \mapsto gag^{-1}$, the map of G onto the conjugacy class of a. This differential is $Id - Ad(a)$, followed by the differential $(d\rho_a)_e : \underline{g} \longrightarrow T(G)_a$ where $\rho_a(g) = ga$.

(2) If $A \in \underline{g}$, define $\alpha_A : G \longrightarrow \underline{g}$ by $\alpha_A(g) = Ad(g)(A) - A$. Then α_A is the composite $G \xrightarrow{Ad-Id} \underline{gl}(\underline{g}) \xrightarrow{\cdot(A)} \underline{g}$, so $(d\alpha_A)_e = d(\cdot(A))_0 \circ (d(Ad\text{-}Id)_e) = \cdot(A) \circ ad$. We use the fact that $\cdot(A)$ is linear, so is its own differential, that $d(Ad)_e = ad$, and that $(dId)_e = 0$ because Id is a constant function. Thus, for $X \in \underline{g}$, we have $(d\alpha_A)_e(X) = ad(X)(A) = [X, A] = -ad(A)(X)$, so

$$(d\alpha_A)_e = -ad(A) \quad .$$

(3) Let $\mathcal{V}$ denote the category of finite dimensional K-modules, and let $F : \mathcal{V} \times \ldots \times \mathcal{V} \longrightarrow \mathcal{V}$ be a functor of n variables which is K-multilinear on the Hom's. Let $\alpha_i : G \longrightarrow GL(V_i)$ be rational representations of an algebraic group G $(1 \leqq i \leqq n)$. Then $\alpha = F(\alpha_1, \ldots, \alpha_n) : G \longrightarrow GL(V)$ is a rational representation on $V = F(V_1, \ldots, V_n)$. Moreover we have

$$d\alpha(X) = \sum_{i=1}^{n} F(1_{V_1}, \ldots, d\alpha_i X, \ldots, 1_{V_n}), \qquad (X \in \underline{g}) \quad .$$

This follows from $\alpha(e^{\delta X}) = e^{\delta d\alpha(X)}$, and

$$\alpha(e^{\delta X}) = F(\alpha_1(e^{\delta X}), \ldots, \alpha_n(e^{\delta X})) =$$

$$= F(e^{\delta d\alpha_1 X}, \ldots, e^{\delta d\alpha_n X}) = F(1_{V_1} + \delta d\alpha_1 X, \ldots, 1_{V_n} + \delta d\alpha_n X) =$$

$$= F(1_{V_1}, \ldots, 1_{V_n}) + \delta(\sum_{i=1}^{n} F(1_{V_1}, \ldots, d\alpha_i X, \ldots, 1_{V_n})) .$$

(4) If $\alpha_i : G \longrightarrow GL(V_i) (i = 1, 2)$ are rational representations and if $\beta : V_1 \longrightarrow V_2$ is a homomorphism of G-representations, i.e. if β is linear and $\beta(\alpha_1(g)v) = \alpha_2(g)\beta(v)$ for $g \in G$ and $v \in V$, then β is also a homomorphism of $\underline{g}$-representations, i.e.

$$\beta(d\alpha_1(X)v) = d\alpha_2(X)\beta(v)$$

for $X \in \underline{g}$ and $v \in V$. For the first formula, applied to the tangent bundles, gives

$$\beta(\alpha_1(e^{\delta X})v) = \alpha_2(e^{\delta X})\beta(v) .$$

The left side is $\beta(e^{\delta d\alpha_1 X}(v)) = \beta(v) + \delta(d\alpha_1 X(v))$, while the right side is $\beta(v) + \delta d\alpha_2 X(\beta(v))$, thus establishing the formula above.

(5) In the setting of (4) we can apply formula (3) to $\alpha = \alpha_1 \otimes \alpha_2 : G \longrightarrow GL(V_1 \otimes_K V_2)$, to obtain

$$d(\alpha_1 \otimes \alpha_2)(X) = (d\alpha_1 X \otimes 1_{V_2}) + (1_{V_1} \otimes d\alpha_2 X) .$$

(6) Let $\alpha : G \longrightarrow GL(V)$ be a rational representation. Then we have $T^n(\alpha) : G \longrightarrow GL(T^n(V))$, where $T^n(V) = V \otimes_K \ldots \otimes_K V$ (n factors) and

$T^n(\alpha) = \alpha \otimes \ldots \otimes \alpha$. From (3) we have

$$d(\alpha \otimes \ldots \otimes \alpha) = \sum_{i=1}^{n} 1_V \otimes \ldots \otimes \underset{i^{\text{th}}\text{ place}}{d\alpha} \otimes \ldots \otimes 1_V \ .$$

Thus, on the tensor algebra $\coprod_n T^n(V)$, we see that the differential of the action of G as algebra automorphisms (extending α in degree 1) is the action of $\underline{g}$ as derivations (extending $d\alpha$ in degree 1).

The passage from the tensor algebra to the symmetric algebra $S(V)$ and the exterior algebra $\Lambda(V)$ can be viewed as epimorphisms of G-representations in each degree. Thus it follows from (4) that the differentials of the actions of G as algebra automorphisms of $S(V)$ and of $\Lambda(V)$ are again given by the actions of $\underline{g}$ as derivations extending $d\alpha$ in degree 1. Explicitly, if $e_1, \ldots, e_n \in V$ then

$$dS^n(\alpha)(X)(e_1 \ldots e_n) = \sum_{i=1}^{n} e_1 \ldots d\alpha X(e_i) \ldots e_n$$

and

$$d\Lambda^n(\alpha)(X)(e_1 \wedge \ldots \wedge e_n) = \sum_{i=1}^{n} e_1 \wedge \ldots \wedge d\alpha X(e_i) \wedge \ldots \wedge e_n \ .$$

(7) If $\dim V = n$ then $\Lambda^n(\alpha) = \det \circ \alpha$ and it follows from the above remarks that

$$d(\det \circ \alpha) = \mathrm{Tr} \circ d\alpha \ .$$

A direct proof of this in $\mathbb{GL}_n$ can be obtained as follows: Let $X = (X_{ij}) \in \underline{gl}_n$. Then $\det(e^{\delta X}) = e^{\delta d(\det)(X)}$, i.e. $\det(I+\delta X) = 1+\delta d(\det)(X)$. Expanding

$$\det\begin{pmatrix} 1+\delta X_{11} & \delta X_{12} \dots \delta X_{1n} \\ \dots & \dots \\ \delta X_{n1} & \delta X_{n2} \dots 1+\delta X_{nn} \end{pmatrix}$$

and using the fact that $\delta^2 = 0$, one sees immediately that $\det(I+\delta X) = 1+\delta(X_{11} + \dots + X_{nn})$. Thus

$$d(\det)(X) = \mathrm{Tr}(X) \qquad (X \in \underline{gl}_n) .$$

(8) Let $\alpha : G \longrightarrow GL(V)$ be a rational representation, and suppose V is a not necessarily associative algebra. Then if G acts via α as algebra automorphisms of V it follows that $\underline{g}$ acts, via $d\alpha$, as derivations. This follows by expanding the formula $\alpha(e^{\delta X})(uv) = \alpha(e^{\delta X})(u)\alpha(e^{\delta X})(v)$ for $X \in \underline{g}$ and $u, v \in V$.

(3.10) PROPOSITION. Let G be an affine algebraic group and let $V \subset A = K[G]$ be a finite dimensional vector space stable under ρ_g for all $g \in G$. Let $\rho : G \longrightarrow GL(V)$ be the rational representation $g \longmapsto \rho_g | V$. Then for $X \in \underline{g}$ and $f \in V$ we have

$$(d\rho)(X)(f) = f*X .$$

PROOF. Recall from (3.4) formula (1) that we have $\rho_g = *e_g$, which is $I\cdot e_g = (I \otimes e_g)\circ\mu_0$, where $I : A \longrightarrow A$ is the identity. Now we see that $I + \delta(d\rho)(X)$ is the restriction to $K[\delta]\otimes_K V \subset K[\delta]\otimes_K A$ of $I\cdot e^{\delta X} = I\cdot(e+\delta X) = I\cdot e+\delta(I\cdot X) = I+\delta(*X)$. Thus $(d\rho)(X) = *X$ as claimed.

COROLLARY. *Under right convolution,* $\underline{g}$ *leaves invariant all subspaces of* $K[G]$ *which are stable under right translation by* G.

Let $D \in K[\mathbb{G}\mathbb{L}_n]$ be the determinant. If $g, h \in \mathbb{G}\mathbb{L}_n$ we have $(\rho_g D)(h) = D(hg) = D(h)D(g)$, so

$$\rho_g D = \det(g)D \quad .$$

Thus the one-dimensional space spanned by D is right invariant. Applying the proposition and (3.9)(7) we obtain:

COROLLARY. *If* $D = \det \in K[\mathbb{G}\mathbb{L}_n]$ *and if* $X \in \underline{gl}_n$ *then* $D*X = Tr(X)D$.

(3.11) PROPOSITION. *Let* G *be an affine algebraic group and let* H *be a closed subgroup with affine algebra* $K[H] = K[G]/J$. *If* $j : H \longrightarrow G$ *is the inclusion then* dj *identifies* $\underline{h} = L(H)$ *with* $\{X \in \underline{g} \mid X(J) = 0\}$. *With this identification we can characterize* $\underline{h}$ *as* $\underline{h} = \{X \in \underline{g} \mid J*X \subset J\}$.

PROOF. Clearly $Der_K(K[G]/J, K(e))$ is identified (by dj) with the set of X in $Der_K(K[G], K(e))$ which kill J; hence the first assertion.

Let $\underline{h}' = \{X \in \underline{g} \mid J*X \subset J\}$. Suppose $X \in \underline{h}$, $f \in J$, and $h \in H$. Then $(f*X)(h) = X(\lambda_{h^{-1}} f) = 0$ because $\lambda_{h^{-1}} J \subset J$ and $X(J) = 0$. Thus $f*X \in J$, so $X \in \underline{h}'$.

Conversely, given $X \in \underline{h}'$ and $f \in J$ we must show that $X(f) = 0$. But $X(f) = X(\lambda_{e^{-1}} f) = (f*X)(e) = 0$ because

$f \in J$, $J*X \subset J$, and $e \in H$.

COROLLARY. Let $G \subset \mathbb{GL}_n$ be a closed subgroup, and let J be the ideal of all polynomials in $A = K[T_{11}, T_{12}, \ldots, T_{nn}]$ vanishing on G. Then

$$G = \{g \in \mathbb{GL}_n \mid \rho_g J = J\}$$

and

$$\underline{g} = \{X \in \underline{gl}_n \mid J*X \subset J\} .$$

PROOF. Put $A' = K[\mathbb{GL}_n] = A[D^{-1}]$, where $D = \det(T_{ij})$, and let J' be the ideal of functions in A' vanishing on G. The proposition above asserts that $\underline{g} = \{X \in \underline{gl}_n \mid J'*X \subset J'\}$, and the fact that $G = \{g \in \mathbb{GL}_n \mid \rho_g J' = J'\}$ is obvious.

Now it is easy to see that $J' = A'J$ and $J' \cap A = J$. Suppose $f \in J$ and $f' \in A'$. Then $\rho_g(ff') = \rho_g(f)\rho_g(f')$ and $(ff')*X = (f*X)f' + f(f'*X)$. Hence $\rho_g J = J \Longrightarrow \rho_g J' = J'$ and $J*X \subset J \Longrightarrow J'*X \subset J'$.

For the converse it suffices to show that each ρ_g and each $*X$ leave $A \subset A'$ stable. For then they leave $J = J' \cap A$ stable as soon as they leave J' stable.

Since $*X = (I \otimes X) \circ \mu_0$ we have $T_{ij}*X = (I \otimes X)(\Sigma_h T_{ih} \otimes T_{hj}) = \Sigma_h T_{ih} X(T_{hj}) \in A$. Similarly, if $g, h \in \mathbb{GL}_n$ then $(\rho_g T_{ij})(h) = T_{ij}(hg) = \Sigma_m T_{im}(h) T_{mj}(g)$, so $\rho_g T_{ij} = \Sigma_m T_{im} T_{mj}(g) \in A$. Thus $A*X \subset A$ and $\rho_g A \subset A$, as required.

REMARK. This corollary is the basis of one of the classical approaches to the Lie algebra of a matric group, using only polynomial functions in the coordinates of the matrices.

(3.12) PROPOSITION. Let M and N be closed subgroups of an affine algebraic group G, and let H be the closure of the commutator group (M, N). Then $\underline{h} = L(H)$ contains all elements of the forms

$$[X, Y] \qquad (X \in \underline{m},\ Y \in \underline{n}) \ ,$$

$$Ad(m)(Y) - Y \quad (m \in M), \qquad Ad(n)(X) - X \quad (n \in N) \ .$$

PROOF. For $m \in M$ define $\alpha_m : N \longrightarrow H$ by $\alpha_m(n) = mnm^{-1}n^{-1}$. Then (see (3.9)(1)) $(d\alpha_m)_e = (Ad(m) - Id) : \underline{n} \longrightarrow \underline{h}$. This secures all elements of the second form, and those of the third form are obtained similarly.

If $A \in \underline{n}$ define $\alpha_A : M \longrightarrow \underline{h}$ by $\alpha_A(m) = Ad(m)(A) - A$. This lies in $\underline{h}$ thanks to the conclusion established above. From (3.9)(2) we have $(d\alpha_A)_e = -ad(A)$ thus securing all elements $[A, X] (X \in \underline{m})$ in $\underline{h}$.

REMARK. The elements in the proposition span $\underline{h}$ if $char(k) = 0$, but not in general (see (3.8)).

§4. JORDAN DECOMPOSITION

(4.1) Nilpotent, unipotent, and semi-simple endomorphisms. Let V be a finite dimensional vector space over K with a k-rational structure $V(k)$. Then $E = End_K(V)$ also has a k-structure given by $E(k) = End_k(V(k))$. An $a \in E$ is called <u>nilpotent</u> if $a^n = 0$ for some $n > 0$, and <u>unipotent</u> if $a - I$ is nilpotent, where I denotes the identity on V. Thus a is nilpotent (resp., unipotent) if and only if all eigenvalues of a are 0 (resp., 1).

(a) <u>If</u> $char(k) = p > 0$ <u>then</u> a <u>is unipotent if and only if</u> $a^{p^r} = I$ <u>for some</u> $r \geqq 0$.

For if $a = I + n$, with n nilpotent, then $a^{p^r} = I + n^{p^r} = I$ for sufficiently large r. Conversely, $a^{p^r} = I$ implies the minimal polynomial of a divides $T^{p^r} - 1 = (T-1)^{p^r}$, so all eigenvalues of a are 1.

(b) <u>Let</u> $a \in E(k)$. <u>We call</u> a <u>semi-simple if it satisfies the following conditions, which are equivalent:</u>

(i) $V(\bar{k})$ <u>is spanned by eigenvectors of</u> a; <u>i.e.</u> a <u>is diagonalizable over</u> $\bar{k}$.

(ii) <u>The algebra</u> $\bar{k}[a] \subset E(\bar{k})$ <u>is semi-simple, i.e. it is a product of copies of</u> $\bar{k}$.

That (i) $\Longrightarrow$ (ii) is obvious once a is put in diagonal form. (Alternatively, $\bar{k}[a] \cong \bar{k}[T]/(P(T))$, where $P(T)$, the minimal polynomial of a, is a product of <u>distinct</u> linear factors.) Conversely, if $\bar{k}[a]$ is a product of copies of $\bar{k}$, then any module over it, e.g. $V(\bar{k})$, is a direct sum of one dimensional submodules.

(c) <u>If</u> $a \in E(k)$ <u>is semi-simple, then the eigenvalues of</u> a <u>are separable over</u> k. <u>Hence</u> a <u>is</u>

diagonalizable over k_s.

For $k[a] \cong k[T]/(P(T))$, P the minimal polynomial of a. Since $a \in E(k)$ we have $\bar{k}[a] = \bar{k} \otimes_k k[a]$, and the absence of nilpotent elements in the latter implies that P has no multiple roots, i.e. that P is a separable polynomial.

(d) Suppose $a, b \in E$ commute. Then:

(i) a, b nilpotent $\Longrightarrow a + b$ is nilpotent.

(ii) a, b unipotent $\Longrightarrow ab$ is unipotent.

(iii) a, b semi-simple $\Longrightarrow ab$ and $a + b$ are semi-simple.

If $a^n = b^m = 0$ then $(a+b)^{n+m} = 0$, thus proving (i). Since $ab - I = (a-I)b + (b-I)$, (ii) follows from (i). Part (iii) is left as an exercise (cf. (4.6)).

Finally, we record the obvious remark:

(e) If a is both semi-simple and nilpotent (resp., unipotent) then $a = 0$ (resp., $a = I$).

(4.2) PROPOSITION. We keep the previous notation. Let $a \in E$.

(1) There exist unique a_s and a_n in E such that a_s is semi-simple, a_n is nilpotent, $a_s a_n = a_n a_s$, and such that $a = a_s + a_n$. We call this the (additive) Jordan decomposition of a.

(2) There are polynomials $P(T)$ and $Q(T)$ in $K[T]$, with zero constant term, such that $a_s = P(a)$ and $a_n = Q(a)$.

(3) The centralizer of a in E centralizes a_s

and a_n. If $A \subset B \subset V$ are subspaces such that $aB \subset A$, then $a_s B \subset A$ and $a_n B \subset A$.

(4) If $A \subset V$ is a subspace invariant under a then the Jordan decomposition of a induces those of $a|A$ and of $a_{V/A}$, the endomorphism a induces on V/A.

(5) If $a \in E(k)$ then $a_s, a_n \in E(k^{p^{-\infty}})$. Moreover, the polynomials P and Q in (2) can be chosen in $k^{p^{-\infty}}[T]$.

PROOF. (1) Write $\det(T-a) = \prod (T-\alpha_i)^{m_i}$ where the α_i are distinct, and put $V_i = \ker(a-\alpha_i I)^{m_i}$. Then it is easy to see that $V = \coprod_i V_i$. Suppose $a = b+c$ with b semi-simple, c nilpotent, and $bc = cb$. Then b commutes with a, hence with $(a-\alpha_i I)^{m_i}$, and so b leaves each V_i invariant. Since $a-b = c$ is nilpotent, a and b have the same eigenvalues on V_i. Since a has only one, α_i, and since b is semi-simple, it follows that $b|V_i = \alpha_i I|V_i$. Therefore b is uniquely determined, and so also is $c = a-b$. On the other hand, if we define a_s by $a_s|V_i = \alpha_i I|V_i$, and $a_n = a-a_s$, then these data clearly satisfy our requirements.

(2) Choose $P(T)$ to solve the congruences

$$P(T) \equiv \alpha_i \mod (T-\alpha_i)^{m_i} \quad \text{and} \quad P(T) \equiv 0 \mod (T) .$$

These are consistent in case some $\alpha_i = 0$, so there is a solution ("Chinese Remainder Theorem"). We take $Q(T) = T - P(T)$.

(3) is an immediate corollary of (2).

(4) Let a' and a'' denote the endomorphisms induced by a on A and V/A, resp. Part (3) implies that a_s and a_n leave A invariant, so we can similarly define a_s', a_s'' and a_n', a_n''. The fact that $a' = a_s' + a_n'$ and $a'' = a_s'' + a_n''$ are Jordan decompositions is obvious.

(5) If $a \in E(k)$ then each of the α_i above are in $\bar{k}$, so the construction in (1) shows that $a_s, a_n \in E(\bar{k})$. If $s \in Gal(\bar{k}/k)$ then s operates on $E(\bar{k})$, and we have $a = s(a) = s(a_s) + s(a_n)$. Since s acts as an algebra automorphism we see that $s(a_n)$ is nilpotent and commutes with $s(a_s)$. Moreover, since $\bar{k}[a_s]$ is a semi-simple algebra (see (4.1)) the same is true of $s(\bar{k}[a_s]) = \bar{k}[s(a_s)]$, so a_s is still semi-simple. Therefore the uniqueness of the Jordan decomposition implies $s(a_s) = a_s$ and $s(a_n) = a_n$. But the elements of $E(\bar{k})$ fixed by $Gal(\bar{k}/k)$ are just $E(k^{p^{-\infty}})$. In particular $a_s, a_n \in \bar{k}[a] \cap E(k^{p^{-\infty}}) = k^{p^{-\infty}}[a]$, so the P and Q in (2) can be chosen with coefficients in $k^{p^{-\infty}}$.

COROLLARY 1. <u>Let</u> $g \in GL(V)$, <u>and put</u> $g_u = I + g_s^{-1} g_n$.

(1) <u>We have</u> $g = g_s g_u = g_u g_s$ <u>with</u> g_s <u>semi-simple and</u> g_u <u>unipotent, and this is the unique factorization of</u> g <u>of this type.</u> (<u>It is called the multiplicative Jordan decomposition of</u> g.)

(2) <u>If</u> $A \subset V$ <u>is a subspace invariant under</u> g, <u>then it is invariant under</u> g_s <u>and</u> g_u, <u>and the Jordan</u>

decomposition of g induces those of the automorphisms induced by g on A and on V/A.

(3) If g is rational over k, then g_s and g_u are rational over $k^{p^{-\infty}}$.

PROOF. (1) Since g_s and g_n commute, $g_u = I + g_s^{-1} g_n$ is unipotent, and $g = g_s g_u = g_u g_s$. Suppose $g = bc = cb$ where b is semi-simple and $n = c - I$ is nilpotent. Then bn is nilpotent and commutes with b, so $g = b + bn$ is the additive Jordan decomposition of g. Hence $b = g_s$ and $bn = g_n$.

In view of the formula for g_u parts (2) and (3) follow immediately from parts (4) and (5), respectively, of the proposition.

COROLLARY 2. If $a, b \in E$ commute then $a+b = (a_s + b_s) + (a_n + b_n)$ is the additive Jordan decomposition of $a+b$. If, moreover, they are invertible, then $ab = (a_s b_s)(a_u b_u)$ is the multiplicative Jordan decomposition. All elements appearing above commute.

PROOF. This follows from (4.1)(c) and from part (3) of the proposition.

COROLLARY 3. If $g \in GL(V)$ and $h \in GL(W)$ then $g \otimes h = (g_s \otimes h_s)(g_u \otimes h_u)$ is the Jordan decomposition of $g \otimes h$.

PROOF. Apply Corollary 2 to $g \otimes 1_W$ and $1_V \otimes h$.

CONVENTION. Suppose that V is not necessarily finite dimensional. We shall say that $a \in E$ is "locally finite" if V is spanned by finite dimensional subspaces stable under a. In this case one says that a is <u>locally nilpotent</u> (resp., <u>unipotent</u>, resp., <u>semi-simple</u>) if its restriction to each finite dimensional a-stable subspace has this property. The uniqueness of the above Jordan decompositions gives us, for a locally finite endomorphism a, a Jordan decomposition $a = a_s + a_n$, and, if a is invertible, $a = a_s a_u$, such that these induce the usual ones on finite dimensional a-stable subspaces. Thus, for example, a_s is locally semi-simple, a_n is locally nilpotent, and $a_s a_n = a_n a_s$. These properties characterize a_s and a_n, and similarly for the multiplicative decomposition.

By abuse of language we shall often drop the word "locally" in the above situation.

Let G be an affine algebraic group. If $g \in G$ and $X \in \underline{g}$ then ρ_g and $*X$ are locally finite endomorphisms of $A = K[G]$ (see (1.9) and (3.10)). Hence we have Jordan decompositions

$$\rho_g = (\rho_g)_s(\rho_g)_u$$

and

$$*X = (*X)_s + (*X)_n \quad .$$

The main result of this section asserts that these

decompositions can be realized already in G and in $\underline{g}$, respectively.

(4.3) We keep the notation and conventions of (4.2).

PROPOSITION. _Let_ $g \in GL(V)$ _and_ $X \in \underline{gl}(V)$, _and let_ $A = K[GL(V)]$.

(1) g _is semi-simple (resp., unipotent) if and only_ ρ_g _is semi-simple (resp., unipotent)_.

(2) X _is semi-simple (resp., nilpotent) if and only if_ $*X$ _is semi-simple (resp., nilpotent)_.

PROOF. We have $A = B[D^{-1}]$ where $B = K[\mathrm{End}(V)]$, and where $D : \mathrm{End}(V) \longrightarrow K$ is the determinant. Since right translation by $GL(V)$ is defined on $\mathrm{End}(V)$, and since $*X$ is its differential (see (3.10)) it follows that ρ_g and $*X$ leave B invariant, and their extensions to A are defined, for $f \in B$, by

$$\rho_g(fD^{-n}) = \rho_g(f)\rho_g(D)^{-n} = D(g)^{-n}\rho_g(f)D^{-n}$$

and

$$\begin{aligned}(fD^{-n})*X &= (f*X)D^{-n} - nfD^{-n-1}(D*X) \\ &= (f*X)D^{-n} - n\mathrm{Tr}(X)fD^{-n} \quad .\end{aligned}$$

Here we have used the fact that $\rho_g(D) = D(g)D$ and $(D*X) = (XD)D = \mathrm{Tr}(X)D$ (see (3.10)). These formulas show that, if f is an eigenvector for ρ_g (resp., $*X$) then so also is fD^{-n} for each $n \geq 0$. This shows that

ρ_g (resp., $*X$) is semi-simple if and only if its restriction to B is.

Suppose ρ_g on B is unipotent. Then since $\rho_g D = D(g)D$, we have $D(g) = 1$. Hence $(\rho_g - I)(fD^{-n}) = ((\rho_g - I)(f))D^{-n}$, and it follows that ρ_g is unipotent on A. The converse is obvious.

Similarly, if $*X$ on B is nilpotent then $(D*X) = Tr(X)D$ implies $Tr(X) = 0$, and hence $(fD^{-n})*X = (f*X)D^{-n}$. This shows $*X$ is nilpotent on A, and the converse is obvious.

These remarks show that it suffices to prove the analogue of the proposition with $B = K[End(V)]$ in place of $A = K[GL(V)]$. Writing $E = End(V)$, B is the symmetric algebra, $S(E^*)$, on the dual $E^* = Hom_K(E, K)$ of E. Moreover, ρ_g and $*X$ are just the automorphism and derivation, respectively, of the algebra $S(E^*)$ induced by (the transposes of) right multiplication on E by $g \in GL(V)$ and by $X \in \underline{gl}(V) = E$, respectively.

If we identify E with $V^* \otimes V(f \otimes v : x \longmapsto f(x)v)$ then right multiplication by $a \in E$ corresponds to $a^* \otimes I$. It suffices to check this for a of the form $g \otimes w$, in which case $(f \otimes v)(g \otimes w) : x \longmapsto f(w)g(x)v = (f(w)g \otimes v)(x)$, and $(a^* \otimes I)(f \otimes v) = a^*(f) \otimes v = f(w)g \otimes v$. Since a is nilpotent (resp., unipotent, resp., semi-simple) if and only if $a^* \otimes I$ is, the proof of the proposition is completed by the next lemma, in which we let E^* play the role of V.

LEMMA. *Let* $g \in GL(V)$ *and* $X \in \underline{gl}(V)$.

(1) g *is semi-simple (resp., unipotent) if and only if the automorphism* $S(g)$ *of* $S(V)$ *induced by* g *is semi-simple (resp., unipotent).*

(2) X *is semi-simple (resp., nilpotent) if and only if the derivation* $s(X)$ *of* $S(V)$ *induced by* X *is semi-simple (resp., nilpotent).*

PROOF. On $S^1(V) = V$ the restrictions of $S(g)$ and $s(X)$ are g and X, respectively, so the only if's are clear.

Since $S^n(g)$ is induced by $T^n(g)$ on $T^n(V) = V \otimes \ldots \otimes V$ by passing to the quotient, the "if" in part (1) follows from corollary 2 in (4.2).

Similarly, $s(X)$ is induced, on passing to the quotient $S^n(V)$ of $T^n(V)$, by $\Sigma_i I \otimes \ldots \otimes X^{i^{th} \text{ place}} \otimes \ldots \otimes I$. These summands commute, and are semi-simple (resp., nilpotent) if X is, so the same is true of their sum. Q. E. D.

(4.4) *Jordan decomposition in affine groups.* Let G be an affine k-group with coordinate ring $A = K[G]$. If $g \in G$ and $X \in \underline{g}$ then ρ_g and $*X$ on A have Jordan decompositions in the sense of the convention of (4.2).

THEOREM. *Let* $g \in G$ *and* $X \in \underline{g}$.

(1) *There is a unique factorization* $g = g_s g_u$ *in* G *such that* $\rho_g = \rho_{g_s} \rho_{g_u}$ *is the (multiplicative) Jordan decomposition of* ρ_g. *If* $g \in G(k)$ *then* $g_s, g_u \in G(k^{p^{-\infty}})$.

(2) <u>There is a unique decomposition</u> $X = X_s + X_n$ <u>in</u> $\underline{g}$ <u>such that</u> $*X = (*X_s) + (*X_n)$ <u>is the (additive) Jordan decomposition of</u> $*X$. <u>If</u> $X \in \underline{g}(k)$ <u>then</u> $X_s, X_n \in \underline{g}(k^{p^{-\infty}})$.

(We refer to the above as the <u>Jordan decompositions</u> of g in G and of X in $\underline{g}$, respectively.)

(3) <u>In case</u> $G = GL(V)$, <u>and so</u> $\underline{g} = \underline{gl}(V)$, <u>then the Jordan decompositions above coincide with those defined in</u> (4.2).

(4) <u>If</u> $\alpha : G \longrightarrow G'$ <u>is a morphism of affine groups then</u> α <u>and</u> $d\alpha$ <u>preserve Jordan decompositions in the groups and Lie algebras, respectively</u>.

PROOF. <u>Case</u> 1. $G = GL(V)$ and $\underline{g} = \underline{gl}(V)$. Let $g = g_s g_u$ and $X = X_s + X_n$ be the Jordan decompositions of (4.2). Then Proposition (4.3)(1) implies ρ_{g_s} is semi-simple and ρ_{g_u} is unipotent. Since $g \longmapsto \rho_g$ is a group homomorphism, ρ_{g_s} and ρ_{g_u} commute, so $\rho_g = \rho_{g_s} \rho_{g_u}$ is the Jordan decomposition. Similarly, (4.3)(2) implies $*X_s$ is semi-simple and $*X_n$ is nilpotent. Since $X \longmapsto *X$ is a Lie algebra homomorphism, $*X_s$ and $*X_n$ commute, so $*X = (*X_s) + (*X_n)$ is the Jordan decomposition of $*X$. Both $g \longmapsto \rho_g$ and $X \longmapsto *X$ are compatible with k-structures, so the rationality assertions follow from those of (4.2).

The uniqueness in this, as in the general, case

follows from the faithfulness of $g \mapsto \rho_g$ (see (1.10)) and of $X \mapsto *X$ (see (3.4)).

General case. Choose a k-rational embedding $G \subset GL(V)$ for some V (see (1.10)), so that $\underline{g} \subset \underline{gl}(V)$. Then ρ_g and $*X$ are induced, on passing to the quotient A of $B = K[GL(V)]$, by the corresponding actions on B. Hence we have $g = g_s g_u$ in $GL(V)$ and $X = X_s + X_n$ in $\underline{gl}(V)$, from case 1, and if we show that $g_s, g_u \in G$ and $X_s, X_n \in \underline{g}$, then they will give the required decompositions of g and X. Moreover the uniqueness and rationality properties will follow just as in case 1.

Let J be the ideal in B defining G. According to (3.11),

$$G = \{g \in GL(V) \mid \rho_g J = J\}$$

and

$$\underline{g} = \{X \in \underline{gl}(V) \mid J*X \subset J\} \quad .$$

But (4.2) implies that for $g \in G$ and $X \in \underline{g}$, J is invariant under $(\rho_g)_s$, $(\rho_g)_u$, $(*X)_s$, and $(*X)_n$, and case 1 implies these are ρ_{g_s}, ρ_{g_u}, $*X_s$, and $*X_n$, respectively. This completes the proof of (1), (2), and (3).

Proof of (4). By factoring α through $\alpha(G)$ it suffices to treat the two cases

(i) α is the inclusion of a closed subgroup,

and

(ii) α is surjective.

In case (i) we have $G \subset G'$ and the compatibility of Jordan decompositions follows from (3) after embedding G' in a linear group.

In case (ii) the comorphism $\alpha_0 : A' \longrightarrow A$ is injective, so we can view A' as a subring of A. Then, for $g \in G$ and $X \in \underline{g}$ we have $\rho_{\alpha(g)} = \rho_g | A'$ and $*d\alpha(X) = *X | A'$. Hence, we have the corresponding relationships between the Jordan decompositions according to (4.2).

COROLLARY. (1) _If_ $g, h \in G$ _commute then_ $gh = (g_s h_s)(g_u h_u)$ _is the Jordan decomposition of_ gh, _and all elements appearing commute._

(2) _If_ $X, Y \in \underline{g}$ _commute (i.e._ $[X, Y] = 0$) _then_ $X + Y = (X_s + Y_s) + (X_n + Y_n)$ _is the Jordan decomposition of_ $X + Y$, _and all elements appearing commute._

PROOF. After embedding G in a $GL(V)$ this follows from (4.2), corollary 2.

(4.5) _Semi-simple and unipotent elements in affine groups._ For an affine k-group G they are the elements of

$$G_s = \{g \in G | g = g_s\}$$

and of

$$G_u = \{g \in G | g = g_u\} ,$$

respectively. We define the analogous sets,

$$\underline{g}_s = \{X \in \underline{g} | X = X_s\} \text{ and } \underline{g}_n = \{X \in \underline{g} | X = X_n\}$$

of semi-simple and nilpotent elements, respectively, in $\underline{g}$.

It follows from part (4) of Theorem (4.4) that, if $\alpha : G \longrightarrow G'$ is a morphism of affine k-groups, then

$$\alpha(G_s) \subset G'_s, \ \alpha(G_u) \subset G'_u$$
$$(d\alpha)(\underline{g}_s) \subset \underline{g}'_s, \quad (d\alpha)(\underline{g}_n) \subset \underline{g}'_n \ .$$

In fact we have $\alpha(G_s) = \alpha(G)_s$ and $\alpha(G_u) = \alpha(G)_u$, and similarly for $\underline{g}$. Moreover, the corollary to Theorem (4.4) implies that a product of two commuting elements in G_s (resp., G_u) is again in G_s (resp., G_u). Similarly for sums of commuting elements in $\underline{g}_s$ (resp., $\underline{g}_n$). In particular, <u>if</u> G <u>is commutative then</u> G_s <u>and</u> G_u <u>are subgroups of</u> G, <u>and</u> $\underline{g}_s$ <u>and</u> $\underline{g}_n$ <u>are subspaces of</u> $\underline{g}$. Moreover, in general, it follows from (4.1)(d) that

$$G_s \cap G_u = \{e\} \ \underline{\text{and}} \ \underline{g}_s \cap \underline{g}_n = 0 \ .$$

If we embed G in a GL(V) then the elements of G_u (resp., $\underline{g}_n$) are defined by the equation $(g-e)^n = 0$ (resp., $X^n = 0$) in End(V) (for large enough n). These equations, with respect to a k-rational basis for V, have coefficients in $\mathbb{Z}$, so we conclude that:

G_u <u>is a</u> k-<u>closed subset of</u> G

and

$\underline{g}_n$ <u>is a</u> k-<u>closed subset of</u> $\underline{g}$.

(4.6) <u>Trigonalization and diagonalization</u>. Let M be a subset of $\underline{gl}_n$. We say that M is trigonalizable (over k) if there is a $g \in \mathbb{GL}_n$ (resp., $g \in \mathbb{GL}_n(k)$) such that gMg^{-1} is in upper triangular form (i.e. lies in $L(\mathbb{T}_n)$). We say M is diagonalizable (over k) if there is a $g \in \mathbb{GL}_n$ (resp., $g \in \mathbb{GL}_n(k)$) such that gMg^{-1} is in diagonal form (i.e. lies in $L(\mathbb{D}_n)$).

More generally, if V is any finite dimensional vector space with a k-structure V(k) then we can speak of trigonalizing or diagonalizing (over k) a family of endomorphisms of V. This means they assume triangular or diagonal form, respectively, with respect to a suitable (k-rational) basis of V.

PROPOSITION. Let $M \subset \underline{gl}_n(k)$ be a commuting family of endomorphisms, and let L be the field extension of k generated by the eigenvalues of elements of M.

(a) M is trigonalizable over L.

(b) If M consists of semi-simple endomorphisms then $L \subset k_s$ and M is diagonalizable over L.

PROOF. The fact that $L \subset k_s$ in case (b) follows from (4.1)(c). For the rest of the proof therefore we can replace k by L and assume all eigenvalues of elements of M are in k.

If $X \in M$ and if $a \in k$ then $W = \ker(X-aI)$ is visibly defined over k, and it is stable under all Y commuting with X, in particular all Y in M.

If M does not consist of scalar matrices

(otherwise there is nothing to prove) then we can choose X so that $0 \neq W \neq V$. Then, by induction on dimension, we can find an $e_1 \in W(k)$ which spans an M-stable line. Applying induction to V/Ke_1 we can complete e_1 to a k-rational basis $e_1, \ldots, e_n$ such that M leaves $Ke_1 + \ldots + Ke_i$ invariant for each $i = 1, \ldots, n$. This proves (a).

To prove (b) we can again assume there is a non-scalar X in M. Write $V = V_1 \oplus \ldots \oplus V_r$ where $V_i = \ker(X - a_i I)$ and $a_1, \ldots, a_r$ are the distinct eigenvalues of X. Then each V_i is defined over k and stable under M so, by induction on $\dim V$, we can diagonalize over k the action of M on each V_i. This yields the desired diagonalization of M on V.

(4.7) THEOREM. _Let_ G _be a commutative_ k-_group. Then_ G_s _and_ G_u _are closed subgroups and the product morphism_

$$\alpha : G_s \times G_u \longrightarrow G$$

is an isomorphism of algebraic groups.

PROOF. We have already seen in (4.5) that G_u is a k-closed subgroup and that G_s is a subgroup meeting G_u in e. Hence α is an isomorphism of abstract groups.

Embed G in some $\mathbb{GL}_n$. Using (4.6)(b) we can further arrange that $G_s = G \cap \mathbb{D}_n$. In particular it follows that G_s is a closed subgroup, and clearly α is then a morphism of algebraic groups.

Write $K^n = V_1 \oplus \ldots \oplus V_r$ where the V_i are the distinct simultaneous eigenspaces for G_s. Then G_u leaves each V_i stable so we can, by (4.6(a)), trigonalize the action of G_u in each V_i. Thus we can assume $G \subset \mathbb{T}_n$ and G_s still equals $G \cap \mathbb{D}_n$.

If $g \in G$ then $g_s \in G_s \subset \mathbb{D}_n$ so it follows easily (for example, from the fact that g is triangular and that g_s is a polynomial in g) that g_s is just the projection of g onto its diagonal component, $g \longmapsto \mathrm{diag}(g_{11}, \ldots, g_{nn})$. This is clearly a morphism. Hence $g \longmapsto g_u = g_s^{-1} g$ is likewise a morphism, so $g \longmapsto (g_s, g_u)$ gives the required inverse to α.

REMARK. We have seen in (4.5) that G_u is k-closed. It will further be shown in §10 that G_s is defined over k. If $\mathrm{char}(k) = 0$ this follows from the obvious invariance of $G_s(\bar{k})$ under $\mathrm{Gal}(\bar{k}/k)$. If $\mathrm{char}(k) = p > 0$ then, if $G \subset \mathbb{GL}_n$, we have $g_u^{p^n} = e$ for all $g \in G$. Hence $\beta : G \longrightarrow G$, $\beta(g) = g^{p^n}$, is a k-morphism of k-groups, clearly, with image in G_s. In fact it will be seen in §8 that the pth power map in G_s is surjective. From this it follows that $G_s = \beta(G)$ is defined over k.

(4.8) Trigonalizing unipotent groups. Let Λ be the algebra of upper triangular matrices, $\begin{pmatrix} * & & * \\ & \ddots & \\ 0 & & * \end{pmatrix}$, and let N be the ideal in Λ of matrices with zero diagonal. Then $N^n = 0$, so $U = I + N = \left\{ \begin{pmatrix} 1 & & * \\ & \ddots & \\ 0 & & 1 \end{pmatrix} \right\}$ is a unipotent group, i.e. one consisting of unipotent elements. It is easy to verify that the $I + N^i$ $(1 \leq i \leq n)$ are normal subgroups of U satisfying the commutator formula: $(I + N^i, I + N^j) \subset I + N^{i+j}$. In particular, taking $i = 1$ and varying j, we see that U is a nilpotent group. Its Lie algebra $\underline{u}$ is the set of all upper triangular matrices with eigenvalues zero, hence it consists of nilpotent matrices.

THEOREM. Let G be a not necessarily closed unipotent subgroup of $\mathbb{GL}_n(k)$. Then G is conjugate over k to a subgroup of U. In particular, G is a nilpotent group, and its Lie algebra consists of nilpotent elements.

PROOF. In view of the remarks made above, it suffices to prove the first assertion. For this, it suffices to show that there is a line L in V fixed by G. For then the set W of fixed points under G is a non zero subspace of V defined over k, and we can finish by applying induction to the induced action of G in V/W.

Henceforth, we may assume therefore that k is algebraically closed. Using induction on $\dim V$ we may further assume that V is an irreducible G-module. Then the vector space A spanned by G is a k-algebra acting irreducibly on V, so (by Wedderburn theory) it must be all of $\mathrm{End}(V)$.

Every $g = I + x \in G$ is unipotent, so $\mathrm{Tr}(g) = \mathrm{Tr}(I) = \dim V$ is independent of g. If also $g' \in G$ then $\mathrm{Tr}(xg') = \mathrm{Tr}((g-I)g') = \mathrm{Tr}(gg') - \mathrm{Tr}(g') = 0$, therefore.

But we saw above that such g' span $\mathrm{End}(V)$, and hence $x = 0$, i.e. $g = I$. This means $G = \{I\}$ so $\dim V = 1$. Q.E.D.

COROLLARY. <u>Let</u> G <u>be a unipotent algebraic group (i.e.</u> $G = G_u$). <u>Then</u> G <u>is isomorphic to a closed subgroup of</u> $U \subset \mathbb{GL}_n$ <u>for some</u> n. <u>Hence</u> $L(G)$ <u>consists of nilpotent elements</u>.

PROOF. We apply the theorem to an immersive representation $\pi : G \longrightarrow \mathbb{GL}_n$ (see (1.10)) to embed G in U. Then $L(G)$ is embedded in $L(U)$ which consists of upper triangular matrices with zeroes on the diagonal.

(4.9) REMARK. It will be shown later that an element $X \in \underline{g}$ is nilpotent (resp. semi-simple) if and only if it is tangent to a closed unipotent subgroup (resp. to a torus, cf. §8).

<u>Bibliographical Note</u>. The Jordan decomposition in algebraic groups is discussed in [1]. However, its existence is equivalent to the theorem 4.7 on commutative algebraic groups, proved earlier by Kolchin [12]. The proof given here is different from the one of [1], and follows a suggestion made by Springer for the Lie algebra case. Jordan decomposition in the Lie algebra is introduced in [2]. However, the definition adopted there and in [3] is more stringent, and the existence proof is less elementary. Here, it becomes the theorem mentioned in 4.9 to be

proved in (11.8) and (14.17).

CHAPTER II

HOMOGENEOUS SPACES

§5. SEMI-INVARIANTS

In this section *all algebraic groups are affine*. The results here prepare the way for the construction of quotients in §6.

(5.1) THEOREM. *Let* G *be a* k-*group and let* H *be a closed subgroup defined over* k. *Then there is an immersive representation* $\alpha : G \longrightarrow GL(E)$ *defined over* k, *and a line* $D \subset E$ *defined over* k, *such that*

$$H = \{g \in G \mid \alpha(g)D = D\} \quad \text{and} \quad \underline{h} = \{X \in \underline{g} \mid d\alpha(X)D \subset D\} .$$

PROOF. Let I denote the ideal in $A = K[G]$ of functions vanishing on H; it is generated by $I_k = I \cap k[G]$, and even by a finite subset of I_k. Therefore, using (1.9), we can find a finite dimensional right G-invariant subspace V of A, defined over k, and such that, if $W = V \cap I$, the ideal

I is generated by W_k.

Both V and I are right H-invariant and defined over k, so the same is true of W. We claim now that

$$H = \{g \in G \mid \rho_g W = W\} \text{ and } \underline{h} = \{X \in \underline{g} \mid W*X \subset W\} .$$

We know from (3.11) that the analogous equations hold if we replace W by I.

We have already remarked that W is right H-invariant, so it is $\underline{h}$-invariant also because convolution is the differential of right translation (3.10).

Conversely, suppose $g \in G$ and $\rho_g W = W$. Since ρ_g is an algebra automorphism we have $\rho_g I = \rho_g(WA) = \rho_g(W)A = WA = I$, so $g \in H$. Similarly, if $X \in \underline{g}$ and $W*X \subset W$, then

$$I*X = (WA)*X \subset (W*X)A + W(A*X) \subset WA = I, \quad \text{so } X \in \underline{h} .$$

Now put $E = \Lambda^d(V)$, where $d = \dim W$, and let $D = \Lambda^d W \subset E$. The representation $\rho : G \longrightarrow GL(V)$ induces $\alpha = \Lambda^d \rho : G \longrightarrow GL(E)$, a k-rational representation. In case α is not immersive replace E by $E \oplus F$ using any k-rational immersive representation $G \longrightarrow GL(F)$. Then all the conditions of the theorem are achieved thanks to the following lemma from linear algebra.

LEMMA. <u>Let</u> W <u>be a</u> d-<u>dimensional subspace of a vector space</u> V, <u>and let</u> $D = \Lambda^d W \subset E = \Lambda^d V$. <u>Let</u>

$g \in GL(V)$ and let $X \in \underline{gl}(V)$. Then

(1) $$(\Lambda^d g)D = D \Longleftrightarrow gW = W \quad ,$$

(2) $$(d\Lambda^d)(X)D \subset D \Longleftrightarrow XW \subset W \quad .$$

PROOF. In both cases the implication $\Longleftarrow$ is clear.

Let $(e_i)(1 \leqq i \leqq m)$ be a basis for V such that $e_1, \ldots, e_d$ span W. In case (1) we can further arrange that, for some $n \geqq 1$, $e_n, \ldots, e_{n+d-1}$ span gW. Then $(\Lambda^d g)(e_1 \wedge \ldots \wedge e_d)$ is a multiple of $e_n \wedge \ldots \wedge e_{n+d-1}$, so $(\Lambda^d g)D = D$ implies $n = 1$, i.e. $gW = W$.

In case (2) we can replace X by $X-Y$ for some Y leaving W stable, if necessary, to achieve the condition $W \cap XW = 0$. Then we can choose the basis above so that Xe_i is a multiple of $e_{d+i}(1 \leqq i \leqq d)$. In this case

$$(d\Lambda^d)_e(X)e_1 \ldots e_d)$$

$$= \sum_{1 \leqq i \leqq d} e_1 \wedge \ldots \wedge e_{i-1} \wedge Xe_i \wedge e_{i+1} \wedge \ldots \wedge e_d \quad .$$

Since the vectors $e_1 \wedge \ldots \wedge e_{i-1} \wedge e_{d+i} \wedge e_{i+1} \wedge \ldots \wedge e_d$ are part of a basis of $\Lambda^d V$ that includes $e_1 \wedge \ldots \wedge e_d$, it follows that the sum above can be a multiple of $e_1 \wedge \ldots \wedge e_d$ only if each $Xe_i = 0$, i.e. only if $X = 0$.

(5.2) Characters and semi-invariants. Let G and G' be k-groups. We shall write $Mor(G, G')$ for the algebraic group morphisms from G to G', and $Mor(G, G')_k$ for the set of those defined over k.

Recall from (AG. 14. 3) that $\Gamma = \mathrm{Gal}(k_s/k)$ operates on $\mathrm{Mor}(G, G')_{k_s}$, and ${}^s\alpha$, for $s \in \Gamma$ and $\alpha \in \mathrm{Mor}(G, G')_{k_s}$, is characterized by:

$$({}^s\alpha)(g) = s(\alpha(s^{-1}g)) \qquad (g \in G(k_s)) \ .$$

Moreover we have

$$\mathrm{Mor}(G, G')_k = \mathrm{Mor}(G, G')_{k_s}^{\Gamma} \ ,$$

i.e. α is defined over k if and only if α is defined over k_s and is a Γ-equivariant homomorphism of $G(k_s)$ into $G'(k_s)$.

Note that when G' is commutative, Mor(G, G') is an abelian group and $\mathrm{Mor}(G, G')_{k_s}$ is a Γ-module, the product in Mor(G, G') being defined by: $aa'(g) = a(g)\cdot a'(g)$.

We shall write

$$X(G) = \mathrm{Mor}(G, \mathbb{GL}_1)$$

and call its elements characters of G. Thus $\chi \in X(G)$ means $\chi \in K[G]$, and $\chi(g) \neq 0$ and $\chi(gg') = \chi(g)\chi(g')$ for all $g, g' \in G$. The condition $\chi \in X(G)_k$ just means that moreover $\chi \in k[G]$.

Let $\alpha : G \longrightarrow GL(V)$ be a k-rational representation. A semi-invariant of G in V is a non-zero vector $v \in V$ spanning a G-stable line in V. Thus we can write

$$\alpha(g)v = \chi(g)v$$

for some function $\chi : G \longrightarrow K^*$, and evidently χ is a character, which is defined over k if $v \in V(k)$. This character is called the weight of the semi-invariant v.

We shall also use the term semi-invariant with respect to the action by translation of functions induced by an action of G on a variety.

With V as above and $\chi \in X(G)$ write

$$V_\chi = \{v \in V \mid \alpha(g)v = \chi(g)v \text{ for all } g \in G\} .$$

We can even restrict to $g \in G(k_s)$ here, because $G(k_s)$ is dense in G (see (AG.13.3)). If, further, χ is defined over k_s, then the equation $\alpha(g)v = \chi(g)v$ is a linear equation in v defined over k_s, so we see that V_χ is defined over k_s if $\chi \in X(G)_{k_s}$.

Suppose $\chi \in X(G)_{k_s}$, $g \in G(k_s)$, $v \in V_\chi(k_s)$, and $s \in \Gamma$. Then

$$\begin{aligned}
({}^s\chi)(g)(sv) &= (s(\chi(s^{-1}g)))(sv) \\
&= s(\chi(s^{-1}g)(v)) \quad (\Gamma \text{ acts semi-linearly}) \\
&= s(\alpha(s^{-1}g)(v)) \quad (v \in V_\chi) \\
&= ({}^s\alpha(g))(sv) \\
&= \alpha(g)(sv) \qquad (\alpha \text{ is defined over } k).
\end{aligned}$$

This shows that $sV_\chi(k_s) \subset V_{({}^s\chi)}(k_s)$, and the reverse inclusion follows by applying s^{-1} to this. Thus we have

$$sV_\chi(k_s) = V_{({}^s\chi)}(k_s)$$

for $\chi \in X(G)_{k_s}$ and $s \in \Gamma$. In particular (see (AG. 14.1)):

<u>If</u> χ <u>is defined over</u> k, <u>then</u> V_χ <u>is defined over</u> k.

A <u>weight</u> of G in V is a $\chi \in X(G)$ such that $V_\chi \neq 0$.

LEMMA. <u>The subspaces</u> V_χ $(\chi \in X(G))$ <u>of</u> V <u>are linearly independent</u>. <u>In particular</u> G <u>has only finitely many weights in</u> V.

PROOF. If not, choose n minimal such that there exist distinct $\chi_i (1 \leq i \leq n)$ and non-zero $v_i \in V_{\chi_i}$ such that $v_1 + \ldots + v_n = 0$. Clearly $n > 1$, so there is a $g \in G$ such that $\chi_1(g) \neq \chi_2(g)$. Since $\Sigma \chi_i(g) v_i = 0$ we can subtract $\chi_1(g)^{-1}$ times the last equation from the first to obtain a non trivial dependence relation of length $< n$; contradiction.

(5.3) COROLLARY. <u>In the setting of</u> (5.1), <u>there exist a</u> $\chi \in X(H)_k$, <u>and functions</u> $f_1, \ldots, f_n \in k[G]$, <u>which are semi-invariants of the same weight</u>, χ, <u>for</u> H <u>under right translation, such that</u>

(1) $$H = \{g \in G \mid \rho_g f_i \in K f_i,\ 1 \leq i \leq n\},$$

(2) $$\underline{h} = \{X \in \underline{g} \mid f_i * X \in Kf_i, \ 1 \leq i \leq n\} .$$

PROOF. With E and D as in (5.1), let $e_1, \ldots, e_n$ be a k-rational basis of E such that $D = Ke_1$, and let T_{ij} denote the (i, j) coordinate function on $\underline{gl}(E) \cong \underline{gl}_n$, the isomorphism being defined relative to the basis above.

In this coordinate system we can paraphrase Theorem (5.1) as follows:

(*) $$H = \{g \in G \mid T_{i1}(\alpha(g)) = 0 \text{ for } i > 1\}$$

(**) $$\underline{h} = \{X \in \underline{g} \mid T_{i1}((d\alpha)X) = 0 \text{ for } i > 1\} .$$

The first formula implies that $\chi = T_{11} \circ \alpha$ is a character on H, evidently defined over k. Put $f_i = T_{i1} \circ \alpha (1 < i \leq n)$. Then $f_i \in k[G]$, and, for $g \in G$ and $h \in H$, we have

$$(\rho_h f_i)(g) = f_i(gh) = T_{i1}(\alpha(gh)) =$$

$$= \Sigma_j T_{ij}(\alpha(g))T_{j1}(\alpha(h)) = T_{i1}(\alpha(g))T_{11}(\alpha(h)) = \chi(h)f_i(g) .$$

Thus each f_i is a semi-invariant of weight χ for H. If $g \in G$ and $\rho_g f_i \in Kf_i$ then $\rho_g f_i(e)$ is a multiple of $f_i(e) = T_{i1}(\alpha(e)) = 0$, for each $i > 1$. Thus $g \in H$, thanks to (*). This proves (1).

It remains to be shown that if $X \in \underline{g}$ and if $f_i * X \in Kf_i$ for all $i > 1$ then $X \in \underline{h}$. The identification of the Lie algebra of $\mathbb{GL}_n$ with $\underline{gl}_n$ assigns the tangent vector Y to the matrix $(Y(T_{ij}))$ (see (3.6)). Viewing the T_{ij} as coordinate functions on the Lie algebra, we have $T_{ij}(Y) = Y(T_{ij})$. Applying this to the X above, we have $T_{i1}((d\alpha)(X)) = (d\alpha)(X)(T_{i1}) = X(T_{i1} \circ \alpha) = Xf_i = (f_i * X)(e) =$ (a multiple of $f_i(e)$) = (a multiple of $T_{i1}(\alpha(e))) = 0$ for all $i > 1$. Hence (**) implies $X \in \underline{h}$.

(5.4) COROLLARY. Let $G \subset \mathbb{GL}_n$ be an algebraic matric group defined over k. Then there exists $\chi \in X(G)_k$ and polynomials $f_1, \ldots, f_m \in k[T_{11}, \ldots, T_{nn}]$ which are semi-invariants of weight χ for G with respect to right translation, such that

$$G = \{g \in \mathbb{GL}_n \mid \rho_g f_i \in Kf_i,\ 1 \leqq i \leqq m\} ,$$

$$\underline{g} = \{X \in \underline{gl}_n \mid f_i * X \in Kf_i,\ 1 \leqq i \leqq m\} .$$

PROOF. $k[\mathbb{GL}_n] = k[T_{11}, T_{12}, \ldots, T_{nn}, D^{-1}]$ where $D = \det(T_{ij})$. From (5.3) we obtain functions $f_i' \in k[\mathbb{GL}_n](1 \leqq i \leqq m)$ which are semi-invariants of some weight $\chi' \in X(G)_k$, and which satisfy conditions of the above type. For r large enough we can write $f_i' = D^{-r} f_i$ with f_i a polynomial $(1 \leqq i \leqq m)$. Evidently D is a semi-invariant of weight D for $\mathbb{GL}_n$. Consequently the f_i are semi-invariants for G of weight $\chi = (D|G)^r \chi'$. One sees immediately that χ and $f_1, \ldots, f_m$ satisfy the conditions above.

(5.5) Invariants. It is not true in general that Theorem (5.1) and its corollaries can be strengthened to give invariants (i.e. $\chi = 1$) instead of semi-invariants. However, there are two important cases when this can be done. One, clearly, is when $X(H)_k = \{1\}$. Another case is deduced as follows: Let $\alpha : G \longrightarrow GL(E)$ be as in Theorem (5.1), and let χ be the character by means of which H acts on D. Suppose we can find a second representation $\alpha' : G \longrightarrow GL(E')$ and a $D' \subset E'$ with the analogous properties, but so that H acts on D' via χ^{-1}. Then $\alpha \otimes \alpha'$ gives a representation of G on $E \otimes_K E'$ so that H acts trivially on $D \otimes_K D'$. Moreover, if $D = Kv$ and $D' = Kv'$ then it is easy to see that H is exactly the isotropy group of $v \otimes v'$ and $\underline{h}$ is the isotropy algebra of $v \otimes v'$.

How can we find such an E' and D'? We can try the contragredient representation $\alpha^* : G \longrightarrow GL(E^*)$. Then the one dimensional H-invariant subspace D of weight χ leads to a one dimensional quotient space D^* of E^* on which H acts via χ^{-1}. To lift D^* H-equivariantly back into E^* it would suffice to know that H acts completely reducibly on E. In characteristic zero this happens if H is a reductive group.

(5.6) THEOREM. Let G be a k-group, and let N be a normal k-subgroup. Then there is a linear representation $\alpha : G \longrightarrow GL(V)$ defined over k such that $N = \ker(\alpha)$ and such that $\underline{n} = \ker(d\alpha)$.

PROOF. Theorem (5.1) gives us an $\alpha : G \longrightarrow GL(E)$ and a line $D \subset E$, all defined over k, such that N is the stability subgroup of D in G and such that $\underline{n}$ is the stability subalgebra of D in $\underline{g}$.

The action of N on D is via some $\chi \in X(N)_k$. Let F denote the sum of all the subspaces E_φ, φ ranging over $X(N)_{k_s}$. We saw above (5.2) that this sum is direct. If $x \in E_\varphi$, $g \in G(k_s)$, and $n \in N$, then $\alpha(n)\alpha(g)x = \alpha(g)\alpha(g^{-1}ng)x = \varphi(g^{-1}ng)\alpha(g)x$. Thus, if we define $(g\varphi)(n) = \varphi(g^{-1}ng)$, then $g\varphi \in X(N)_{k_s}$, and

$$\alpha(g)E_\varphi = E_{(g\varphi)}, \quad (g \in G(k_s),\ \varphi \in X(N)_{k_s}) \ .$$

It follows that F is G-invariant. Moreover, F is defined over k_s and invariant under $Gal(k_s/k)$ (see (5.2)) so F is defined over k. Finally, since $D \subset F$, there is no loss in assuming that E = F; otherwise follow α by restriction to F.

This done, let $V \subset \underline{gl}(E)$ be the set of endomorphisms of $E = \coprod E_\varphi (\varphi \in X(N)_{k_s})$ which leave each of the E_φ stable. Evidently $V = \coprod \underline{gl}(E_\varphi)$. If $g \in G(k_s)$ and if $v \in V$ then, for each $\varphi \in X(N)_{k_s}$,

$$\begin{aligned}\alpha(g)v\alpha(g)^{-1}E_\varphi &= \alpha(g)vE_{(g^{-1}\varphi)} \\ &= \alpha(g)E_{(g^{-1}\varphi)} \\ &= E_\varphi \ .\end{aligned}$$

Thus $\alpha(G)$ normalizes V, so we can define $\beta : G \longrightarrow GL(V)$ by $\beta(g)(v) = \alpha(g)v\alpha(g)^{-1}$. Since β is just the restriction to V of α followed by Ad on GL(E), it is a morphism. To see that V, and hence also β, are defined over k, take $s \in \mathrm{Gal}(k_s/k)$ and $v \in V(k_s)$. Then $({}^s v)E_\varphi(k_s) = (s \cdot v \cdot s^{-1})E_\varphi(k_s) = svE_{({}^{s^{-1}}\varphi)}(k_s) = sE_{({}^{s^{-1}}\varphi)}(k_s) = E_\varphi(k_s)$. Thus V is a subspace defined over k_s, and $V(k_s)$ is $\mathrm{Gal}(k_s/k)$ stable, so V is defined over k (see (AG.14.1)).

If $n \in N$ then $\alpha(n)$ is a multiple of the identity on each E_φ, so $\alpha(n)$ centralizes V, and hence $\beta(n) = e$. Conversely, if $\beta(g) = e$ then $\alpha(g)$ must leave each E_φ stable and induce a scalar multiplication in each one. (This is a simple calculation in $\underline{gl}(E)$.) Since $D \subset E_\chi$ it follows that $\alpha(g)$ leaves D stable, so $g \in N$. This shows that $N = \ker(\beta)$, and hence that $\underline{n} \subset \ker(d\beta)$.

Since β is the restriction to V of $\mathrm{Ad}_{GL(E)} \circ \alpha$ it follows that $d\beta$ is the restriction to V of $\mathrm{ad} \circ d\alpha$. Therefore $X \in \ker(d\beta) \Longrightarrow \mathrm{ad}((d\alpha)(X))V = 0 \Longrightarrow (d\alpha)(X)$ centralizes $V \Longrightarrow (d\alpha)(X)$ leaves each E_φ stable and induces a scalar multiplication in each one (same calculation as above) $\Longrightarrow (d\alpha)(X)$ leaves $D \subset E_\chi$ stable $\Longrightarrow X \in \underline{n}$.

§6. HOMOGENEOUS SPACES

Given an algebraic group G and a closed subgroup H we want to give the coset space G/H the structure of a variety in a natural way, for example, so that the projection $\pi : G \longrightarrow G/H$ is a morphism satisfying a suitable universal mapping property. We shall do this here for G affine. The method is to use the results of §5 to realize G/H as the orbit of a point with isotropy group H under a suitable action of G on a projective space. In order to verify that this construction of G/H has the required properties we shall have to invoke several results from algebraic geometry which are quoted in Chapter AG.

We hasten to point out that the use of the term "quotient" here is not the categorical one, and hence it should be regarded as a provisional terminology adjusted to our present needs.

(6.1) Quotient morphisms. Let $\pi : V \longrightarrow W$ be a k-morphism of k-varieties. We say π is a quotient morphism (over k) if

(1) π is surjective and open.

(2) If $U \subset V$ is open, then π_0 induces an isomorphism from $K[\pi(U)]$ onto the set of $f \in K[U]$ which are constant on the fibres of $\pi | U$.

Recall from (AG. 8.2) that (1) implies that π is dominant.

UNIVERSAL MAPPING PROPERTY: Let $\pi : V \longrightarrow W$ be a quotient morphism over k. If $\alpha : V \longrightarrow Z$ is any morphism constant on the fibres of π then there is a unique morphism $\beta : W \longrightarrow Z$ such that $\alpha = \beta \circ \pi$. If α is a k-morphism of k-varieties then so also is β.

PROOF. It is clear that β exists and is unique topologically because π is open. It remains to show that if U is open in Z, then $f \longmapsto f \circ \beta$ carries $K[U]$ into $K[\beta^{-1}(U)]$. But π_0 identifies $K[\beta^{-1}(U)] = K[\pi(\alpha^{-1}(U))]$ with the set of $h \in K[\alpha^{-1}(U)]$ which are constant on the fibres of $\pi|\alpha^{-1}(U)$. Since α_0 maps $K[U]$ into the ring of such functions in $K[\alpha^{-1}(U)]$ (because α is constant on the fibres of π) it follows indeed that $\beta_0 K[U] \subset K[\beta^{-1}(U)]$. Thus β is a morphism of varieties.

In the above argument β_0 was seen to be the unique map rendering the diagram

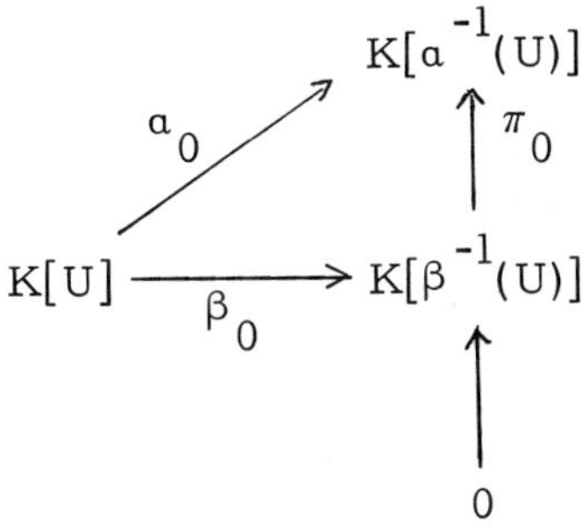

commutative. If U is k-open then so also are $\alpha^{-1}(U)$ and $\beta^{-1}(U) = \pi(\alpha^{-1}(U))$ (see (AG. 14. 5)). Moreover α_0 and π_0 are defined over k, so it follows that β_0 is also defined over k.

COROLLARY. <u>A bijective quotient morphism is an isomorphism.</u>

For if π is bijective we can apply the universal mapping property to $\alpha = 1_V$ to obtain π^{-1}.

(6.2) LEMMA. Let $\pi : V \longrightarrow W$ be a surjective open separable morphism of irreducible varieties, and assume W is normal. Then β is a quotient morphism.

PROOF. We must verify condition (2) of the definition of quotient morphism for each open U in V. Since $\pi | U : U \longrightarrow \pi(U)$ inherits all of the hypotheses made on π it suffices to treat the case $U = V$. Then we must show that every $f \in K[V]$ constant on the fibres of π lies in the subring $\pi_0 K[W]$. According to (AG.18.2, Prop.) f is purely inseparable over $\pi_0 K(W)$, so the separability of π implies that $f = \pi_0 f'$ for some $f' \in K(W)$. It remains to be shown that f' is everywhere defined. If f' is not defined at $\pi(x)$, then, because W is normal, it follows from (AG.18.3; Lem.) that there is a point $\pi(y)$ where $1/f'$ is defined and vanishes. But then $1/f = \pi_0(1/f')$ is defined and vanishes at y, contrary to the fact that $f \in K[V]$.

(6.3) The quotient of V by G. For the next few sections (until (6.7)) we fix a k-group G acting k-morphically on a k-variety V. An orbit map is a surjective morphism $\pi : V \longrightarrow W$ of varieties such that the fibres of π are the orbits of G in V. A quotient of V by G over k is an orbit map $\pi : V \longrightarrow W$ which is a quotient morphism over k in the sense of (6.1). In particular such a π satisfies the following:

UNIVERSAL MAPPING PROPERTY: If $\alpha : V \longrightarrow Z$ is any morphism constant on the orbits of G there is a unique morphism $\beta : W \longrightarrow Z$ such that $\alpha = \beta \circ \pi$. If α is a k-morphism of k-varieties so also is β.

It follows that the quotient, if it exists, is unique up to a unique k-isomorphism. We are thus permitted to denote it by the symbol $G \backslash V$. If the action is defined so that G operates on the right on V, as with right translation in a larger group containing G, then we shall use the symbol V/G.

In general quotients do not exist. For example, the next proposition shows that the existence of a quotient implies that the dimensions of the orbits cannot vary. Moreover: if an orbit map $\pi : V \longrightarrow W$ exists, then the orbits of G in V are closed. This is because they are inverse images of points under a morphism.

(6.4) PROPOSITION. Let $\pi : V \longrightarrow W$ be a dominant orbit map and assume that W is irreducible.

(a) G acts transitively on the set of irreducible components of V. In particular, if G is connected, then V is irreducible.

Assume now that the irreducible components of V are open.

(b) The orbits of G in V have constant dimension $d = \dim V - \dim W$.

(c) If W is normal then π is open.

PROOF. (a) Let F and F' be irreducible components of V. Since π is dominant and W is irreducible it follows that πF and $\pi F'$ contain dense open sets in W. Hence $\pi^{-1}(\pi F') = G \cdot F'$ contains a non-empty, hence dense, open set in F. But $G \cdot F'$ is the union of those irreducible components of V into which G transforms F'. In particular it is closed, so it contains F, and hence $F = gF'$ for some $g \in G$ because F is irreducible. The stability group H of F in G is a closed subgroup of finite index, so H contains G^0 (see (1.2)). This proves (a).

To prove (b) and (c) we replace V by F and G by H, and thus reduce to the case when V is irreducible. This reduction is justifiable in view of (a) and of the disjointness of the irreducible components of V.

Now that V is irreducible part (c) is a consequence of (b), by virtue of (AG. 18. 4), so it remains to prove (b). For this we use the results of (AG. 10. 2) on the dimension of the fibres of a morphism. The orbits are homogeneous so all irreducible components of an orbit have the same dimension. Moreover, $\dim G(x) \geqq d$, with equality whenever $\pi(x) \in U$, where U is some dense open set in W

Next consider the graph of the action of G on V: $\Gamma = \{(g, x, gx) \in G \times V \times V\}$. Let D be the diagonal in $V \times V$, put $Z = \Gamma \cap (G \times D)$, and let $p : Z \longrightarrow D$ be the projection. If $x \in V$, then $p^{-1}(x, x) = \{(g, x, x) \mid g \in G, gx = x\} = G_x \times \{(x, x)\}$. Hence all irreducible components of the fibre of p over (x, x) have the same dimension. Let Z_0 be an irreducible component of Z containing $\{e\} \times D$, and let $p_1 : Z_0 \longrightarrow D$ be the restriction of p. Then p_1 is surjective, and $p_1^{-1}(x, x)$ is a non-empty union of irreducible components of $p^{-1}(x, x)$. Thus by applying the theorems on fibres of a morphism (AG.10.2) to p_1 we see that

$$\dim G_x \geqq d' = \dim Z_0 - \dim D$$

with equality whenever $x \in U'$, where U' is some open dense set in V. Combining this and the above, we have, for all $x \in V$,

$$d \leqq \dim G(x) = \dim G - \dim G_x \leqq \dim G - d' \quad .$$

Choosing $x \in U' \cap \pi^{-1}(U)$, which is possible because the latter set is open dense, we see that the inequalities become equalities, so $d = \dim G - d'$. Hence $\dim G(x) = d$ for all x.

(6.5) <u>The function field of a quotient</u>. If U is a dense open set in V and if $g \in G$ then $g^{-1}U$ is also open dense, and we have the comorphism $\lambda_g : K[g^{-1}U] \longrightarrow K[U]$ (where $(\lambda_g f)(x) = f(g^{-1}x)$). As U varies we obtain an automorphism of the direct system of $K[U]$'s, and hence of their direct limit $K(V)$. If $f \in K(V)$ has domain of definition U, then $\lambda_g f$ has domain of definition gU. In this way G acts, by left translation, as a group of K-algebra automorphisms of $K(V)$, and we denote the fixed ring by $K(V)^G$.

PROPOSITION. Suppose a quotient $\pi : V \longrightarrow W$ of V by G exists. Then π is a separable morphism and π_0 induces an isomorphism of $K(W)$ onto $K(V)^G$. If V is irreducible then, for each $x \in V$, π_0 maps $\mathcal{O}_{W,\pi(x)}$ isomorphically onto $\mathcal{O}_{V,x} \cap K(V)^G$.

PROOF. Since π is dominant, π_0 induces a monomorphism of $K(W)$ into $K(V)$ whose image clearly lies in $K(V)^G$. On the other hand, if $f \in K(V)^G$, then the domain of definition U of f is G-stable, and f is constant on the fibres of $\pi|U$. Hence the definition of quotient implies that f lies in the image of $\pi_0 : K[\pi(U)] \longrightarrow K[U]$.

To show that π is separable, therefore, it suffices to prove that if F is a finite product of fields, and if H is a group of automorphisms of F, then F is separable over $E = F^H$. To a decomposition of E as a product of fields corresponds a decomposition of F which is clearly G-stable, so we can reduce to the case when E is a field. Then G operates transitively on the factors of F; otherwise we could separate the latter into G-orbits and this would yield a product decomposition of F^G.

If L is one of the fields into which F factors we must show that L is separable over E. But the remarks above imply that $E = L^{H'}$ where H' is the stability group of L in H. Hence the desired separability follows from (AG. 2. 4).

If V is irreducible, then the field $K(V)$ contains all the local rings $\mathcal{O}_{V,x}$ $(x \in V)$. Identifying $K(W)$ with

$K(V)^G$, we have $\mathcal{O}_{W,\pi(x)} \subset (\mathcal{O}_{V,x} \cap K(V)^G)$, and the map $\pi_0 : \mathcal{O}_{W,\pi(x)} \longrightarrow \mathcal{O}_{V,x}$ is just the inclusion. It remains to show that every $f \in \mathcal{O}_{V,x} \cap K(V)^G = \mathcal{O}_{V,x} \cap K(W)$ lies in $\mathcal{O}_{W,\pi(x)}$. If U is an open neighborhood of x on which f is defined, then the definition of a quotient implies that, as an element of K[U], f lies in $\pi_0 K[\pi(U)]$. In particular, as a rational function on W, f is defined at $\pi(x)$, i.e. $f \in \mathcal{O}_{W,\pi(x)}$.

(6.6) PROPOSITION. Suppose $\pi : V \longrightarrow W$ is a separable orbit map, and assume that W is normal and that the irreducible components of V are open. Then (W, π) is the quotient of V by G.

PROOF. We can easily reduce to the case when W is connected, and hence (being normal) irreducible. Then it follows from (6.4)(c) that π is open, and from (6.4)(a), that G operates transitively on the components of V. Since these components are disjoint we can replace V by one of them and G by its stability group, and retain all of our hypotheses. Thus we see that it suffices to prove the proposition when V is also irreducible. But then the fact that π is a quotient morphism follows from Lemma (6.2).

COROLLARY. Let G_1, G_2 be k-groups, and V_1, V_2 k-varieties. Assume that G_i operates k-morphically on V_i and that V_i/G_i exists and is normal $(i = 1, 2)$. Then $(V_1 \times V_2)/(G_1 \times G_2)$ exists and is canonically isomorphic to

$(V_1/G_1) \times (V_2/G_2)$.

The product $V_1/G_1 \times V_2/G_2$ is normal (AG. 18.1). The projections $V_i \longrightarrow V_i/G_i$ are separable (6.5), hence their product is (AG. 17.3, Cor.). The fibres of the latter map are the orbits of $G_1 \times G_2$; we may then apply the proposition.

(6.7) PROPOSITION. Suppose $x \in V(k)$, and let $\pi : G \longrightarrow G(x)$ be the k-morphism $g \longmapsto g \cdot x$. Then $G(x)$ is a smooth variety defined over k and locally closed in V. Moreover π is an orbit map for the action of G_x on G by right translation. The following conditions are equivalent:

(a) π is a quotient of G by G_x.

(b) π is separable, i.e. $(d\pi)_e : L(G) \longrightarrow T(G(x))_x$ is surjective.

(c) The kernel of $(d\pi)_e$ is contained in $L(G_x)$.

When these conditions hold G_x is defined over k, and hence π is a quotient of G by G_x over k.

PROOF. The first assertion follows from (1.8), and the second one is obvious.

In view of the homogeneity of G and of G(x) the interpretation of separability given in (b) is justified by (AG. 17.3). We obtain (a) $\Longrightarrow$ (b) from (6.5) and (b) $\Longrightarrow$ (a) from (6.6). Since $\dim G = \dim G_x + \dim G(x)$, and since the tangent spaces to a smooth variety have the same dimension as the variety, the equivalence of (b) and (c) follows from the obvious inclusion $L(G_x) \subset \ker(d\pi)_e$.

If π is separable, then it follows from (AG. 13.2) that there is a dense open set $W \subset G(x)$ such that, if $w \in W(k_s)$, the fibre $\pi^{-1}(w)$ has a dense set of separable points. Since W contains a separable point (AG. 13.3) w, we can translate w to deduce the corresponding property for every separable point of $G(x)$. Since x is rational over k, it follows that $G_x = \pi^{-1}(x)$ has a dense and Galois-stable set of separable points, so (AG. 14.4) G_x is defined over k.

REMARK. The above argument shows that the kernel of a separable k-morphism of k-groups is defined over k.

(6.8) THEOREM. _Let_ G _be an affine_ k-_group and let_ H _be a closed subgroup defined over_ k. _Then the quotient_ $\pi : G \longrightarrow G/H$ _exists over_ k, _and_ G/H _is a smooth quasi-projective variety_. _If_ H _is a normal subgroup of_ G, _then_ G/H _is an affine_ k-_group and_ π _is a_ k-_morphism of_ k-_groups_.

PROOF. Theorem (5.1) gives us a k-rational representation $\alpha : G \longrightarrow GL(E)$ and a line D in E defined over k such that

$$H = \{g \in G \mid \alpha(g)D = D\}, \quad \underline{h} = \{X \in \underline{g} \mid d\alpha(X)D \subset D\} .$$

Let $q : E - \{0\} \longrightarrow P$ denote the projection onto the projective space $P = P(E)$ of lines in E, and let $x = q(D - \{0\}) \in P(k)$. Via α, we have a k-morphic action of G on P, and we propose to construct G/H from the orbit map $\pi : G \longrightarrow G(x)$, $\pi(g) = gx$. Since H is the isotropy group of x, clearly, it remains only to show, thanks to (6.7), that $\ker(d\pi)_e = \underline{h}$.

Choose $v \neq 0$ in D and define $\beta : G \longrightarrow E - \{0\}$ by $\beta(g) = \alpha(g)v$. Then $\pi = q \circ \beta$ and $(d\beta)_e(X) = (d\alpha)(X)v$, where, as usual, we identify $T(E - \{0\})_v = T(E)_v$ with E. Therefore, since $\underline{h} = (d\beta)_e^{-1}(D)$, the fact that $\ker(d\pi)_e = \underline{h}$ follows from the fact that the kernel of $(dq)_v : T(E - \{0\})_v \longrightarrow T(P)_{q(v)}$ is just D.

Finally, if H is a normal subgroup of G, then Theorem (5.6) permits us to choose $\alpha : G \longrightarrow GL(E)$ above so that $H = \ker(\alpha)$ and $\underline{h} = \ker(d\alpha)$. It then follows from (1.4) that $G' = \alpha(G)$ is a closed subgroup of $GL(E)$ defined over k. Letting G act, via α, by left translation on $GL(E)$, we can view $\pi : G \longrightarrow G'$, $\pi(g) = \alpha(g)(= \alpha(g)e)$ as the orbit map onto the orbit of e. Since $\ker(d\pi) = \underline{h}$ and since H is the stability group of e under the above action, it follows again from (6.7) that π is the quotient of G by H. This completes the proof of the theorem.

CAUTION. Even though $G \longrightarrow G/H$ is a surjective k-morphism, it is not true in general that $G(k) \longrightarrow (G/H)(k)$ is surjective. This is true if $k = k_s$, and a general study of this problem leads to questions in Galois cohomology which will not be discussed here, (see e.g. [19]).

(6.9) COROLLARY. Let $\alpha : G \longrightarrow G'$ be a morphism of algebraic groups. If G is affine so also is $\alpha(G)$.

PROOF. Let $N = \ker(\alpha)$. Then α induces a bijective morphism $\beta : G/N \longrightarrow \alpha(G)$, and we know that G/N is affine. Hence it follows from (AG.18.3) that $\alpha(G)$ is affine.

(6.10) COROLLARY. Let G be an affine k-group acting k-morphically on a k-variety V, and let N be a closed normal subgroup of G defined over k.

(1) If V/N exists over k and is a normal variety, then G/N acts k-morphically on V/N (in the natural way). In particular, if N acts trivially on V, then G/N acts k-morphically on V.

(2) If, moreover, V/G exists and is a normal variety then the quotient of V/N by G/N exists and is canonically isomorphic to V/G.

PROOF. Let $\alpha : G \times V \longrightarrow V$ be the action and let $\pi : V \longrightarrow V/N$ and $p : G \longrightarrow G/N$ be the quotient morphisms. Using the corollary to 6.6, we see that the vertical arrows in the commutative diagram

$$
\begin{array}{ccc}
G \times V & \xrightarrow{\;\alpha\;} & V \\
{\scriptstyle 1_G \times \pi}\big\downarrow & & \big\downarrow{\scriptstyle \pi} \\
G \times (V/N) & \dashrightarrow{\;\alpha'\;} & V/N \\
{\scriptstyle p \times 1_{(V/N)}}\big\downarrow & \nearrow & \\
(G/N) \times (V/N) & {\scriptstyle \beta} &
\end{array}
$$

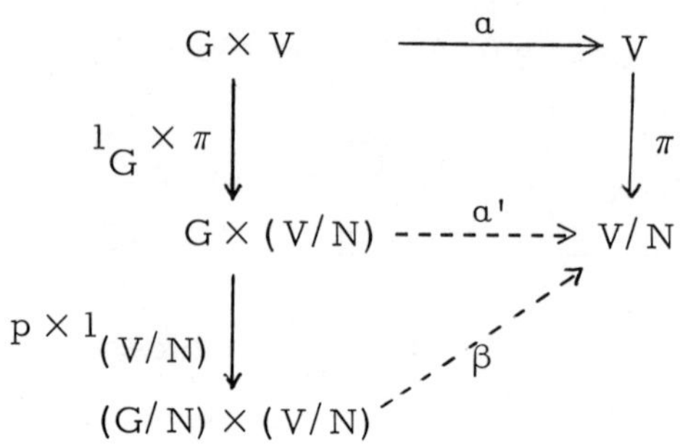

are quotient morphisms.

Now we can fill the diagram with α' and then β using the universal mapping property (6.1) for quotients. The k-action of G/N on V/N is then given by β. In case N acts trivially on V we have V = V/N, so this proves (1).

For part (2) let $\pi_G : V \longrightarrow V/G$ be the quotient. The universal mapping property for π gives us a π' making the triangle

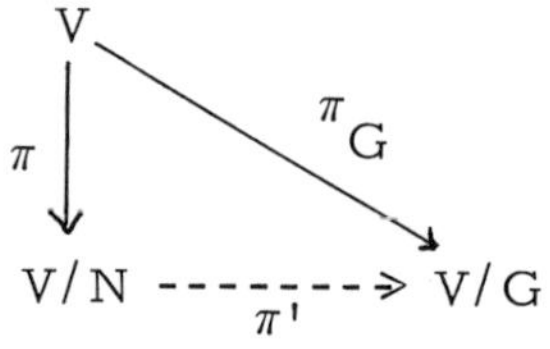

commutative. Clearly π' is an orbit map for the action of G/N on V/N. Since $\pi_G = \pi' \circ \pi$ is separable so also is π'. Hence (6.6) implies that π' is a quotient, because V/G is normal.

(6.11) COROLLARY. <u>Let</u> G <u>be an affine</u> k-<u>group and let</u> N $\subset$ M <u>be closed subgroups of</u> G <u>defined over</u> k <u>such</u>

that N *is normal in* M. *Then* M/N *acts* k-*morphically on* G/N, *the quotient exists and is isomorphic to* G/M. *If* M *and* N *are normal subgroups of* G, *these varieties are isomorphic as* k-*groups*.

PROOF. The first assertion follows by substituting (G, M, N) for (V, G, N) in Corollary (6.10), and the second one is clear.

(6.12) PROPOSITION. *Let* G *be an affine* k-*group, and let* M *and* N *be closed subgroups defined over* k. *Let* $\pi : G \longrightarrow G/N$ *be the quotient morphism. Then* $L(M) \cap L(N) = L(M \cap N)$ *if and only if* π *induces a separable morphism* $\pi' : M \longrightarrow \pi(M)$. *In this case* $M \cap N$ *is defined over* k.

As an immediate consequence we have:

COROLLARY. *If* char(k) = 0, *then* $L(M) \cap L(N) = L(M \cap N)$ *and* $M \cap N$ *is defined over* k.

PROOF. π' is just the map of M onto the M-orbit of $\pi(e) \in G/N$, and the stability group of $\pi(e)$ in M is $M \cap N$. Moreover, $\ker(d\pi')_e = L(M) \cap \ker(d\pi)_e = L(M) \cap L(N)$, so the proposition follows from (6.7).

(6.13) REMARKS. (6.10) is valid without assuming V/N and V/G to be normal (see [18, Prop. 2]). Similarly, it follows from Lemma 3 and Prop. 2 of [18] that the Cor.

of (6.7) is true also if V_i/G_i is not normal (i = 1, 2). However, these facts will not be needed in these Notes.

Theorem 6.8 is proved here for affine groups. It remains true however if affine k-group is replaced by algebraic k-group: the existence of a quotient k-structure on G/H was proved by M. Rosenlicht [16] for k algebraically closed and by Weil [21] in general; the fact that G/H is quasi-projective is due to Chow (Algebraic Geometry and Topology, a Symposium in honor of S. Lefschetz, Princeton Univ. Press 1957, 122-128).

§7. ALGEBRAIC GROUPS IN CHARACTERISTIC ZERO

In this section it is assumed that char(k) = 0, and G is an affine k-group G. Our aim is to obtain some basic results of Chevalley [7a] on the algebraic Lie algebras $\underline{h}$ in $\underline{g} = L(G)$, i.e. on those of the form $\underline{h} = L(H)$ for some closed subgroup H of G.

(7.1) The operators $\mathcal{A}$ and $\underline{a}$. Recall (6.12) that, if H and N are closed subgroups of G then

$$(1) \qquad L(H \cap N) = L(H) \cap L(N) \quad .$$

It follows that if H is connected then

$$(2) \qquad H \subset N \iff L(H) \subset L(N) \quad .$$

In analogy with the notion of group closure in §2, we associate to a subset M of L(G) the intersection of all closed subgroups H of G such that $M \subset L(H)$, to be denoted $\mathcal{A}(M)$. It is connected, and by (7.1), is the smallest closed subgroup of G whose Lie algebra contains M; its Lie algebra,

$$\underline{a}(M) = L(\mathcal{A}(M)) ,$$

is therefore the smallest algebraic Lie algebra in $\underline{g}$ containing M.

We can of course define $\mathcal{A}(M)$ in non-zero characteristic but then $L(\mathcal{A}(M))$ does not necessarily contain M, in fact may be zero even if M is not, and this notion seems uninteresting in that case.

(7.2) PROPOSITION. Let $\pi : G \longrightarrow G'$ be a surjective morphism of algebraic groups, and let $M \subset L(G)$. Then

$$\pi(\mathcal{A}(M)) = \mathcal{A}(d\pi(M)) \text{ and } d\pi(\underline{a}(M)) = \underline{a}(d\pi(M)) .$$

PROOF. If H is a closed subgroup of G, then, since we are in characteristic zero, $\pi : H \longrightarrow \pi(H)$ is separable, and therefore $d\pi(L(H)) = L(\pi(H))$.

It follows from (6.7) that, under $d\pi$, both the images and inverse images of algebraic Lie algebras are algebraic. In particular $d\pi(\underline{a}(M))$ is an algebraic Lie algebra containing $d\pi(M)$, and hence $\underline{a}(d\pi(M))$. The reverse inclusion follows since $d\pi^{-1}(\underline{a}(d\pi(M)))$ is an algebraic Lie algebra containing M, and hence $\underline{a}(M)$.

Now $\pi(\mathcal{A}(M))$ and $\mathcal{A}(d\pi(M))$ are connected subgroups of G' with the same Lie algebra, and hence they are equal (see (7.1)).

(7.3) The structure of $\mathcal{A}(X)$ for $X \in \underline{gl}(V)$.

(1) X is nilpotent, $\neq 0$. Define $\alpha : \mathbb{G}_a \longrightarrow G = GL(V)$ by

$$\alpha(t) = \exp(tX) = \sum_{n \geqq 0} (n!)^{-1}(tX)^n \ .$$

Since X is nilpotent, α is a polynomial map, and it is clearly a homomorphism. The minimal polynomial of X is a monomial, so it follows that the non-zero powers of X are linearly independent. Since $X \neq 0$ this implies α is injective. Hence α induces an isomorphism $\mathbb{G}_a \cong \alpha(\mathbb{G}_a) = H$ of algebraic groups, because we are in characteristic zero. Since $d\alpha : L(\mathbb{G}_a) \longrightarrow \underline{gl}(V)$ is the map $t \longmapsto t \cdot X$, we conclude that $H = \mathcal{A}(X)$, for dimension reasons. Therefore

$$\mathcal{A}(X) \cong \mathbb{G}_a \ .$$

(2) $X = \mathrm{diag}(x_1, \ldots, x_n) \in L(\mathbb{D}_n)$.

This case is included for completeness, though it will not be needed elsewhere.

We shall invoke here some elementary results on tori to be proved below in §8. In particular we shall see in (8.2) that $H = \mathcal{A}(X)$ is the intersection of $\ker \chi$ for all characters $\chi \in X(\mathbb{D}_n)$ such that $\chi(H) = 1$, and the latter condition is equivalent to: $d\chi(L(H)) = 0$. If

$\chi(\mathrm{diag}(t_1, \ldots, t_n)) = t_1^{m_1} \ldots t_n^{m_n}$ then $d\chi(\mathrm{diag}(s_1, \ldots, s_n)) = \Sigma m_i s_i$, where we identify $L(\mathbb{D}_n)$ with the diagonal matrices in $\underline{gl}_n$. Thus, if

$$L = \{(m_i) \in \mathbb{Z}^n \mid \Sigma m_i x_i = 0\}$$

then

$$\mathcal{A}(X) = \{\mathrm{diag}(t_1, \ldots, t_n) \mid \prod t_i^{m_i} = 1 \text{ for all } (m_i) \in L\}$$

and

$$\underline{a}(X) = \{\mathrm{diag}(s_1, \ldots, s_n) \mid \Sigma m_i s_i = 0 \text{ for all } (m_i) \in L\} .$$

(3) *If* $X = X_s + X_n$ *is the Jordan decomposition of* X, *then* $\mathcal{A}(X) = \mathcal{A}(X_s) \cdot \mathcal{A}(X_n)$ *and* $\underline{a}(X) = \underline{a}(X_s) + \underline{a}(X_n)$.

This is clear, and, in fact, these products and sums are direct. In view of (1) and (2), we now have the structure of $\mathcal{A}(X)$ in general.

REMARK. As a group analogue of (1), we have: *if* $u \in GL(V)$ *is unipotent and* $\neq I$, *then* $\mathcal{A}(u) = \mathbb{G}_a$. To see this, write $x = I - u$. This is a nilpotent transformation; hence $X = \log u = \Sigma_{i>0}\, i^{-1}(-x)^i$ is a polynomial in x, with 0 as constant term, and is therefore nilpotent, too. By (1), $\mathcal{A}(X)$ is isomorphic to $\mathbb{G}_a$ and contains $u = \exp X$, hence $\mathcal{A}(u) \subset \mathcal{A}(X)$. But u has infinite order, and therefore $\dim \mathcal{A}(u) \geq 1$, whence $\mathcal{A}(u) = \mathcal{A}(X)$.

(7.4) LEMMA. *Let* $\pi : G \longrightarrow GL(E)$ *be a rational representation, and let* $N \subset M$ *be vector subspaces of* E. *Put*

$$H = \{g \in G \mid \pi(g)N = N, \pi(g)M = M, \pi(g)_{M/N} = e\} .$$

Then

$$L(H) = \underline{tr}(M, N) = \{X \in \underline{g} \mid d\pi(X)M \subset N\} \quad .$$

In particular, $\underline{tr}(M, N)$ is an algebraic Lie algebra.

PROOF. Clearly $\underline{b} = \underline{tr}(M, N)$ is a Lie algebra containing $L(H)$. Conversely, supposing $X \in \underline{b}$, it suffices to show that $\mathcal{a}(X) \subset H$. Since $\pi(\mathcal{a}(X)) = \mathcal{a}(d\pi(X))$ (by (7.2)) we may replace G by $\pi(G)$. Since X_s and X_n are polynomials in X without constant term, it follows that $X_s, X_n \in \underline{b}$ along with X, so we are reduced to the cases $X = X_s$ and $X = X_n$.

If $X = X_n$ then (see (7.3)(1)) $\mathcal{a}(X) = \{\exp(tX)\}$, which clearly lies in H. If $X = X_s$ we may assume X is diagonalized with respect to a basis $e_1, e_2, \ldots$ such that $e_1, \ldots, e_n$ span N, $e_1, \ldots, e_m$ span M, and $e_{n+1}, \ldots, e_m$ span $M' \subset \ker(X)$. It is then clear that $\mathcal{a}(X)$ lies in the group of diagonal matrices $\operatorname{diag}(d_1, \ldots, d_m, \ldots)$ for which $d_{n+1} = \ldots = d_m = 1$. Evidently these matrices belong to H. Q.E.D.

(7.5) PROPOSITION. Let $(H_i)_{i \in I}$ be a family of closed smooth irreducible subvarieties of G such that, for each $i \in I$, $e \in H_i$, and $H_i^{-1} = H_j$ for some j. Let H be the subgroup generated by the H_i's. Then H is closed and $\underline{h} = L(H)$ is spanned by the vector spaces

$$\operatorname{Ad}(h)T(x^{-1}H_i)_e \qquad (h \in H;\ x \in H_i;\ i \in I) \quad .$$

PROOF. According to (2.2) H is closed, and there is a finite sequence $i_1, \ldots, i_s$ in I such that the product map $p : W = H_{i_1} \times \ldots \times H_{i_s} \longrightarrow H$ is surjective. We shall change notation now and write H_j in place of H_{i_j} $(1 \leqq j \leqq s)$. Since p is separable (char. 0) it follows that, for some $w = (w_1, \ldots, w_s) \in W$, $(df)_w : T(W)_w \longrightarrow T(H)_v$ is surjective, where $v = p(w) = w_1 \ldots w_s$.

We now introduce $v_j = w_1 \ldots w_j$, $H'_j = w_j^{-1} H_j$, and $H''_j = v_j H'_j v_j^{-1}$, $(1 \leqq j \leqq s)$. Define $\alpha : W' = H'_1 \times \ldots \times H'_s \longrightarrow W$ by $\alpha(x_1, \ldots, x_s) = (w_1 x_1, \ldots, w_s x_s)$, and put $\beta = \mathrm{Int}(v_1) \times \ldots \times \mathrm{Int}(v_s) : W' \longrightarrow W'' = H''_1 \times \ldots \times H''_s$. We claim that the rectangle

$$\begin{array}{ccccc} W' & \xrightarrow{\alpha} & W & \xrightarrow{p} & H \\ \beta \big\downarrow & & & & \big\downarrow \rho_{v^{-1}} \\ W'' & & \xrightarrow[p'']{\hspace{3em}} & & H \end{array}$$

is commutative, where p'' is the product map. In fact,

$$p''\beta(x_1, \ldots, x_s) = v_1 x_1 v_1^{-1} v_2 x_2 v_2^{-1} \ldots v_{s-1}^{-1} v_s x_s v_s^{-1}$$

$$= w_1 x_1 w_2 x_2 \ldots w_s x_s v^{-1} ,$$

(because $v_{j-1}^{-1} v_j = w_j (1 \leqq j \leqq s)$ and $v_s = v$); hence

$$p''\beta(x_1, \ldots, x_s) = (p\alpha(x_1, \ldots, x_s))v^{-1} .$$

Writing e also for $(e, \ldots, e) \in W'$, we have $\alpha(e) = w$.

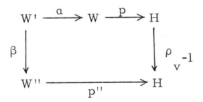

Since α and $\rho_{v^{-1}}$ are isomorphisms of varieties, and since $(dp)_w$ is surjective, it follows that the differential,

$$d(p'' \circ \beta)_e : T(W')_e \longrightarrow T(H)_e = \underline{h} ,$$

of $p'' \circ \beta = \rho_{v^{-1}} \circ p \circ \alpha$ at e is also surjective. If $X = (X_1, \ldots, X_s) \in T(W')_e$, then $d(p'' \circ \beta)_e(X) = \Sigma d(\mathrm{Int}(v_j))_e(X_j) = \Sigma \mathrm{Ad}(v_j)(X_j)$. Thus $\underline{h} = \Sigma \mathrm{Ad}(v_j) T(H_j')_e$. Since $v_j \in H$ and since $H_j' = w_j^{-1} \cdot H_j$, with $w_j \in H_j$, the proposition is proved.

(7.6) THEOREM. In (7.5), suppose that each H_i is a closed subgroup of G, with Lie algebra $\underline{h}_i$. Then $\underline{h}$ is spanned, as a vector space, by the spaces $\mathrm{Ad}(h)(\underline{h}_i)$ $(h \in H; i \in I)$, and it is generated, as a Lie algebra, by the $\underline{h}_i$ $(i \in I)$.

PROOF. If $x \in H_i$ then, since H_i is a group, $x^{-1} H_i = H_i$, so $T(x^{-1} H_i)_e = \underline{h}_i$. Hence the first assertion is just (7.5).

Let M be the Lie subalgebra generated by the $\underline{h}_i (i \in I)$. We must show that the inclusion $M \subset \underline{h}$ is an equality. Thanks to the conclusion above it will suffice to show that M is stable under $\mathrm{Ad}(H)$, i.e. that $H \subset N_G(M) = \mathrm{Tr}(M, M)$. Since the latter is a group, it suffices to show that it contains each H_i. But H_i is connected, so the latter follows if we show that $\underline{h}_i \subset L(\mathrm{Tr}(M, M))$. According to (7.4) (applied to Ad, with $M = N$) we have $L(\mathrm{Tr}(M, M)) = \underline{tr}(M, M)$. Since M

is a Lie algebra containing $\underline{h}_i$ we have $[\underline{h}_i, M] \subset M$. Q.E.D.

(7.7) COROLLARY. The following conditions on a Lie subalgebra $\underline{h}$ of $\underline{g}$ are equivalent:

(1) $\underline{h}$ is algebraic.

(2) If $X \in \underline{h}$ then $\underline{a}(X) \subset \underline{h}$.

(3) $\underline{h}$ is spanned by algebraic Lie algebras.

(4) $\underline{h}$ is generated as a Lie algebra by algebraic Lie algebras.

The implications (1) $\Longrightarrow$ (2) $\Longrightarrow$ (3) $\Longrightarrow$ (4) are clear, and (4) $\Longrightarrow$ (1) follows immediately from (7.6).

(7.8) PROPOSITION. Let $H = (M, N)$, where M and N are closed connected normal subgroups of G. Then $\underline{h} = [\underline{m}, \underline{n}]$, where $\underline{h}$, $\underline{m}$, $\underline{n}$ are the Lie algebras of H, M, N.

PROOF. For $x, y \in G$ write

$$c_x(y) = c'_y(x) = (x, y) = xyx^{-1}y^{-1} .$$

Then H is generated by the sets $H_a = c_a(N)$ and $H'_a = c'_a(N) = H_a^{-1}$ where a varies over M. These sets satisfy the hypotheses of (7.5) because N is a connected closed subgroup. Hence $\underline{h}$ is spanned by subspaces of the form

$$\mathrm{Ad}(h)T(c_a(b)^{-1}H_a)_e \quad \text{and} \quad \mathrm{Ad}(h)T(c'_a(b)^{-1}H'_a)_e \quad ,$$

for $h \in H$, $a \in M$, $b \in N$.

The inclusion $[\underline{m}, \underline{n}] \subset \underline{h}$ follows from (3.12), and the invariance of $[\underline{m}, \underline{n}]$ under $\mathrm{Ad}(G)$ follows from the normality of M and N. Thus, it remains to show that, for $a \in M$ and $b \in N$, we have

$$T(c_a(b)^{-1}H_a)_e,\ T(c'_a(b)^{-1}H'_a)_e \subset [\underline{m}, \underline{n}] \ .$$

Consider $f : N \longrightarrow G$ defined by $f(x) = c_a(b)^{-1}c_a(bx)$. Then $f(e) = e$ and $(df)_e(\underline{n}) = T(c_a(b)^{-1}c_a(N))_e$, clearly. Explicitly,

$$f(x) = bab^{-1}a^{-1}abxa^{-1}(bx)^{-1} = ba\,x\,a^{-1}b^{-1}bx^{-1}b^{-1}$$

$$f(x) = (ba).x.(ba)^{-1}\ .\ bx^{-1}b^{-1}\ .$$

Thus $(df)_e = \mathrm{Ad}(ba) - \mathrm{Ad}(b) = \mathrm{Ad}(b)(\mathrm{Ad}(a) - 1)$. Since $\mathrm{Ad}(b)$ leaves $[\underline{m}, \underline{n}]$ stable it will suffice to show that

$$(\mathrm{Ad}(a) - 1)(\underline{n}) \subset [\underline{m}, \underline{n}] \text{ for } a \in M\ .$$

(The case of $c'_a(b)^{-1}c'_a(N)$ follows from similar arguments which we omit.)

Let $\pi : \underline{g} \longrightarrow \underline{g}' = \underline{g}/[\underline{m}, \underline{n}]$ be the natural projection. Fix $X \in \underline{n}$ and define $\alpha : M \longrightarrow \underline{g}'$ by $\alpha(a) = \pi((\mathrm{Ad}(a) - 1)(X))$. We must show that $\alpha = 0$.

Since $[\underline{m}, \underline{n}]$ is stable under $\mathrm{Ad}\, G$, the quotient $\underline{g}'$ is also a G-module. For $a, a' \in M$ we have $\mathrm{Ad}(aa') - 1 = \mathrm{Ad}(a)(\mathrm{Ad}(a') - 1) + (\mathrm{Ad}(a) - 1)$, from which it follows that $\alpha(aa') = \mathrm{Ad}(a)\alpha(a') + \alpha(a)$. This implies that

$P = \{a \in M | \alpha(a) = 0\}$ is a closed subgroup of M, and that $\alpha(aP) = \alpha(a)$ for all $a \in M$. Hence α can be factored through the quotient:

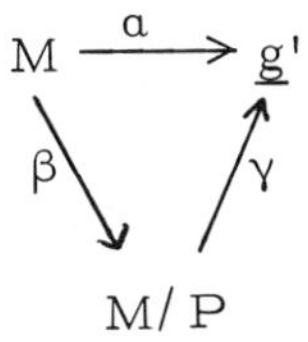

where β is the quotient morphism. Since γ is injective, it is an isomorphism of M/P onto its image (char 0). Since $\alpha(M) = M/P$ is connected we can show it is a single point by proving that $(d\alpha)_e = 0$.

We have $\alpha = \pi \circ \delta$ where $\delta(a) = (\mathrm{Ad}(a) - 1)(X)$ so $(d\alpha)_e = (d\pi)_0 \circ (d\delta)_e = \pi \circ (d\delta)_e$. (Since π is linear $(d\pi)_0 = \pi$.) Now using (3.9)(2), we get $(d\delta)_e(Y) = \mathrm{ad}(Y)(X) = [Y, X]$, so $(d\delta)_e(\underline{m}) = [\underline{m}, X] \subset [\underline{m}, \underline{n}]$. Thus indeed $\pi \circ (d\delta)_e(\underline{m}) = 0$. Q.E.D.

(7.9) COROLLARY. Let $\underline{h}$ be a Lie subalgebra of $\underline{g}$. Then $[\underline{h}, \underline{h}] = [\underline{a}(\underline{h}), \underline{a}(\underline{h})]$, and is an algebraic Lie algebra.

PROOF. $\underline{h} \subset \underline{tr}(\underline{h}, [\underline{h}, \underline{h}])$, clearly, and the latter is algebraic, by (7.4). Therefore $\underline{a}(\underline{h}) \subset \underline{tr}(\underline{h}, [\underline{h}, \underline{h}])$, i.e. $[\underline{a}(\underline{h}), \underline{h}] \subset [\underline{h}, \underline{h}]$. Therefore $\underline{h} \subset \underline{tr}(\underline{a}(\underline{h}), [\underline{h}, \underline{h}])$, so again we see that $\underline{a}(\underline{h}) \subset \underline{tr}(\underline{a}(\underline{h}), [\underline{h}, \underline{h}])$, i.e. $[\underline{a}(\underline{h}), \underline{a}(\underline{h})] \subset [\underline{h}, \underline{h}]$. The opposite inclusion is obvious.

It follows from (7.8) that $[\underline{a}(\underline{h}), \underline{a}(\underline{h})]$ is the Lie algebra of $(\mathfrak{a}(\underline{h}), \mathfrak{a}(\underline{h}))$, and this shows that $[\underline{h}, \underline{h}]$ is algebraic.

BIBLIOGRAPHICAL NOTE

Linear algebraic groups over $\mathbb{C}$ were studied around the end of the XIX-th century by Maurer in a series of papers (see notably Sitz.-Ber. Bayer. Akad. 24 (1894)). One of his main results is the fact that such a group is a rational variety. Later, E. Cartan (C. R. Acad. Sci. Paris 120 (1895), 544-548) announced some further results on algebraic groups, notably Cor. (7.9) above, but never published the proofs. The topic then fell into oblivion. It was revived by Chevalley-Tuan and then by Chevalley [7]. The main results of this paragraph, in particular (7.6) to (7.9), are all proved in [7a]. The main tool of Chevalley is a formal exponential, which allows him to set up an analogue of the familiar correspondence between Lie algebras and Lie groups of Lie group theory. Because of this, he had to restrict himself to groundfields of characteristic zero. Here, we could dispense with this notion by using the structure of variety of the quotient space G/H of an algebraic group by a closed subgroup, and the separability of morphisms in characteristic zero. The latter fact was of course also used in [7a], so that the main point is really the possibility of viewing G/H as an algebraic variety. To see this illustrated concretely, the reader may compare the proof of (7.1)(2) given here with that of [7a, p. 157].

CHAPTER III

SOLVABLE GROUPS

In this chapter, all algebraic groups are affine, unless the contrary is explicitly allowed. G is a k-group.

§8. DIAGONALIZABLE GROUPS AND TORI

(8.1) LEMMA. Let H be an abstract group, and let X denote the set of homomorphisms $H \longrightarrow K^*$. Then X is linearly independent as a set of functions from H to K.

PROOF. If not, let $n > 0$ be minimal such that there exist linearly dependent $\chi_1, \ldots, \chi_n \in X$; say $f = (\sum_{i<n} a_i\chi_i) + \chi_n = 0$. Choose $h_0 \in H$ such that $\chi_n(h_0) \neq \chi_1(h_0)$ (clearly $n > 1$). Then, for all $h \in H$, $0 = f(h_0h) - \chi_n(h_0)f(h) = \sum_{i<n} a_i(\chi_i(h_0) - \chi_n(h_0))\chi_i(h)$. This is a non trivial dependence relation with strictly less than n terms, contradicting the minimality of n.

(8.2) Diagonalizable groups. Let $A = K[G]$. Then the

character group $X(G)$ is a subset of A. We call G diagonalizable if $X(G)$ spans A (as K-module). If, further, $X(G)_k$ spans A, then we shall say G is split over k. Since $A = K \otimes_k A_k$ the latter condition is equivalent to $X(G)_k$ spanning $A_k = k[G]$, as a k-module.

PROPOSITION. Assume $Y \subset X(G)_k$ spans A_k. Then:

(a) $Y = X(G)$. In particular all characters of G are rational over k.

(b) $A_k = k[X(G)]$, the group algebra of the finitely generated abelian group $X(G)$. Moreover the Hopf algebra structure on A_k is induced by the diagonal map $X(G) \longrightarrow X(G) \times X(G)$ and the inverse map $X(G) \longrightarrow X(G)$.

(c) If H is a closed subgroup of G, then H is a diagonalizable group defined and split over k, and H is defined by character equations (i.e. as the intersection of kernels of characters) in G. Moreover, every character on H extends to a character on G.

(d) If $\pi : G \longrightarrow \mathbb{GL}_n$ is a k-rational representation, then $\pi(G)$ is conjugate over k to a subgroup of $\mathbb{D}_n$. In particular G is k-isomorphic to a closed subgroup of $\mathbb{D}_n$.

PROOF. (a) follows immediately from (8.1) applied to $X(G) \subset A$. Moreover (8.1) implies that $X(G)$ is linearly independent over k so that A_k is, indeed, the group algebra of $X(G)$. The description of the Hopf algebra structure follows directly from the definitions. For example, the diagonal is the comorphism of $G \times G \longrightarrow G$, and the restriction of this comorphism to characters $X(G) \longrightarrow X(GxG) = X(G) \times X(G)$, is easily seen to be the diagonal map of $X(G)$. Since A_k is a finitely generated k-algebra it follows easily that $X(G)$ must be a finitely generated abelian group. This proves (b).

To prove (c) we first note that $B = K[H]$ is a residue class ring of A, and hence B is spanned by the image of $X(G)$. The latter elements are the restrictions to H of characters on G so it follows that H is diagonalizable, and therefore $B = K[X(H)]$. Since $p : A \longrightarrow B$ is surjective and sends $X(G)$ to $X(H)$ it follows that p is just the group algebra homomorphism induced by a surjection $X(G) \longrightarrow X(H)$. Since $X(G) = X(G)_k$ it follows that H is defined by character equations over k, and that $X(H) = X(H)_k$. This proves (c).

(d) A generating set of $X(G)$ gives an injective morphism of G into $(\mathbb{GL}_1)^d$ for some d, so G is a commutative group of semi-simple elements. It follows therefore, from (4.6), that for any rational linear representation $\pi : G \longrightarrow GL(V)$, $\pi(G)$ is diagonalizable. The diagonal entries are then characters of G. Now suppose π is defined over k. Then, since each $\chi \in X(G)$ is defined over k, the eigenspace $V_\chi = \{x \in V \mid \pi(g)x = \chi(g)x \ \forall g \in G\}$ is also defined over k (see (5.2)). Thus $\pi(G)$ is diagonalizable in $GL(V)$ over k. In case π is immersive this yields a k-isomorphism of G with a closed subgroup of $\mathbf{D}_n$, and the existence of a k-rational immersive π is confirmed by (1.10). Q.E.D.

COROLLARY. Let G be diagonalizable. Then G splits over k if and only if $X(G) = X(G)_k$. For any $g \in G$,

$$\mathcal{A}(g) = \{h \in G \mid \chi(g) = 1 \Longrightarrow \chi(h) = 1 \text{ for all } \chi \in X(G)\} .$$

The Lie algebra of G consists of semi-simple elements.

EXAMPLE. Assume $k = \mathbb{Q}$, and let $m > 2$ be an integer. Let μ_m denote the kernel of $x \longmapsto x^m$ in $\mathbb{GL}_1$. Thus $\mu_m(k')$ is the group of mth roots of unity in k' for any k-algebra k'. The definition makes it clear that μ_m is a diagonalizable k-group split over k. Explicitly,
$k[\mu_m] = k[t] = k[T]/(T^m-1)$. Moreover
$X(\mu_m) = \{1, t, \ldots, t^{m-1}\}$.

Let $\pi : \mu_m \longrightarrow \mathbb{GL}_n$ be a faithful rational representation defined over k. Then the Proposition above guarantees that $\pi(\mu_m)$ is conjugate, over k, to a diagonal group. At first sight this appears unreasonable, since k does not contain the eigenvalues of a generator, x, of $\pi(\mu_m)$. The point is that $x \in \mathbb{GL}_n$ will not be in $\mathbb{GL}_n(k)$, even though π is defined over k, but x can nevertheless be diagonalized by conjugation by an element of $\mathbb{GL}_n(k)$.

(8.3) COROLLARY. The contravariant functor $G \longmapsto X(G)$ is fully faithful (see proof for definition) from the category of diagonalizable groups split over k and their morphisms as algebraic groups to the category of finitely generated $\mathbb{Z}$-modules. In particular, all morphisms between such groups are defined over k.

PROOF. Let G, G' be two k-split diagonalizable groups, with affine rings A, A' respectively. Consider the commutative triangle

$$\begin{array}{ccc} & \mathrm{Mor}_{\text{alg. grp.}}(G, G')_k & \\ {\scriptstyle \alpha}\swarrow & & \searrow{\scriptstyle X} \\ \mathrm{Mor}_{\text{Hopf alg.}}(A'_k, A_k) & \xleftarrow[\beta]{} & \mathrm{Mor}_{\mathbb{Z}\text{-mod}}(X(G'), X(G)) \end{array}$$

The bijectivity of α is essentially by definition (cf. (1.5)). The existence and injectivity of β follows from part (b) of Proposition (8.2). It follows therefore that all three arrows are bijective. The first assertion of the corollary is the bijectivity of X. The last assertion follows because the target of X is independent of k, and therefore so is its source.

REMARK. If X is a finitely generated abelian group, then A = K[X] is a Hopf algebra, and therefore it defines a diagonalizable group with character group X provided A has no nilpotent elements. A has nilpotent elements if and only if char(k) = p > 0 and X has elements of order p.

(8.4) PROPOSITION. The following conditions are equivalent:

(1) G is diagonalizable.

(2) G is isomorphic to a subgroup of $\mathbb{D}_n$ for some n > 0.

(3) For any rational representation

$\pi : G \longrightarrow \mathbb{GL}_n$, $\pi(G)$ is conjugate to a subgroup of $\mathbb{D}_n$.

(4) G contains a dense commutative subgroup consisting of semi-simple elements.

The corresponding assertion in the split case is:

PROPOSITION'. The following conditions are equivalent:

(1') G is diagonalizable and split over k.

(2') G is k-isomorphic to a subgroup of $\mathbb{D}_n$ for some $n > 0$.

(3') If $\pi : G \longrightarrow \mathbb{GL}_n$ is a rational representation defined over k then $\pi(G)$ is conjugate over k to a subgroup of $\mathbb{D}_n$.

PROOF'. (1') $\Longrightarrow$ (2') follows from (8.2)(d), (2') $\Longrightarrow$ (1') from (8.2)(c), (1') $\Longrightarrow$ (3') from (8.2)(d), and (3') $\Longrightarrow$ (2') from the existence of an immersive k-rational representation $\pi : G \longrightarrow \mathbb{GL}_n$ (see (1.10)).

PROOF. The equivalence of (1), (2), and (3) follows by taking $k = K$ above. (2) $\Longrightarrow$ (4) is obvious, and (4) $\Longrightarrow$ (3) follows from (4.6).

COROLLARY. Suppose G is diagonalizable (and split over k). Then the same is true of each subgroup of G, and of the image of G under any morphism (defined over k

PROOF. For subgroups use condition (8.2)(c). If $\pi : G \longrightarrow G'$ is a morphism (defined over k) then embed

G' in $\mathbb{GL}_n$ (over k) and apply condition (3) (resp., (3')) to get $\pi(G)$ conjugate (over k) to a subgroup of $\mathbb{D}_n$. Then apply (2) (resp. (2')).

(8.5) Tori. The diagonal group $\mathbb{D}_n$ is a closed subgroup of $\mathbb{GL}_n$ which is evidently isomorphic, over the prime field, to $(\mathbb{GL}_1)^n$. An algebraic group isomorphic to $\mathbb{D}_n$ is called an n-dimensional torus.

The terminology stems from the fact that these groups play a role here analogous to that played by topological tori (i.e. products of circle groups) in the theory of compact Lie groups. Note however that, if $K = \mathbb{C}$, the tori considered here are not compact. If they are defined over $\mathbb{R}$ their groups of real points may or may not be compact (see (8.15)).

PROPOSITION. The following conditions on an algebraic group T are equivalent:

(1) T is an n-dimensional torus.

(2) T is a connected diagonalizable group of dimension n.

(3) T is a diagonalizable group and $X(T) = \mathbb{Z}^n$.

PROOF. (1) $\Longrightarrow$ (2) follows from (8.4)(2).
(2) $\Longrightarrow$ (3). Since $\mathbb{GL}_1$ is connected and of dimension 1, its only connected subgroups are $\{e\}$ and $\mathbb{GL}_1$. Applying this to images of characters we see that the character group of a connected group T is torsion free. If further T is diagonalizable then $K[T] = K[X(T)]$, and clearly

dim T (i.e. $\text{tr.deg.}_K K(T)$) is the rank of the free abelian group X(T).

(3) $\Longrightarrow$ (1). Let $\alpha_1, \ldots, \alpha_n$ be a basis for X(T). Then $K[T] = K[\alpha_1, \alpha_1^{-1}, \ldots, \alpha_n, \alpha_n^{-1}]$ and evidently $\alpha : t \longmapsto \text{diag}(\alpha_1(t), \ldots, \alpha_n(t))$ gives the required isomorphism $T \longrightarrow \mathbb{D}_n$. (For the comorphism $\alpha_0 : K[\mathbb{D}_n] \longrightarrow K[T]$ is visibly surjective, and both groups are connected, of dimension n.)

COROLLARY. <u>A closed connected subgroup</u> S <u>of a torus</u> T <u>is a torus and a direct factor</u>.

By the proposition, S is a torus and X(S) is free. The restriction homomorphism $X(T) \longrightarrow X(S)$ is surjective (8.2)(c) hence split, and S is a direct factor by (8.3).

(8.6) <u>The multiplicative one parameter subgroups</u> in a k-group G are the elements of

$$X_*(G) = \text{Mor}(\mathbb{GL}_1, G) .$$

Since $X(G) = \text{Mor}(G, \mathbb{GL}_1)$ we can compose to obtain a map

$$X(G) \times X_*(G) \longrightarrow \mathbb{Z} = X(\mathbb{GL}_1) .$$

given by

$$\langle \chi, \lambda \rangle = m \text{ if } (\chi \circ \lambda)(x) = x^m .$$

If G is commutative this is a bilinear map of abelian groups. It follows easily from (8.3) and (8.4) (or even directly) that:

PROPOSITION. *If* T *is a torus then*

$$X(T) \times X_*(T) \longrightarrow \mathbb{Z}$$

is a dual pairing over $\mathbb{Z}$.

(8.7) PROPOSITION. *Let* G *be diagonalizable and split over* k. *Then* G *is a direct product* $G = G^0 \times F$, *where* F *is a finite group, and* G^0 *is a torus defined and split over* k.

PROOF. Thanks to (8.2)(d) we may assume that G is a closed subgroup of some $\mathbb{D}_n$. Moreover (8.4) and (8.2)(c) imply that all closed subgroups of $\mathbb{D}_n$ are defined and split over k, and (8.5) implies that G^0 is a torus.

According to (8.2)(c), the restriction homomorphism $X(\mathbb{D}_n) \cong \mathbb{Z}^n \longrightarrow X(G^0)$ is surjective. Since G^0 is connected, (8.5) implies that $X(G^0)$ is free, so the epimorphism splits. In other words we can find a basis $\chi_1, \ldots, \chi_n$ for $X(\mathbb{D}_n)$ so that $\chi_1, \ldots, \chi_d$ generate the group of characters which annihilate G^0. Then the k-automorphism $x \longmapsto \mathrm{diag}(\chi_1(x), \ldots, \chi_n(x))$ of $\mathbb{D}_n$ maps G^0 onto $\{\mathrm{diag}(x_1, \ldots, x_n) \mid x_i = 1, 1 \leqq i \leqq d\}$. Thus $\mathbb{D}_n = \mathbb{D}_d \times G^0$.

It follows that, as a group, $G = F \times G^0$ where

$F = G \cap \mathbb{D}_d$. Then clearly $F \cong G/G^0$ so F is a finite group, and the product map $\alpha : F \times G^0 \longrightarrow G$ is a group isomorphism. That it is also an isomorphism of varieties follows because it is so on pairs of corresponding connected components.

(8.8) PROPOSITION. If k is not an algebraic extension of a finite field then $T = (\mathbb{GL}_1)^n$ contains an element t, rational over k, that generates a dense subgroup.

PROOF. If $t = (t_1, \ldots, t_n)$, then t generates a dense subgroup if and only if no non-trivial character of T kills t. Since the characters are all of the form $t \longmapsto t_1^{m_1} \ldots t_n^{m_n}$ this requirement is just that $t_1, \ldots, t_n$ be multiplicatively independent. Hence we want k^* to contain free abelian groups of arbitrarily large finite rank. If $\mathrm{char}(k) = 0$ this follows from the infinitude of primes in $\mathbb{Z}$. If $\mathrm{char}(k) = p > 0$, and if $x \in k$ is transcendental over the prime field $\mathbb{F}_p$, then this follows from the infinitude of primes in the polynomial ring $\mathbb{F}_p[x]$.

REMARK. The Proposition above is valid without assuming that T is split over k, but the proof of the general case is somewhat more delicate. (See Tits, Yale lectures, 1967).

(8.9) Torsion in tori. Let p denote the characteristic

exponent of k, and let T be a d-dimensional torus defined over k. For $m \in \mathbb{Z}$ define

$$\alpha_m : T \longrightarrow T, \qquad \alpha_m(x) = x^m .$$

PROPOSITION. Assume $m > 0$.

(a) α_m is surjective.

(b) If m is a power of p, then α_m is bijective.

(c) If $(m, p) = 1$ then α_m is separable, $\ker(\alpha_m) \cong (\mathbb{Z}/m\mathbb{Z})^d$ (as a group) and $\ker(\alpha_m) \subset T(k_s)$.

(d) If m is not a power of p then the union of the groups $\ker(\alpha_{m^n})$ $(n > 0)$ is a dense subgroup of T.

PROOF. K^* is a divisible group in which the Frobenius map, $x \longmapsto x^p$, is bijective. This implies (a) and (b).

(c): Since $(d\alpha_m) : X \longmapsto mX$ we see that α_m is separable because $(m, p) = 1$. It follows that $\ker(\alpha_m)$ is defined over k (see (6.7), Remark), so its points rational over k_s are dense. Once we prove that $\ker(\alpha_m)$ is finite, it will follow therefore that all of its points are rational over k_s. Finally, the fact that $\ker(\alpha_m) \cong (\mathbb{Z}/m\mathbb{Z})^d$ follows from the fact that the mth roots of unity in K^* are a cyclic group of order m.

Part (d) follows from the case $d = 1$. Then $T = \mathbb{GL}_1$ is irreducible of dimension one, so $\bigcup_{n>0} \ker(\alpha_{m^n})$ is dense as soon as it is infinite, and part (c) implies that this is the case if m is not a power of p.

COROLLARY. *Let* G *be diagonalizable. For each* $m > 0$ *the elements of order dividing* m *in* G *are a finite group. The torsion subgroup of* G *is dense in* G.

This follows from (8.7) and the proposition above, for (8.7) says G is the direct product of a torus with a finite group.

(8.10) *Rigidity of diagonalizable groups*. This refers to the fact that they do not admit a non trivial connected family of automorphisms. This property is shared by abelian varieties, and for that reason we do not require the algebraic groups in the following proposition to be affine.

PROPOSITION. *Let* $\alpha : V \times H \longrightarrow H'$ *be a morphism of varieties such that:*

(i) H' *is an algebraic group containing, for each* $m > 0$, *only finitely many elements of order* m;

(ii) H *is an algebraic group in which the elements of finite order are dense; and*

(iii) V *is a connected variety and, for each* $x \in V$, $\alpha_x : h \longmapsto \alpha(x, h)$ *is a homomorphism.*

Then the map $x \longmapsto \alpha_x$ *is constant.*

PROOF. For $h \in H$ write $\beta_h(x) = \alpha(x, h)$. Then $\beta_h : V \longrightarrow H'$ is a morphism from a connected variety. Its image, when h has finite order, is finite, by (i) and (iii). Hence β_h is constant when h has finite order. Therefore, if $x, y \in V$, the morphism

$\gamma : H \longrightarrow H'$, $\gamma(h) = \alpha_x(h)\alpha_y(h)^{-1}$, sends every element of finite order to e. Condition (ii) then implies that $\gamma(h) = e$ for all h.

COROLLARY 1. *Let* $H \subset H'$ *be closed subgroups of* G, *and let* V *be the connected component of* e *in* $\mathrm{Tran}(H, H') = \{g \in G \mid gHg^{-1} \subset H'\}$. *Suppose* H' *and* H *satisfy conditions* (i) *and* (ii) *above*. *Then* $V = Z_G(H)^0$.

PROOF. Apply the proposition to $\alpha(x, h) = xhx^{-1}$, to conclude that $\alpha(x, h) = \alpha(e, h)$ for all $x \in V$. This shows that $V \subset Z_G(H)^0$; the reverse inclusion is obvious.

In case $H = H'$ is diagonalizable (8.9) permits us to conclude:

COROLLARY 2. *Let* H *be a diagonalizable subgroup of an algebraic group* G. *Then* $N_G(H)^0 = Z_G(H)^0$.

(8.11) PROPOSITION. *Let* G *be diagonalizable*. *Then* G *splits over a finite separable extension of* k.

PROOF. Choose a k-embedding $G \subset \mathbb{GL}_n$. Then it suffices to diagonalize $G(k_s)$ by conjugation by an element of $\mathbb{GL}_n(k_s)$, because $G(k_s)$ is dense in G. But the possibility of doing this follows directly from (4.6).

REMARK. One can also argue as above using the elements of finite order in G. It follows from (8.9) that the latter are dense in G and lie in $G(k_s)$.

COROLLARY 1. *Let* T *be a torus defined over* k *and let* $\Gamma = \mathrm{Gal}(k_s/k)$.

(a) $X(T) = X(T)_{k_s}$ *and* $X_*(T) = X_*(T)_{k_s}$. *Hence* $X(T)_k = X(T)^\Gamma$ *and* $X_*(T)_k = X_*(T)^\Gamma$.

(b) *The natural pairing*

$$X(T) \times X_*(T) \longrightarrow \mathbb{Z}$$

makes $X(T)$ *and* $X_*(T)$ *a dual pair of* Γ-*modules*.

PROOF. Since T is split over k_s we have $X(T) = X(T)_{k_s}$. This implies (see (8.3)) that $\mathrm{Mor}(G, T) = \mathrm{Mor}(G, T)_{k_s}$ for any diagonalizable group G split over k_s. With $G = \mathbb{GL}_1$ this gives $X_*(T) = X_*(T)_{k_s}$, thus proving (a).

The pairing in (b) is a separating duality over $\mathbb{Z}$ (see (8.5)) so we need only to check its compatibility with the action of each $s \in \Gamma$. We must show that $\langle {}^s\alpha, {}^s\lambda \rangle = \langle \alpha, \lambda \rangle$ for $\alpha \in X(T)$ and $\lambda \in X_*(T)$. We have, for $x \in k_s^*$,

$$x^{\langle {}^s\alpha, {}^s\lambda \rangle} = ({}^s\alpha \circ {}^s\lambda)(x) = ({}^s\alpha)(s\lambda(s^{-1}x)) = s\alpha(s^{-1}s\lambda(s^{-1}x)) =$$
$$= s(\alpha \circ \lambda)(s^{-1}x) = s(s^{-1}x)^{\langle \alpha, \lambda \rangle} = x^{\langle \alpha, \lambda \rangle}.$$

COROLLARY 2. *With* T *as above*, T *is split over* k *if and only if* $X_*(T) = X_*(T)_k$.

PROOF. Γ operates trivially on the free abelian group $X(T)$ if and only if it operates trivially on its dual, $X_*(T)$.

(8.12) <u>The category of diagonalizable</u> k-<u>groups</u>. We have seen in (8.11) that such a group, G, is split over k_s. Thus, if $A = K[G]$, it follows from (8.2) that $A_{k_s} = k_s[X(G)]$, the group algebra of X(G). If $s \in \Gamma = \mathrm{Gal}(k_s/k)$ then the action of s on this group algebra is given by

$$^s(\Sigma a_\alpha \alpha) = \Sigma\, {}^s a_\alpha\, {}^s\alpha \ .$$

This action determines $A_k = A_{k_s}^{\Gamma}$, and thus we see that G, as a k-group, is completely determined by X(G) with its structure as a Γ-module. For knowledge of the latter permits us to construct A_{k_s} and the action of Γ on A_{k_s}, and hence A_k. As a Γ-module, X(G) is finitely generated as a $\mathbb{Z}$-module, and the action of Γ is continuous, i.e. some open subgroup of finite index in Γ acts trivially on X(G) (because G is split by a finite extension of k). If $p = \mathrm{char}(k) > 0$, moreover, X(G) has no p-torsion because K[X(G)] is reduced.

Let $\alpha : G \longrightarrow G'$ be a morphism of diagonalizable k-groups. It follows from (8.3) that α is defined over k_s. Moreover the following conditions are equivalent:

(1) α is defined over k.

(2) $\alpha_0 : A'_{k_s} \longrightarrow A_{k_s}$ (where $A' = K[G']$) is Γ-equivariant.

(3) $X(\alpha) : X(G') \longrightarrow X(G)$ is Γ-equivariant.

The equivalence of (1) and (2) follows from (AG. 14. 3), and the equivalence of (2) and (3) follows from the description above of the action of Γ on the affine algebras, via its action on the character groups.

Now we can consider X to be a (contravariant) functor,

$$X : \mathcal{A} \longrightarrow \mathcal{B}$$

where the two categories are defined as follows:

obj $\mathcal{A}$: diagonalizable k-groups.

mor $\mathcal{A}$: k-morphisms.

obj $\mathcal{B}$: finitely generated $\mathbb{Z}$-modules, without p-torsion if char(k) = p > 0, on which Γ acts continuously.

mor $\mathcal{B}$: Γ-equivariant homomorphisms.

It follows from (8. 3) and the remarks above that the functor X is fully faithful. In fact:

PROPOSITION. $X : \mathcal{A} \longrightarrow \mathcal{B}$ <u>is an equivalence of categories.</u>

There remains only to be shown that every $M \in$ obj $\mathcal{B}$ is the character module of some $G \in$ obj $\mathcal{A}$. The group algebra A = K[M] is a Hopf algebra, and a reduced affine K-algebra, because M is finitely generated and without p-torsion. Hence $G = \mathrm{spec}_K(A)$ is an affine group. Moreover M is naturally a group of characters on G, so G is diagonalizable, with character group M (see (8.2)).

We must now give G a k-structure inducing the given action of Γ on M. First we give A the k_s-structure $k_s[M]$. Let $s \in \Gamma$ operate on $k_s[M]$ by ${}^s(a\alpha) = {}^s a\, {}^s\alpha$ ($a \in k_s$; $\alpha \in M$). This defines a continuous action of Γ on $k_s[M]$, i.e. one for which each element of $k_s[M]$ has an open isotropy subgroup. It follows therefore from (AG. 14. 2) that $A_k = k_s[M]^\Gamma$ is a k-structure on A. This k-structure clearly meets our requirements.

(8.13) EXAMPLES. (1) Suppose $M = \mathbb{Z}[\Gamma/U]$ where U is an open subgroup of Γ. Then, for any Γ-module N we have

$$\mathrm{Hom}_{\Gamma\text{-mod}}(M, N) = \mathrm{Hom}_{\mathbb{Z}\text{-mod}}(M, N)^\Gamma = N^U .$$

Let k' be any k-algebra and let Γ act on $k_s \otimes_k k'$ via its action on k_s. Then clearly $(k_s \otimes_k k')^U = L \otimes_k k'$, where $L = k_s^U$, and therefore also $(k_s \otimes_k k')^{*U} = (L \otimes_k k')^*$, the notation referring to the groups of invertible elements in these algebras.

Now put $A = K[M]$ with k-structure $A_k = k_s[M]^\Gamma$. Then $G = \mathrm{spec}_K(A)$ is a diagonalizable k-group with character module M. The functor of points of G is described as follows, where k' is a variable k-algebra:

$$\begin{aligned} G(k') &= \mathrm{Hom}_{k\text{-alg}}(A_k, k') \\ &= \mathrm{Hom}_{k_s\text{-alg}}(A_{k_s}, (k_s \otimes_k k'))^{\Gamma} \\ &= \mathrm{Hom}_{\mathbb{Z}\text{-mod}}(M, (k_s \otimes_k k')^*)^{\Gamma} \\ &= (k_s \otimes_k k')^{*U} = (L \otimes_k k')^* . \end{aligned}$$

Thus we see that G is the multiplicative group $\mathbb{GL}_1(L)$ of the k-algebra L (see (1.6), Example (9)). It follows, in particular, that G is k-rational, i.e. that the function field $k(G)$ is purely transcendental (loc. cit.).

(2) Let T be a k-torus and put $N = X(T)$. Some open normal subgroup U of Γ operates trivially, so N is a $\mathbb{Z}$-free representation of finite rank of the finite group $\Gamma' = \Gamma/U$. Hence there is a monomorphism $\alpha_0 : N \longrightarrow M$ where M is a free $\mathbb{Z}[\Gamma']$-module. (For example one can take $M = N''$, where, for a Γ'-module H, we write $H' = \mathrm{Hom}_{\mathbb{Z}\text{-mod}}(H, \mathbb{Z}[\Gamma'])$.) The monomorphism α_0 corresponds to an epimorphism $\alpha : S \longrightarrow T$, where S is the torus with character module M. Thus we have an embedding of function fields $\alpha_0 : k(T) \longrightarrow k(S)$. It follows from example (1) above that $k(S)$ is purely transcendental. This shows that:

A k-<u>torus</u> T <u>is unirational over</u> k, i.e $k(T)$ is contained in a purely transcendental extension of k. In particular, if k is infinite, $T(k)$ is dense in T.

(8.14) <u>Anisotropic tori</u>. Write $\mathcal{B}_{\mathbb{Q}}$ for the category of finite dimensional $\mathbb{Q}$-modules on which Γ operates continuously, i.e. via finite quotient groups. Then (cf. Curtis-Reiner, for example) $\mathcal{B}_{\mathbb{Q}}$ is a semi-simple category, i.e. all short exact sequences split.

We have the exact functor $\mathcal{B} \longrightarrow \mathcal{B}_{\mathbb{Q}}$ (see (8.12) for notation) which sends M to $M_{\mathbb{Q}} = \mathbb{Q} \otimes_{\mathbb{Z}} M$. If M is torsion free we can view M as embedded in $M_{\mathbb{Q}}$ as a lattice. Thus:

$$M^{\Gamma} = M \cap M_{\mathbb{Q}}^{\Gamma},$$

$$M^{\Gamma} = 0 \Longleftrightarrow M_{\mathbb{Q}}^{\Gamma} = 0, \quad \text{and}$$

$$M^{\Gamma} = M \Longleftrightarrow M_{\mathbb{Q}}^{\Gamma} = M_{\mathbb{Q}} .$$

A k-torus T is said to be <u>anisotropic over</u> k if $X(T)_k = \{1\}$, i.e. if $X(T)^{\Gamma} = \{1\}$. This is equivalent to the existence of no non-trivial Γ-fixed points in $\mathbb{Q} \otimes_{\mathbb{Z}} X(T)$, by the remarks above. The semi-simplicity of the category $\mathcal{B}_{\mathbb{Q}}$ implies that the functor "fixed points" is exact on $\mathcal{B}_{\mathbb{Q}}$. Thus:

COROLLARY. *Let* $e \longrightarrow T' \longrightarrow T \longrightarrow T'' \longrightarrow e$ *be an exact sequence over* k *of* k-*tori*. *Then* T *is split (resp., anisotropic) over* k *if and only if* T' *and* T'' *are split (resp., anisotropic) over* k.

(8.15) T_a *and* T_d. Let T be a torus defined over k. The subtori of T correspond, in view of (8.5) and (8.12), to the Γ-module quotients of $X(T)$ which are torsion free.

One such quotient clearly is

$$X(T_a) = X(T)/X(T)_k = X(T)/X(T)^{\Gamma} ,$$

where (see (8.2)(c))

(a) $$T_a = \bigcap_{\alpha \in X(T)_k} \ker(\alpha) .$$

By construction it is clear that $X(T_a)^{\Gamma} = \{1\}$, i.e. that T_a is anisotropic, and that it is the largest anisotropic subtorus of T.

There is also a largest split subtorus, T_d, of T. To obtain T_d as above we would first take the largest quotient of $X(T)$ on which Γ acts trivially, and then reduce this quotient modulo its torsion submodule. However, it is more natural here to work in the dual module $X_*(T)$ (see (8.11), Cor. 1). Then we can describe T_d as follows:

$$X_*(T_d) = X_*(T)_k = X_*(T)^{\Gamma} ;$$

(d) T_d is the subgroup generated by

$$\{\operatorname{im}(\lambda) \mid \lambda \in X(T)_k\} .$$

This last description shows that T_d is a k-split torus, and that it contains all other such subtori of T.

A subtorus of $T_a \cap T_d$ must be both split and anisotropic (see (8.14)) and hence trivial. Thus $(T_a \cap T_d)^0$ is trivial, and so $T_a \cap T_d$ is finite.

Let $r = \operatorname{rank} X(T)^{\Gamma}$ and let $r_* = \operatorname{rank} X_*(T)^{\Gamma}$. Then $\dim T_a = n-r$ (where $n = \dim T$) and $\dim T_d = r_*$. These ranks can be computed as $\mathbb{Q}$-dimensions after tensoring the modules with $\mathbb{Q}$. Moreover $X(T)_{\mathbb{Q}}$ and $X_*(T)_{\mathbb{Q}}$ remain a dual pair of $\mathbb{Q}$-Γ-modules. Since the trivial representations of Γ are self dual it follows that $X(T)_{\mathbb{Q}}^{\Gamma}$ and $X_*(T)_{\mathbb{Q}}^{\Gamma}$ have the same dimension (thanks to the fact that these are semi-simple Γ-modules). Thus $r = r_*$ and so $\dim T_a + \dim T_d = \dim T$. This implies, in view of the last paragraph, that the product morphism $T_a \times T_d \longrightarrow T$ is surjective.

We summarize:

PROPOSITION. *Let* T *be a torus defined over* k, *and let* T_a *and* T_d *be defined by* (a) *and* (d) *above.*

(1) (a) T_a *is the largest anisotropic subtorus of* T *defined over* k. (b) T_d *is the largest split subtorus of* T *defined over* k.

(2) $T_a \cap T_d$ *is finite and* $T = T_a \cdot T_d$.

(3) *If* $\alpha : T \longrightarrow T'$ *is a* k-*morphism of* k-*tori then* $\alpha T_a \subset T'_a$ *and* $\alpha T_d \subset T'_d$. *In other words* $T \longmapsto T_a$ *and* $T \longmapsto T_d$ *are functorial.*

The last assertion is clear from the definitions, and all others were proved above.

(8.16) *Examples over* $k = \mathbb{R}$. The group $\Gamma = \mathrm{Gal}(\mathbb{C}/\mathbb{R})$ has order two.

(1) If $\dim T = 1$ there are two possibilities: (a) T *is split*. $T(\mathbb{R}) = \mathbb{R}^*$ and $X(T) = \mathbb{Z}$ with trivial Γ-action. (b) T *is anisotropic*. $X(T) = \mathbb{Z}$ with the generator of Γ acting by $\chi \longmapsto -\chi$. The group T is

$\mathbb{SO}(2)$, the real special orthogonal group in two variables, and $T(\mathbb{R})$ is the compact group of orientation preserving rotations of the plane.

(2) In the general case T is anisotropic if and only if $T(\mathbb{R})$ is compact (in the real topology). This can be deduced easily from example (1), with the aid of (8.15), and using the fact that there are only two irreducible $\mathbb{Q}$-Γ-modules.

(8.17) Weights and roots of diagonalizable groups. Let T be a diagonalizable group. We shall sometimes write the groups $X(T)$ of characters, and $X_*(T)$ of one parameter subgroups, additively. When doing this we shall employ an exponential notation, as follows:

$$\begin{aligned} t^{\alpha} &= \alpha(t) && (t \in T,\ \alpha \in X(T)) \\ x^{\lambda} &= \lambda(x) && (x \in \mathbb{GL}_1,\ \lambda \in X_*(T)) \\ (x^{\lambda})^{\alpha} &= x^{\langle \alpha, \lambda \rangle} && \text{(see (8.5)).} \end{aligned}$$

Let $T \longrightarrow GL(V)$ be a rational representation of T. If $\alpha \in X(T)$ we write

$$V_{\alpha} = \{v \in V \mid t \cdot v = \alpha(t)v \ \text{ for all } \ t \in T\} .$$

Since T is diagonalizable V is the direct sum of the V_{α}'s. Those α for which $V_{\alpha} \neq 0$ are called the weights of T in V. They are evidently finite in number.

Suppose T acts on G. Then T acts on $\underline{g} = L(G)$, and the set $\Phi(T, G)$ of non zero weights of T in $\underline{g}$ is called the set of roots of G relative to T. Thus

$$\underline{g} = \underline{g}^T \oplus \coprod_{\alpha \in \Phi(T,G)} \underline{g}_\alpha .$$

In case T and G are given as subgroups of some larger group in which T normalizes G then $\Phi(T, G)$ will always refer to the action of T on G by conjugation. Of course, by taking the semi-direct product $T \cdot G$, the general case reduces to one of this type.

Suppose T acts on G as above and that H is a T-invariant closed subgroup of G. Then $\underline{h} = L(H)$ is also T-invariant. For each $\alpha \in \Phi(T, G)$ we can write $\underline{g}_\alpha = \underline{h}_\alpha \oplus \underline{g}'_\alpha$ for some complement $\underline{g}'_\alpha$ of $\underline{h}_\alpha = \underline{h} \cap \underline{g}_\alpha$. We shall write

$$\begin{aligned} \Phi(T, G/H) &= \{\alpha \in \Phi(T, G) \mid \underline{g}'_\alpha \neq 0\} \\ &= \{\alpha \in \Phi(T, G) \mid \underline{h}_\alpha \neq \underline{g}_\alpha\} . \end{aligned}$$

Then we have

$$\underline{g} = (\underline{g}^T + \underline{h}) \oplus \coprod_{\alpha \in \Phi(T, G/H)} \underline{g}'_\alpha .$$

In case $H \subset G^T$ we have $\underline{h} \subset \underline{g}^T$ and hence $\Phi(T, G/H) = \Phi(T, G)$. We shall sometimes refer to $\Phi(T, G/H)$ as the set of "roots of G outside of H (relative to T)," or of complementary roots of G, with respect to H.

(8.18) PROPOSITION. We keep the notation of (8.17).

Assume T _to be connected and_ k _infinite. Then there is a_ $t \in T(k)$ _such that_

$$Z_H(t) = Z_H(T), \qquad Z_{\underline{h}}(t) = Z_{\underline{h}}(T) \ .$$

PROOF. We can assume $G = GL(V)$ for some vector space V defined over k. Write $V = V_1 \oplus \dots \oplus V_n$, where the V_i are the eigenspaces for the distinct weights $\chi_1, \dots, \chi_n$ of T on V. Since T is unirational over k ((8.13)(2)) and k is infinite, T(k) is dense in T, and we can choose $t \in T(k)$ such that $\chi_i(t) \neq \chi_j(t)$ for $i \neq j$. An obvious computation shows then that

$$Z_H(t) = Z_H(T) = M \cap H \ ,$$

$$Z_{\underline{h}}(t) = Z_{\underline{h}}(T) = L(M) \cap \underline{h} \ ,$$

where $M = GL(V_1) \times \dots \times GL(V_n)$.

BIBLIOGRAPHICAL NOTE

Tori are introduced in [1], the groups of their characters and of their one parameter subgroups in [8, Exp. 4]. That a k-torus T splits over a finite separable extension of k is pointed out while showing that T is unirational over k in [16, Prop. 10]. Another proof, due to J. Tate, is given in [4, §1]. The equivalence of categories (8.12), at least for tori, is proved in [15]. In fact, most of the results proved in this paragraph may be found in one of these references.

§9. CONJUGACY CLASSES AND CENTRALIZERS OF SEMI-SIMPLE ELEMENTS

In this section it is shown that conjugacy classes of semi-simple elements are closed (9.2), and that their global and infinitesimal centralizers correspond (9.1). The action of a semi-simple element s on a connected unipotent group U is studied and it is shown (9.3) that $Z_U(s)$ is connected. Applications are then made to group actions of diagonalizable groups (9.4).

(9.1) <u>The conjugacy class morphisms</u>. In this section we fix a closed subgroup H of G defined over k.

H acts on G by conjugation, and we write $C_H(s)$ for the orbit of an element $s \in G$; this is the H-<u>conjugacy class</u> of s.

$$\alpha : H \longrightarrow C_H(s), \qquad \alpha(h) = hsh^{-1} ,$$

is then the orbit map, and the isotropy group of s is the <u>centralizer</u> $Z_H(s)$. We can now apply (6.7) to this to determine when α is a quotient morphism. In order to make the statement more explicit we shall first determine $(d\alpha)_e$. Since $\alpha(h)s^{-1} = (h, s)$ is the commutator, it follows from (3.9)(1) that the latter has differential $(\mathrm{Id} - \mathrm{Ad}(s))|\underline{h}$, which maps $\underline{h}$ to $T(C_H(s)s^{-1})_e$. Thus its kernel is $\underline{h} \cap \underline{z}_{\underline{g}}(s)$, where $\underline{z}_{\underline{g}}(s) = \ker(\mathrm{Id} - \mathrm{Ad}(s))$. Since translation is an isomorphism, we conclude also that $(d\alpha)_e : \underline{h} \longrightarrow T(C_H(s))_s$ has kernel $\underline{h} \cap \underline{z}_{\underline{g}}(s)$. We shall denote the latter by $\underline{z}_{\underline{h}}(s)$, so that

$$\underline{z}_{\underline{h}}(s) = \{X \in \underline{h} \mid Ad(s)X = X\} \quad ,$$

even though we have not assumed that $Ad(s)$ leaves $\underline{h}$ invariant. In any case we certainly have

$$L(Z_H(s)) \subset \underline{z}_{\underline{h}}(s) \quad ,$$

and we can now apply (6.7) to conclude:

(*) Assume $s \in G(k)$. Then $C_H(s)$ is a smooth variety defined over k, and α is a k-morphism which induces a bijective k-morphism

$$\alpha' : H/Z_H(s) \longrightarrow C_H(s) \quad .$$

The following conditions are equivalent: (a) α' is an isomorphism; (b) α is separable; (c) $L(Z_H(s)) = \underline{z}_{\underline{h}}(s)$. When these conditions hold, $Z_H(s)$ is defined over k.

Next we discuss the infinitesimal analogue of the above situation. Namely, H acts on $\underline{g}$ via Ad_G, and we denote the H-orbit of an $X \in \underline{g}$ by $\underline{c}_H(X)$. Let

$$\beta : H \longrightarrow \underline{c}_H(X), \qquad \beta(h) = Ad(h)X \quad ,$$

be the orbit map. The stability group of X is denoted $Z_H(X)$, and it is called the centralizer of X in H. Before applying (6.7) we again compute first the differential of β. Following β by translation by $-X$, and using (3.9)(2), we see that the differential at e is $-ad(X)$.

Thus

$$\ker(d\beta)_e = \underline{z}_{\underline{h}}(X) = \{Y \in \underline{h} \mid [X, Y] = 0\} ,$$

and this clearly contains $L(Z_H(X))$. Now we apply (6.7) again to conclude:

(*) Assume $X \in \underline{g}(k)$. Then $\underline{c}_H(X)$ is a smooth variety defined over k, and β is a k-morphism which induces a bijective k-morphism

$$\beta' : H/Z_H(X) \longrightarrow \underline{c}_H(X) .$$

The following conditions are equivalent: (a) β' is an isomorphism; (b) β is separable; (c) $L(Z_H(X)) = \underline{z}_{\underline{h}}(X)$. When these conditions hold, $Z_H(X)$ is defined over k.

Note that, if char(k) = 0, conditions (b) of (*) and of (*) are automatic. More generally, they hold if s and X are semi-simple and normalize H.

PROPOSITION. (1) If, in (*), s is semi-simple and normalizes H, then conditions (a), (b), and (c) hold.

(1) If, in (*) X is semi-simple and normalizes H then conditions (a), (b), and (c) hold.

We say X normalizes H if $\mathrm{Ad}(h)X - X \in \underline{h}$ for all $h \in H$. This implies that X normalizes $\underline{h}$, i.e. that $[X, \underline{h}] \subset \underline{h}$ (see (3.9)(2)).

PROOF. After choosing a k-rational immersive representation we can enlarge G and assume $G = GL(V)$ for some vector space V with k-structure.

Case 1. $H = G$.

(1) Write $V = V_1 \oplus \dots \oplus V_t$ where the V_i are eigenspaces for the distinct eigenvalues of s (which is semi-simple). Then a simple direct calculation shows that $Z_G(s) = GL(V_1) \times \dots \times GL(V_t)$. If $Y \in \underline{g} = \underline{gl}(V)$ then $Ad(s)Y = sYs^{-1}$ so we conclude similarly that $\underline{z}_{\underline{g}}(s) = \underline{gl}(V_1) \oplus \dots \oplus \underline{gl}(V_t)$. The latter is just $L(Z_G(s))$, thus establishing condition (c).

($\underline{1}$) The proof is completely parallel, using a decomposition of V for the semisimple endomorphism $X \in \underline{gl}(V)$.

General case. Write $c : G \longrightarrow M$, where $M = C_G(s).s^{-1}$ and $c(g) = gsg^{-1}s^{-1}$, and write $c' : H \longrightarrow M'$, where $c' = c|H$ and $M' = C_H(s)s^{-1}$. Then c' is just a followed by right translation by s^{-1}, so we have only to show that $(dc')_e : \underline{h} \longrightarrow T(M')_e$ is surjective (condition (b) of (*)). We know from case 1 that $(dc)_e : \underline{g} \longrightarrow T(M)_e$ is surjective. Since $(dc)_e = Id - Ad(s)$ we see therefore that $T(M)_e = \underline{m}$, where $\underline{g} = \underline{z}_{\underline{g}}(s) \oplus \underline{m}$ and $\underline{m}$ is the sum of the eigenspaces of $Ad(s)$ corresponding to eigenvalues different from 1. Since s normalizes H, it follows that $\underline{h} = \underline{z}_{\underline{h}}(s) \oplus \underline{m}'$, where $\underline{m}' = \underline{m} \cap \underline{h}$ is similarly defined. Since $(dc')_e = (dc)_e|\underline{h}$ it follows that $(dc')_e(\underline{h}) = \underline{m}'$. Hence the proof of surjectivity of $(dc')_e$ will be finished once we show that $T(M')_e \subset \underline{m}' = \underline{m} \cap \underline{h}$. Evidently $T(M')_e \subset \underline{m} = T(M)_e$. On the other hand, since s

normalizes H, we have $M' = C_H(s)s^{-1} \subset H$, and so $T(M')_e \subset \underline{h}$ also.

The proof of ($\underline{1}$) is similar to the proof of (1) above. We introduce $a : G \longrightarrow \underline{c}$, where $\underline{c} = \underline{c}_G(X) - X$ and $a(g) = Ad(g)X - X$, and the morphism $a' : H \longrightarrow \underline{c}' = \underline{c}_H(X) - X$ where $a' = a|H$. We want to show that $(da')_e$ is surjective, and we know from case 1 that $(da)_e = -ad(X) : \underline{g} \longrightarrow T(\underline{c})_0$ is surjective. It follows that $\underline{g} = \underline{z}_{\underline{g}}(X) \oplus \underline{m}$ where $\underline{m} = T(\underline{c})_0$ is the sum of the eigenspaces of $ad(X)$ corresponding to eigenvalues different from 0. Since X normalizes $\underline{h}$ we can similarly write $\underline{h} = \underline{z}_{\underline{h}}(X) \oplus \underline{m}'$ where $\underline{m}' = \underline{m} \cap \underline{h}$. Since $(da')_e = (da)_e|\underline{h}$ it follows that $(da')_e(\underline{h}) = ad(X)(\underline{h}) = \underline{m}'$. Hence the surjectivity of $(da')_e$ will follow once we show that $T(\underline{c}')_0 \subset \underline{m}' = \underline{m} \cap \underline{h}$. Evidently $T(\underline{c}')_0 \subset \underline{m} = T(\underline{c})_0$. On the other hand, since X normalizes H, we have $\underline{c}' = \underline{c}_H(X) - X \subset \underline{h}$, and so $T(\underline{c}')_0 \subset \underline{h}$ also.

REMARK. Let $p : M' \times Z_H(s) \longrightarrow H$ be the product morphism, with differential $(dp)_{(e,e)} : \underline{m}' \oplus L(Z_H(s)) \longrightarrow \underline{h}$. The proof above shows that $L(Z_H(s)) = \underline{z}_{\underline{h}}(s)$, and hence that $(dp)_{(e,e)}$ is an isomorphism. Moreover the differential of $c|M' : M' \longrightarrow M'$ at e is $Id - Ad(s)|\underline{m}' : \underline{m}' \longrightarrow \underline{m}'$, which is clearly also an isomorphism.

(9.2) THEOREM. _We keep the notation of_ (9.1).

(1) _If_ $s \in G$ _is semi-simple and normalizes_ H,

<u>then</u> $C_H(s)$ <u>is closed</u>.

(<u>l</u>) <u>If</u> $X \in \underline{g}$ <u>is semi-simple and normalizes</u> H <u>then</u> $\underline{c}_H(X)$ <u>is closed</u>.

Recall that X normalizes H if $Ad(h)X - X \in \underline{h}$ for all $h \in H$.

PROOF. After choosing a faithful representation, we may assume $G = GL(V)$. If $A \in End(V)$ write $C(A, T)$ for the characteristic polynomial of A, and $M(A, T)$ for the minimal polynomial of A. With this notation we define

$$W = \{x \in N_G(H) \,|\, M(s, x) = 0 \text{ and } C(Adx|\underline{h}, T) = C(Ads|\underline{h}, T)\} \quad .$$

Clearly $s \in W$, and W is stable under H operating by conjugation. If $x \in W$ then $M(x, T)$ divides $M(s, T)$, and the latter is a product of distinct linear factors because s is semi-simple; hence x is likewise semi-simple. We can therefore apply (9.1) to obtain

$$\dim C_H(x) = \dim H - \dim Z_H(x) =$$
$$= \dim H - \dim \underline{z}_{\underline{h}}(x) = \dim H - m_1(x) \quad ,$$

where $m_1(x)$ is the multiplicity of 1 as an eigenvalue of $Adx|\underline{h}$. But the second condition defining W implies that $m_1(x) = m_1(s)$. Therefore, under the action of H by conjugation on W, the orbits $C_H(x)$ have constant dimension. It therefore follows from the closed orbit lemma (1.8) that the orbits are closed in W. But evidently W is closed in

$N_G(H)$, and the latter is closed in G (see (1.7)). This proves that $C_H(s)$ is closed.

The proof that $C_H(X)$ is closed is similar. It uses

$$W = \{Y \in \underline{n}_{\underline{g}}(H) \mid M(X, Y) = 0 \text{ and } C(\mathrm{ad}Y|\underline{h}, T) = C(\mathrm{ad}X|\underline{h}, T)\} \quad .$$

Here $\underline{n}_{\underline{g}}(H)$ is the set of Y in $\underline{g}$ that "normalize H" in the sense of (9.1). This set W is closed in $\underline{g}$, it contains X, and it is stable (via Ad) under H. Using (9.1) one can argue as above to show that the H-orbits in W have constant dimension, and hence are closed.

COROLLARY. *Let* L *be a (not necessarily closed) subgroup of* G, *which is commutative, consists of semi-simple elements, and normalizes* H. *Then*

$$L(Z_H(L)) = \underline{z}_{\underline{h}}(L) \quad .$$

If either $L \subset G(k)$, *or* L *is closed, defined over* k, *then* $Z_H(L)$ *is defined over* k.

PROOF. We may assume that $G = H$. Clearly the right side contains the left one, so, in case $G^0 \subset Z_G(L)$, the left side equals $\underline{g}$ and equality is forced. We complete the proof by induction on $\dim G$. Choose $s \in L$ so that $G' = Z_G(s)$ does not contain G^0, and hence $\dim G' < \dim G$. Part (1) of (9.1) Proposition tells us that $\underline{g}' = L(Z_G(s)) = \underline{z}_{\underline{g}}(s)$, from which it follows that

$\underline{z}_{\underline{g}}(L) = \underline{z}_{\underline{g}'}(L)$. Moreover it is clear that $Z_G(L) = Z_{G'}(L)$, and $L \subset G'$ because L is commutative. By induction we have $L(Z_{G'}(L)) = \underline{z}_{\underline{g}'}(L)$, so this proves the first assertion. If $L \subset G(k)$, the same induction, and (9.1), show that $Z_H(L)$ is defined over k. Let now L be closed, defined over k. Then, by the above $Z_H(L(k_s))$ is defined over k_s. But $L(k_s)$ is Zariski dense in L (AG.13.3), hence $Z_H(L(k_s)) = Z_H(L)$. On the other hand, $Z_H(L)$ is clearly k-closed. Therefore it is defined over k.

(9.3) PROPOSITION. Let G be a k-group and let U be a connected unipotent subgroup defined over k. Let $s \in G(k)$ be a semi-simple element that normalizes U. Put $M = C_U(s)s^{-1}$ and write $c_s(g) = gsg^{-1}s^{-1}$ for $g \in G$, so that $M = c_s(U)$.

(1) $Z_U(s)$ and M are closed subvarieties of U defined over k.

(2) The product morphism $\alpha : M \times Z_U(s) \longrightarrow U$ is an isomorphism of varieties. Hence $Z_U(s)$ is connected.

(3) c_s induces an isomorphism of the variety M onto itself.

PROOF. It follows from (9.1)(1) that $Z_U(s)$ and M are smooth varieties defined over k, and clearly $Z_U(s)$ is closed. The fact that M is closed is just (9.2)(1). This proves (1).

It further follows from the Remark in the proof of (9.1)(1) that α and $c_s : M \longrightarrow M$ are separable, once we know they are dominant. Therefore it suffices, to conclude the proof, to show that α and $c_s : M \longrightarrow M$ are bijective. We shall do this in several steps. Write $Z = Z_U(s)$.

(a) $c_s(u) = c_s(v) \Longleftrightarrow uZ = vZ$ for $u, v \in U$. This is because c_s is conjugation of s followed by right translation by s^{-1}, and Z is the stability group of s under conjugation.

(b) If $u, v \in U$ then $c_s(uv) = uc_s(v)u^{-1}c_s(u)$. Hence, if $u \in Z(U)$ we have $c_s(uv) = c_s(v)c_s(u) = c_s(vu)$, and $c_s(u^{-1}) = c_s(u)^{-1}$. For $c_s(uv) = uvs(uv)^{-1}s^{-1} = u(vsv^{-1}s^{-1})u^{-1}(usu^{-1}s^{-1})$. If $u \in Z(U)$ then $uc_s(v)u^{-1} = c_s(v)$ and $uv = vu$, so the second assertion follows from the first. The third one clearly follows from the second one.

(c) $M \cap Z = \{e\}$. Suppose $z = c_s(u) \in Z$ with $u \in U$. Then $zs = usu^{-1}$ is the Jordan decomposition of the semi-simple element usu^{-1}, so the unipotent part, z, equals e.

(d) $\alpha : M \times Z \longrightarrow U$ is bijective if U is abelian. Part (b) implies that $c_s : U \longrightarrow U$ is a homomorphism. It has kernel Z, by (a), and image M, so $\dim U = \dim M + \dim Z$. Moreover part (c) implies that α is injective. (Note that α is a group morphism now by (b).) Since U is connected, the dimension formula above implies that α is also surjective.

(e) α is bijective. Since U is nilpotent we can find a connected central subgroup $N \neq \{e\}$ of U

normalized by s (e.g. the last non trivial term of the descending central series of U). If $N = U$ we can apply (d). If not, we can assume, by induction on dimension, that the analogue of our assertion is valid for the pairs (s, N) and (s', U'), where $U' = U/N$ and s' is the image of s in the quotient modulo N of the normalizer of N. Let π denote this quotient morphism.

Put $Z' = Z_{U'}(s')$ and $M' = c_{s'}(U') = \pi(M)$. The induction hypothesis says that the product morphism $\alpha' : M' \times Z' \longrightarrow U'$ is bijective. Similarly, $c_s(N) \times Z_N(s) \longrightarrow N$ is bijective.

To show that α is injective suppose we have $xa = yb$ with $a, b \in Z$ and $x, y \in M$. Replacing a by ab^{-1} we can assume $b = e$. Applying π we conclude from the injectivity of α' that $\pi(a) = e$, so that $a \in N$. If $x = c_s(u)$ and $y = c_s(v)$ we have $usu^{-1}s^{-1}a = vsv^{-1}s^{-1}$ and $a(\in N \cap Z)$ centralizes U and s. Therefore we have $(usu^{-1})a = (vsv^{-1})$, which is the Jordan decomposition of the semi-simple element vsv^{-1}, so the unipotent part, a, equals e. This shows that α is injective.

We next claim that the inclusion $c_s(N) \subset M \cap N$ is an equality. For any $n \in N$ can be written as ma with $m \in c_s(N)$ and $a \in Z_N(s)$, by induction. If also $n \in M$, the injectivity of α implies $a = e$.

Now we will show that $\pi : Z \longrightarrow Z'$ is surjective. Suppose $x \in U$ and $\pi(x) \in Z'$. Then $c_{s'}(\pi(x)) = e$ so $c_s(x) \in \ker(\pi) \cap M = N \cap M = c_s(N)$, by the last paragraph. Say

$c_s(x) = c_s(n)$ with $n \in N$. Since $N \subset Z(U)$ it follows from (b) that $c_s(n^{-1}x) = c_s(x)c_s(n^{-1}) = c_s(x)c_s(n)^{-1} = e$. Thus $n^{-1}x \in Z$ and $\pi(n^{-1}x) = \pi(x)$, so we have lifted $\pi(x)$ to an element of Z, as required.

Now we can show that α is surjective:

$$
\begin{aligned}
U &= MZN, && \text{(because } U' = M'Z',\ \pi M = M', \text{ and } \pi Z = Z'\text{)},\\
&= MNZ, && (N \subset Z(U)),\\
&= Mc_s(N)Z_N(s)Z, && \text{(by induction)},\\
&= MZ, && \text{(because } Z_N(s) \subset Z\text{) and } Mc_s(Z(U)) = M, \text{ by (b))} .
\end{aligned}
$$

(f) $c_s : M \longrightarrow M$ <u>is bijective</u>. Using part (a) and the surjectivity of α we have $M = c_s(U) = c_s(MZ) = c_s(M)$. If $u, v \in M$ and $c_s(u) = c_s(v)$ then (a) implies $u = vz$ for some $z \in Z$. Thus $\alpha(u, e) = \alpha(v, z)$ so the injectivity of α implies that $z = e$. Q.E.D.

(9.4) <u>Group actions of diagonalizable groups</u>. We fix a diagonalizable group T, a morphic action of T on G, and a T-invariant closed subgroup H of G containing $G^T = Z_G(T)$. With respect to the action of T on the Lie algebras $\underline{g} = L(G)$ and $\underline{h} = L(H)$ we have (see (8.17) for the notation)

$$\underline{g} = \underline{g}^T \oplus \coprod_{\alpha \in \Phi(T, G)} \underline{g}_\alpha$$

$$\underline{g} = (\underline{g}^T + \underline{h}) \oplus \coprod_{\alpha \in \Phi(T, G/H)} \underline{a}_\alpha ,$$

where $\underline{a}_\alpha$ is a complement for $\underline{h}_\alpha$ in $\underline{g}_\alpha$. Finally, we write $T_\alpha = \ker(\alpha)$, $(\alpha \in X(T))$.

PROPOSITION. (1) We have $L(G^T) = \underline{g}^T$, and hence $\underline{g}^T \subset \underline{h}$. If G is connected and unipotent, then G^T is connected.

(2) The following conditions on a subgroup S of T are equivalent: (a) $(G^S)^0 \subset H$; (b) $\underline{g}^S \subset \underline{h}$; (c) S is contained in no T_α for $\alpha \in \Phi(T, G/H)$.

(3) If G^S is connected, then $G^S = G^T \Longleftrightarrow S$ is contained in no $T_\alpha (\alpha \in \Phi(T, G))$.

(4) If G is connected and if $G \neq G^T$, then G is generated by the subgroups $Z_G(T^\alpha)$, $(\alpha \in \Phi(T, G))$.

PROOF (1). The first assertion is a special case of the Corollary to 9.2 (applied to the semi-direct product of T and G).

The second assertion of (1) is proved by induction on dim G: If $G = G^T$, then G^T is connected, by hypothesis. Otherwise choose s such that $G \not\subset Z_G(s)$. By (9.3)(2), G^s is connected. One argues then as in the proof of the Corollary to 9.2.

Proof of (2): (a) $\Longrightarrow$ (b). If $(G^S)^0 \subset H$ then $L(G^S) \subset \underline{h}$, and (1) implies that $L(G^S) = \underline{g}^S$.

(b) $\Longrightarrow$ (a). Since $\underline{h} \subset \underline{g}$ we obtain $\underline{h}^S \subset \underline{g}^S$, clearly, and $\underline{g}^S \subset \underline{h}$ implies $\underline{h}^S = \underline{g}^S$. Thus the dimension equality implies $(H^S)^0 = (G^S)^0 \subset H$, using (1).

(b) $\Longleftrightarrow$ (c). Writing

$$\underline{g} = \underline{h} \oplus \coprod_{\alpha\in\Phi} \underline{a}_\alpha \quad (\Phi = \Phi(T,\ G/H))$$

we have

$$\underline{g}^S = \underline{h}^S \oplus \coprod_{\alpha\in\Phi} \underline{a}_\alpha^S = \underline{h}^S \oplus \coprod_{\alpha\in\Phi,\ \alpha(S)=\{1\}} \underline{a}_\alpha \ .$$

Thus $\underline{g}^S \subset \underline{h} \iff \alpha(S) \neq \{1\}$ for all $\alpha \in \Phi$, as claimed.

(3) Since $G^T \subset G^S$ this follows by applying (1) and (2) ((a) $\iff$ (c)) with $H = G^T$.

(4) Let G' denote the subgroup generated by all G^{T_α} ($\alpha \in \Phi(T, G)$). The condition $G^T \neq G$ implies that $\Phi(T, G)$ is not empty. Since $L(G^{T_\alpha})$ equals $\underline{g}^{T_\alpha}$ by (1), and hence contains $\underline{g}^T + \underline{g}_\alpha$, it follows that $L(G')$ contains $\underline{g}^T + \sum_{\alpha\in\Phi_T(G)} \underline{g}_\alpha = \underline{g}$. Hence $G' \supset G^0 = G$.

This completes the proof.

(9.5) COROLLARY. Keep the notation of (9.4).

(1) If $\lambda \in X_*(T)$ and if $S = \text{im}(\lambda)$, then $(G^S)^0 \subset H$ if and only if $\langle\alpha, \lambda\rangle \neq 0$ for all $\alpha \in \Phi(T, G/H)$. In particular $(G^S)^0 = (G^T)^0$ if and only if $\langle\alpha, \lambda\rangle \neq 0$ for all $\alpha \in \Phi(T, G)$.

(2) Suppose T is a torus and $G \neq G^T$. Then G^0 is generated by the $(G^{T_\alpha^0})^0$. Moreover, if k is infinite there is a $t \in T(k)$ such that $t^\alpha \neq 1$ for all $\alpha \in \Phi(T, G)$, and for such a t we have $Z_G(t)^0 = (G^T)^0$.

Part (1) follows directly from (9.4)(2). Since the centralizer of T^0 contains that of T, the first assertion of (2) is a consequence of (9.4)(4). The existence of t follows from the fact that T(k) is dense in T ((8.13)(2)). The last equality of (2) then follows from (9.4)(2), applied to $H = G^T$ and to the subgroup S generated by t.

(9.6) PROPOSITION. Let $\pi : G \longrightarrow G'$ be a surjective and T-equivariant morphism of k-groups on which the diagonalizable group T acts. Then the induced homomorphism $(G^T)^0 \longrightarrow (G'^T)^0$ is surjective.

PROOF. Since $N = \ker(\pi)$ is T-invariant there is an action of T on G/N, and π factors through a T-equivariant and bijective morphism $G/N \longrightarrow G'$. Hence we may assume that $G' = G/N$. In this case $(d\pi)_e : \underline{g} \longrightarrow \underline{g}'$ is surjective. Since T is diagonalizable $\underline{g}^T \longrightarrow \underline{g}'^T$ is also surjective. According to (9.4)(1), however, the latter is the differential of $G^T \longrightarrow G'^T$, so the proposition follows.

REMARK. The proof shows even that $(G^T)^0 \longrightarrow (G'^T)^0$ is a quotient morphism if π is a quotient morphism.

BIBLIOGRAPHICAL NOTE

The Proposition in (9.1) and Theorem (9.2) are proved in [4, §10] for groups, and in [2, 3] for Lie algebras. Proposition (9.3) is proved in [1, lemme 9.6] when U is commutative, and in [4, §11.1] in the general case. In [1], there is a counterpart where s is unipotent, and U is a torus, but it will not be needed in these Notes. (9.5) generalizes a result proved in [8, Exp. 9, No. 1] for actions of tori on unipotent groups.

§10. CONNECTED SOLVABLE GROUPS

The analysis of a general affine group proceeds via a study of its connected solvable subgroups. This is because the latter have a number of special properties which make them easier to work with. The main ones are the fixed point theorem (10.4) and the structure theorem (10.6).

(10.1) Complete varieties. We shall collect here some properties of complete varieties to be used below. Recall (AG.7.4) that V is complete if, for all varieties X, the projection $V \times X \longrightarrow X$ is a closed map. Properties (1), (2), and (3) which follow are taken from (AG.7.4).

(1) *A closed subvariety of a complete variety is complete. The image of a complete variety under a morphism is closed and complete. Products of complete varieties are complete.*

(2) *A morphism from a connected complete variety into an affine variety is constant.*

(3) *Projective varieties are complete.*

(4) *Let* $\alpha : V \longrightarrow W$ *be a bijective morphism. If* W *is normal and complete then* V *is also complete.* (See (AG.18.3).)

Finally, from (AG.18.5(d)) we have:

(5) *Let* $\alpha : V \longrightarrow W$ *be a morphism from an*

irreducible smooth curve V into a complete variety W. Then α extends to a morphism $\bar{\alpha} : \bar{V} \longrightarrow W$ from the complete smooth curve $\bar{V}$ containing V.

(10.2) A composition series for $\mathbb{T}_n$. Recall the following subgroups of $\mathbb{GL}_n$:

$$\mathbb{T}_n = \{g = (g_{ij}) \mid g_{ij} = 0 \text{ for } j < i\}$$

$$= \left\{ \begin{pmatrix} * & & * \\ & \ddots & \\ 0 & & * \end{pmatrix} \in \mathbb{GL}_n \right\}$$

$$\mathbb{U}_n = \{g \in \mathbb{T}_n \mid g_{ii} = 1, \ 1 \leqq i \leqq n\}$$

$$= \left\{ \begin{pmatrix} 1 & & * \\ & \ddots & \\ 0 & & 1 \end{pmatrix} \right\}$$

$$\mathbb{D}_n = \{g \in \mathbb{GL}_n \mid g_{ij} = 0 \text{ for } i \neq j\}$$

$$= \{\mathrm{diag}(t_1, \ldots, t_n) \mid t_i \in K^*\} \ .$$

The following facts are readily checked:

$$\mathbb{U}_n = (\mathbb{T}_n)_u = (\mathbb{T}_n, \mathbb{T}_n) \ ,$$

$$\mathbb{D}_n \cong (\mathbb{GL}_1)^n, \ \mathbb{T}_n = \mathbb{D}_n \cdot \mathbb{U}_n \ .$$

$\mathbb{T}_n$ is the group of invertible elements in the algebra A of all upper triangular matrices. The set N of matrices in A with zeroes on the diagonal is an ideal (in fact the radical) of A. The two sided ideal N^h is spanned by the basic matrices e_{ij} for which $j \geqq i + h$. Moreover, the image of $e_{i,i+h}$ in N^h/N^{h+1} spans a one dimensional two sided ideal in A/N^{h+1} since it is killed by N and is an eigenvector for the diagonal matrices. Thus the vector space $A_{h\ell}$ spanned by $\{e_{ij} \mid j > i+h, \text{ or } j = i+h \leqq \ell\}$ is a two sided ideal in A for $0 \leqq h < n$ and $1 \leqq \ell \leqq n-h$. If we order the pairs (h, ℓ) lexicographically we obtain a descending chain of two sided ideals, starting with $A = A_{0,0}$, ending with $A_{n-1,1} = Ke_{nn}$, and such that each has codimension one in the next larger one. Writing $\mathbb{T}_{h\ell} = \{g \in \mathbb{T}_n \mid g \equiv I \bmod A_{h\ell}\}$ we therefore obtain a descending chain of normal subgroups of $\mathbb{T}_n$. Note that $N = A_{1,n-1}$, and hence $\mathbb{T}_{1,n-1} = \mathbb{U}_n$. Thus one sees that the first n quotients are isomorphic to $\mathbb{GL}_1$, and the remaining ones are isomorphic to $\mathbb{G}_a$. In summary:

> $\mathbb{T}_n$ <u>is filtered by a chain of normal subgroups with successive quotients isomorphic to</u> $\mathbb{GL}_1$ <u>or</u> $\mathbb{G}_a$.

(10.3) <u>Grassmannians and flag varieties.</u> Let V be an n-dimensional vector space. We propose to put on the set $G_d(V)$ of d-dimensional subspaces of V the structure of a projective variety. Define

$$f : G_d(V) \longrightarrow \mathbb{P}(\Lambda^d V)$$

by sending W to the point in the projective space corresponding to the line $\Lambda^d W \subset \Lambda^d V$. It is easily checked (and well known) that f is injective (cf. (5.1) Lemma), so we need only show that its image is closed.

$\mathbb{P}(\Lambda^d V)$ is covered by (affine) open sets U of the following type relative to a suitable basis $e_1, \ldots, e_n$ for $V : U$ consists of all points whose homogeneous coordinates, in the basis of $\Lambda^d V$ defined by $e_1, \ldots, e_n$, are such that the coefficient of $e = e_1 \wedge \ldots \wedge e_d$ is not zero. Thus U is the complement of a linear variety.

Write $V = W_0 \oplus W'_0$ where W_0 and W'_0 are spanned by $e_1, \ldots, e_d$ and $e_{d+1}, \ldots, e_n$, respectively. Then, for $W \in G_d(V)$, we have $f(W) \in U$ if and only if the projection maps W isomorphically onto W_0. In this case W has a unique basis of the form $e_1 + x_1(W), \ldots, e_d + x_d(W)$, with $x_i(W) \in W'_0$. Say $x_i(W) = \sum_{j>d} a_{ij} e_j$. Then $f(W)$ is the projection into $\mathbb{P}(\Lambda^d V)$ of the vector $e + (\sum_{1 \leqq i \leqq d} e_1 \wedge \ldots \wedge x_i(W) \wedge \ldots \wedge e_d) + (*)$, where $(*)$ involves basis vectors omitting two or more of $e_1, \ldots, e_d$. Now

$$e_1 \wedge \ldots \wedge x_i(W) \wedge \ldots \wedge e_d = \sum_{j>d} a_{ij} e_1 \wedge \ldots \wedge e_j \wedge \ldots \wedge e_d ,$$

so we see that, in $(e_1 + x_1(W)) \wedge \ldots \wedge (e_d + x_d(W))$, we recover a_{ij} as the coefficient of the basis vector $e_1 \wedge \ldots \wedge e_j \wedge \ldots \wedge e_d$, $(1 \leqq i \leqq d;\ j > d$, e_j at the ith place), and these coefficients, which determine W, may be prescribed arbitrarily. The coefficients of the remaining vectors in $\Lambda^d V$ are polynomial functions of the a_{ij}. Thus, $f(G_d(V))$ is essentially the graph of a morphism from the space of (a_{ij})'s to another linear space. In particular, it is closed.

Suppose $W \in G_d(V)$ and $W' \in G_{d'}(V)$, with $d \leqq d'$. Then the condition that $W \subset W'$ can be expressed by algebraic equations on the coordinates in $\mathbb{P}(\Lambda^d V) \times \mathbb{P}(\Lambda^{d'} V)$. Thus $\{(W, W') \in G_d(V) \times G_{d'}(V) \mid W \subset W'\}$ is a closed subvariety. The flag variety, $\mathcal{F}(V)$, is

$$\{(V_1, \ldots, V_n) \in G_1(V) \times \ldots \times G_n(V) \mid V_i \subset V_{i+1}, 1 \leqq i < n\} .$$

The remarks above show that $\mathcal{F}(V)$ is a projective variety. Hence, by (10.1)(3), $\mathcal{F}(V)$ is complete.

The following remarks on $GL(V)$ illustrate certain theorems to be proved below for arbitrary connected groups.

If $e_1, \ldots, e_n$ is a basis for V we can define

$$\varphi : GL(V) \longrightarrow \mathcal{F}(V)$$

by $\varphi(g) = (V_1, \ldots, V_n)$, where V_i is the space spanned by $ge_1, \ldots, ge_i$ $(1 \leqq i \leqq n)$. It is clear that $GL(V)$ operates transitively on the flags in V, the operation being such that φ is equivariant. Therefore φ induces a bijective morphism $\alpha : GL(V)/B \longrightarrow \mathcal{F}(V)$, where B is the isotropy group of the flag $\varphi(e)$. Under the isomorphism $GL(V) \longrightarrow \mathbf{GL}_n$ defined by the basis above one sees that B corresponds to $\mathbf{T}_n$. Write U^- for the unipotent subgroup corresponding to lower triangular matrices. It is easy to check that $U^- \cdot B$ contains an open set in $GL(V)$. In fact, it corresponds to the set of $g = (g_{ij})_{1 \leqq i, j \leqq n}$ in $\mathbf{GL}_n$ such that, for each $d \leqq n$, $\det(g_{ij})_{1 \leqq i, j \leqq d} \neq 0$, and this is clearly open.

In terms of the projective coordinates introduced on each $G_d(V)$, we see that the coordinates of $\varphi(g)$ are given by $(ge_1, ge_1 \wedge ge_2, \ldots, ge_1 \wedge \ldots \wedge ge_n)$. If $g \in U^-$ then $ge_i = e_i + \sum_{j>i} a_{ij}e_j$, so $ge_1 \wedge \ldots \wedge ge_i =$

$(ge_1 \wedge \ldots \wedge ge_{i-1} \wedge e_i) + (\sum_{j>i} a_{ij} ge_1 \wedge \ldots \wedge ge_{i-1} \wedge e_j)$.

Thus we see, by induction on i, that the ge_i can be determined algebraically from the projective coordinates of $\varphi(g)$, for $g \in U^-$. As a consequence, φ induces an isomorphism of U^- onto its image. Since, as we saw above, $\varphi(U^-)$ contains an open set in $\varphi(GL(V))$, it follows that the differential of φ is surjective, i.e. φ is separable. This proves:

> $\varphi : GL(V) \longrightarrow \mathcal{F}(V)$ _induces an isomorphism of varieties_ $\alpha : GL(V)/B \longrightarrow \mathcal{F}(V)$. _In particular_, $GL(V)/B$ _is a projective variety_.

The above proof is a little sketchy, but an independent, and much more general, one will be given in (11.1).

(10.4) THEOREM. _Let_ G _be a connected solvable group operating morphically on a non-empty complete variety_ V. _Then_ G _has a fixed point in_ V.

PROOF. We argue by induction on $d = \dim G$. If $d = 0$ then $G = \{e\}$, so assume $d > 0$. Then $N = (G, G)$ is connected and of smaller dimension, so the set F of fixed points of N in V is a non-empty, closed, and hence complete, variety. Since N is normal in G, it follows that F is stable under G.

By the closed orbit lemma (1.8) there is an $x \in F$ such that $G(x)$ is closed. Since $N \subset G_x$, it follows that G_x is normal in G. Thus

$$G/G_x \longrightarrow G(x)$$

is a bijective morphism from a connected affine variety to a complete one. Since $G(x)$ is smooth, and hence normal, it follows from (10.1)(4) that G/G_x is complete. Now (10.1)(2) implies that G/G_x is a point. Q.E.D.

(10.5) COROLLARY (Lie-Kolchin Theorem). *If* $\pi : G \longrightarrow GL(V)$ *is a linear representation of a connected solvable group, then* $\pi(G)$ *leaves a flag in* V *invariant. I.e.* $\pi(G)$ *can be put in triangular form.*

PROOF. G has a fixed point for the action induced by π on the variety $\mathcal{F}(V)$ because, by (10.3), $\mathcal{F}(V)$ is complete.

Here is a purely algebraic corollary:

COROLLARY. *Let* M *be a solvable, not necessarily closed, subgroup of* $GL(V)$. *Then some subgroup of finite index in* M *can be put in triangular form.*

PROOF. Let $H = \mathcal{A}(M)$. We know from (2.4) Cor. 2 that H is solvable. Now apply the last corollary to H^0. Then $H^0 \cap M$ has finite index in M, and hence solves our problem.

(10.6) THEOREM. Let G be connected, solvable.

(1) G_u is a connected normal k-closed subgroup of G containing $DG = (G, G)$.

(2) G/G_u is a torus, and G_u contains a chain of closed connected subgroups, normal in G, such that the successive quotients have dimension one.

(3) G is nilpotent if and only if G_s is a subgroup of G. In this case, G_s is a closed subgroup defined over k, and G is the direct product $G_s \times G_u$.

(4) The maximal tori in G are conjugate by $C^{\infty}G$. If T is a maximal torus, then $G = T \cdot G_u$ (semi-direct product). $L(G_u)$ is the union of the nilpotent elements of $L(G)$.

(5) Let S be a not necessarily closed subgroup of G, consisting of semi-simple elements. Then

(i) S is contained in a torus, and

(ii) $G^S = Z_G(S)$ is connected and equal to $N_G(S)$.

PROOF. (1) Using the Lie-Kolchin Theorem we can embed G in $\mathbf{T}_n$. Then $\mathbf{U}_n = (\mathbf{T}_n)_u = D\mathbf{T}_n$ is a closed normal subgroup of $\mathbf{T}_n$, so G_u is a closed normal subgroup of G containing DG. It follows from (4.5) that G_u is k-closed. Let $\pi : G \longrightarrow G' = G/DG$ be the canonical projection. By (4.7), $G' = G'_s \times G'_u$, hence G'_u is connected. We claim that $G_u = \pi^{-1}(G'_u)$. If $x \in G_u$, then $\pi(x) \in G'_u$ by (4.4). Let now $x \in \pi^{-1}(G'_u)$ and $x = x_s \cdot x_u$ its Jordan decomposition. Then, by (4.4), $x_s, x_u \in \pi^{-1}(G'_u)$, and $x_s \in DG$. But $DG \subset G_u$, hence $x_s = e$ and $x \in G_u$, which shows that $G_u = \pi^{-1}(G'_u)$. Since DG and G'_u are connected, it follows that G_u is connected.

(2) G/G_u injects into $\mathbf{T}_n/\mathbf{U}_n \cong \mathbf{D}_n$ so G/G_u is a commutative connected group consisting of semi-simple elements, and hence is a torus (see (8.4) and (8.5)). Starting with a chain of connected normal subgroups N_i of $\mathbf{T}_n$ contained in $\mathbf{U}_n$ and with successive quotients isomorphic to $\mathbf{G}_a$ (see (10.2)) we obtain from the groups $(N_i \cap G)^0$ a chain of connected normal subgroups of G contained in G_u with successive quotients of dimension $\leqq 1$. Eliminating repetitions, the quotients will then have dimension one.

(3) Suppose first that G_s is a subgroup of G. It projects injectively into G/G_u, so G_s is commutative. Hence we can use (4.6) to diagonalize G_s under some faithful rational representation of G in a $GL(V)$. It is then clear that the closure of G_s is a diagonalizable subgroup of G, necessarily equal to G_s, clearly. By rigidity (8.10) we have $Z_G(G_s) = N_G(G_s)^0$. But evidently G_s is normal in G, so, since G is connected, G_s is central in G. The quotient G/G_s is unipotent, and hence nilpotent (4.8), so it follows that G is nilpotent, as claimed.

Suppose, conversely, that G is nilpotent. We claim then that G_s lies in the center of G.

Let $a \in G_s$ and put $U = G_u$. Write $c_a(x) = xax^{-1}a^{-1}$ for $x \in G$ and put $M = c_a(U)$. According to (9.3)(3) c_a

induces a bijection $M \longrightarrow M$, so $M \subset C^{\infty}G$. Since G is nilpotent we conclude that $M = \{e\}$, i.e. that a centralizes U. Hence G^a contains DG, so it is a normal subgroup. In order to prove that $G^a = G$, it suffices then, in view of (4.4), (4.7), to show that $G^a \supset G_s$.

Suppose then that $t \in G_s$. Then $c_a(t) \in U$, so a commutes with $c_a(t)$. Therefore $c_a(t)a = tat^{-1}a^{-1}a = tat^{-1}$ is the Jordan decomposition of the semi-simple element tat^{-1}, so the unipotent part, $c_a(t)$, is e.

Now that G_s is central it follows as above that G_s is a closed diagonalizable subgroup of G. The Jordan decomposition in G and in $L(G)$ shows that $G = G_s \times G_u$ (group direct product) and that $L(G_s) \cap L(G_u) = 0$. Thus G is the direct product of G_s and G_u as an algebraic group, because $G_s \times G_u \longrightarrow G$ is bijective and separable.

It remains to be shown that G_s is defined over k.

(a) $p = \text{char } k = 0$. The Jordan factors of a $g \in G(\bar{k})$ are in $G_s(\bar{k}) \times G_u(\bar{k})$, and the action of $\Gamma = \text{Gal}(\bar{k}/k)$ evidently preserves Jordan decomposition. Therefore G_s and G_u each have dense sets of $\bar{k}$-points which are Γ-stable, so they are subgroups defined over k.

(b) $p > 0$. There is a $q = p^r (r > 0)$ such that $u^q = e$ for all $u \in G_u$. (If $G \subset \mathbf{GL}_n$ then $r = n-1$ works.) Then the Jordan decomposition shows that $g \longmapsto g^q$ defines a morphism $G \longrightarrow G_s$, evidently defined over k. It follows from (8.9)(b) that its restriction to G_s is bijective. Thus G_s, being the image of a k-morphism, is defined over k.

(4) We first claim, by induction on dim G, that there is a torus T in G that projects onto G/G_u. It will then follow that $G = T \cdot G_u$ (semi-direct product of algebraic groups) because the Jordan decompositions imply that $T \cap G_u = \{e\}$ and $L(T) \cap L(G_u) = 0$.

If G is nilpotent we take $T = G_s$ as in (3). If not then there is an $s \in G_s$ which is not central, so $\dim G^s < \dim G$, where we write $G^s = Z_G(s)$. Moreover it follows from (9.6) that $(G^s)^0 \longrightarrow (G/G_u)^s = G/G_u$ is surjective. Hence we can find the required T in $(G^s)^0$, by induction.

Next we claim:

(*) Suppose $G = T \cdot G_u$ as above. Then every $s \in G_s$ is conjugate by an element of $C^\infty G$ to an element of T.

We prove (*) by induction on dim G. In case G is nilpotent it follows from part (3) above that G_s is the unique maximal torus, so we may assume G is not nilpotent, i.e. that $C^\infty G \neq \{e\}$. Let N be the identity component of the center of $C^\infty G$. Then $N \neq \{e\}$, for $C^\infty G$ is connected and unipotent, and N contains the last non-trivial term of the descending central series of $C^\infty G$, which is also connected (see (2.3)).

Let $\pi : G \longrightarrow G' = G/N$ be the natural projection. Then $G' = T' \cdot G'_u$ (semi-direct) where $T' = \pi(T)$. By induction, there is a $g' \in C^\infty G'$ such that $g'\pi(s)g'^{-1} \in T'$.

Choosing $g \in C^{\infty}G$ such that $\pi(g) = g'$, and replacing s by gsg^{-1}, therefore, we may assume $s \in T \cdot N$. We want to conjugate s into T by an element of N.

Write $s = nt$ with $n \in N$ and $t \in T$. We apply (9.3) to t and N in order to write $n = c_t(u)z$ where $u \in N$, $c_t(u) = utu^{-1}t^{-1}$, and where $z \in Z_N(t)$. Thus $s = utu^{-1}t^{-1}zt = utu^{-1}z$. Since z is unipotent and commutes with t and u, the equation $s = (utu^{-1})z$ is the Jordan decomposition of the semi-simple element s, and hence $z = e$. Thus $u^{-1}su = t \in T$, thus proving (*).

To conclude the proof of the first assertion in (4) suppose T' is another maximal torus in G. Choose $s \in T'$ so that $s^{\alpha} \neq 1$ for all $\alpha \in \Phi_{T'}(G)$. Then it follows from (9.4) that s and T' have centralizers in G with the same connected component of e. Using (*) above we can conjugate s into T with an element of $C^{\infty}G$. Conjugating T' likewise we are reduced to the case, therefore, where $T \subset (G^s)^0 = (G^{T'})^0$. From (*) we conclude that each element of T' is conjugate in $(G^{T'})^0$ to an element of T. But T' is central in $(G^{T'})^0$, so we have $T' \subset T$, and hence $T' = T$, by maximality.

Let $\pi : G \longrightarrow G/G_u$ be the canonical projection. Its restriction to T is an isomorphism of T onto G/G_u. In particular $L(G/G_u)$ consists of semi-simple elements, and (4.4) shows that if $X \in \underline{g}$ is nilpotent, then $X \in \ker d\pi = L(G_u)$. Since $L(G_u)$ consists of nilpotent elements (4.8), this ends the proof of (4).

(5) Let S be a subgroup of G consisting of

semi-simple elements, and let $\pi : G \longrightarrow G/G_u$ be the canonical projection. Then the restriction of π to S is injective, hence S is commutative since G/G_u is. Moreover, if $n \in G$ normalizes S, then $\pi(n)$ centralizes $\pi(S)$, and therefore (since π_S is injective) n centralizes S. This proves that $Z_G(S) = N_G(S)$. The group $\overline{S} = \mathcal{A}(S)$ is a closed diagonalizable subgroup of G, and we have $Z_G(\overline{S}) = Z_G(S)$, which reduces us to the case where S is closed for the proof of the remaining assertions. Let T be a maximal torus of G.

Case 1. S <u>is central</u>. If $s \in S$, some conjugate of s lies in T by (4), so $s \in T$. Thus $S \subset T$ and $G^S = G$ is connected.

Case 2. S <u>is not central</u>. Choose a non central $s \in S$. Replacing T by a conjugate we can assume $s \in T$. Then $T \subset G^s = T \cdot G_u^s$, and (9.3) implies that G_u^s is connected. Therefore G^s is connected, has smaller dimension than G, and contains S. By induction S is conjugate in G^s to a subgroup of T, and $(G^s)^S = G^S$ is connected.

This completes the proof of (5), and hence also of Theorem (10.6).

(10.7) <u>Curves with a connected group of automorphisms</u>. The structure theorem (10.6) has one glaring deficiency; it gives no accounting of groups of dimension one. These appear as the "composition factors" of G_u in part (2) of the theorem.

In fact the only one dimensional connected groups are $\mathbb{GL}_1$ and $\mathbb{G}_a$. This will be shown in (10.9). We shall deduce this fact from the following proposition, which, in turn, is a corollary of the classification of one-dimensional groups.

The proof we give of the proposition uses facts about Jacobians of curves, which are in the spirit of, but outside the framework of, these notes.

PROPOSITION. Let X be a complete, smooth, irreducible algebraic curve. Suppose that a connected group G of dimension $\geqq 1$ operates non trivially on X with a fixed point. Then X is isomorphic to the projective line, $\mathbb{P}_1$.

PROOF. We must show that the genus, gen X of X, is zero. Let $f : X \longrightarrow J$ be the canonical morphism of X into its Jacobian J. (See Lang, Abelian varieties, Ch. II, §2.) J is an abelian variety (= complete connected algebraic group) whose dimension equals gen X, and $f(X)$ generates J. Moreover (loc. cit., Theorem 9) any rational map $h : X \longrightarrow A$, where A is an abelian variety, induces a unique homomorphism $\alpha : J \longrightarrow A$ such that $h(x) = \alpha(f(x)) + a$ for some $a \in A$ independent of $x \in X$. (We are, of course, writing + for the group operation in the abelian varieties here.) In fact this "universal mapping property" clearly determines f up to translation by an element of J. We shall normalize f so that $f(p) = 0$, where $p \in X$ is some fixed point of G (which is assumed to exist).

If $g \in G$ the universal mapping property implies that $f \circ g : X \longrightarrow J$ is of the form $\alpha_g \circ f + a_g$ for some group morphism $\alpha_g : J \longrightarrow J$ and some $a_g \in J$. Evaluating at $p = g(p)$ shows that $a_g = 0$, so $f \circ g = \alpha_g \circ f$. We are now tempted to assert that we have an action $G \times J \longrightarrow J$, giving a connected family of automorphisms of J, and to invoke the rigidity of abelian varieties (cf. (8.10)).

Rather than justify that assertion we argue directly: If $a \in J$ define $\beta_a : G \longrightarrow J$ by $\beta_a(g) = \alpha_g(a)$. In case $a = f(x)$ for some $x \in X$ this is the composite map $G \xrightarrow{\beta_x} X \xrightarrow{f} J$, where $\beta_x(g) = g(x)$, and this is a morphism. In general we can write $a = \Sigma f(x_i)$ for suitable $x_i \in X$ so $\beta_a = \Sigma \beta_{f(x_i)}$ is again a morphism.

Let ${}_mJ = \ker(a \longmapsto ma)$ in J, where m is a positive integer. Then ${}_mJ$ is finite (loc. cit.), and it is clearly stable under each α_g. Hence $\beta_a(G)$ is finite for each $a \in {}_mJ$. Since G is connected and $\beta_a(e) = a$, it follows that $\beta_a(G) = \{a\}$.

Thus, for $g \in G$, $\alpha_g : J \longrightarrow J$ fixes all elements of finite order. But the latter are dense in J (loc. cit), so $\alpha_g = 1_J$.

We conclude that $f : X \longrightarrow J$ is a G-equivariant map with G operating trivially on the right. Hence f collapses each G-orbit in X to a point. Since G acts non trivially on the irreducible curve X some G-orbit must contain an open dense set. The complement of the latter is finite, so X has only finitely many G-orbits.

It follows that J is generated by a <u>finite</u> set f(X). This is clearly impossible unless $J = \{0\}$, i.e. unless $\dim J (= \text{gen } X) = 0$. Q.E.D.

(10.8) <u>The automorphism group of</u> $\mathbb{P}_1$ <u>is</u> $\mathbb{PGL}_2$. We shall write

$$G = \mathbb{PGL}_2 = \mathbb{GL}_2/S ,$$

where

$$S = Z(\mathbb{GL}_2) = \{aI \mid a \in K^*\}$$

is the group of scalar 2×2 matrices. The projection $\mathbb{GL}_2 \longrightarrow G$ will be denoted

$$\begin{pmatrix} a & b \\ c & d \end{pmatrix} \longrightarrow \begin{bmatrix} a & b \\ c & d \end{bmatrix} .$$

In order to avoid confusion the projection

$$\underline{gl}_2 \longrightarrow \underline{g} = \underline{pgl}_2 = \underline{gl}_2/K \cdot I$$

will be denoted

$$\begin{pmatrix} a & b \\ c & d \end{pmatrix} \longrightarrow \begin{bmatrix} a & b \\ c & d \end{bmatrix}_L .$$

Consider the torus $T = \mathbb{D}_2/S$ in G. We have the isomorphism

$$\lambda : \mathbb{GL}_1 \longrightarrow T, \qquad a \longmapsto a^\lambda = \begin{bmatrix} a & 0 \\ 0 & 1 \end{bmatrix} .$$

Let $\alpha \in X(T)$ be such that $\langle \alpha, \lambda \rangle = 1$, i.e. such that $(a^\lambda)^\alpha = a$ for $a \in \mathbb{GL}_1$. Next define

$$u_\alpha, u_{-\alpha} : \mathbb{G}_a \longrightarrow G$$

by

$$u_\alpha(b) = \begin{bmatrix} 1 & b \\ 0 & 1 \end{bmatrix} \quad \text{and} \quad u_{-\alpha}(c) = \begin{bmatrix} 1 & 0 \\ c & 1 \end{bmatrix} .$$

The images of u_α and $u_{-\alpha}$ will be denoted U_α and $U_{-\alpha}$, respectively. A direct calculation shows that

$$\text{(1)} \qquad \begin{aligned} tu_\alpha(b)t^{-1} &= u_\alpha(t^\alpha b), \quad \text{and} \\ tu_{-\alpha}(c)t^{-1} &= u_{-\alpha}(t^{-\alpha}c) \end{aligned}$$

for $t \in T$ and $b, c \in \mathbb{G}_a$. The resulting commutator formulas,

$$(t, u_\alpha(b)) = u_\alpha((t^\alpha - 1)b), \quad \text{and}$$

$$(t, u_{-\alpha}(c)) = u_{-\alpha}((t^{-\alpha} - 1)c) \ ,$$

show that the derived group DG contains U_α and $U_{-\alpha}$. The subgroup generated by U_α and $U_{-\alpha}$ clearly has dimension > 2. Since $\dim G = 3$ and G is connected we conclude:

(2) $G = DG$, <u>and</u> G <u>is generated by</u> U_α <u>and</u> $U_{-\alpha}$.

The Lie algebras $L(T)$, $L(U_\alpha)$, and $L(U_{-\alpha})$ are spanned by

$$(3)\ H = \begin{bmatrix} 1 & 0 \\ 0 & 0 \end{bmatrix}_L, \quad X_\alpha = \begin{bmatrix} 0 & 1 \\ 0 & 0 \end{bmatrix}_L, \quad \text{and} \quad X_{-\alpha} = \begin{bmatrix} 0 & 0 \\ 1 & 0 \end{bmatrix}_L ,$$

respectively. Moreover it follows from (1) that X_α and $X_{-\alpha}$ are semi-invariants of weights α and $-\alpha$, respectively, for T under Ad_G. Therefore

$$\begin{aligned} \underline{g} &= L(T) \oplus L(U_\alpha) \oplus L(U_{-\alpha}) \\ &= \underline{g}^T \oplus \underline{g}_\alpha \oplus \underline{g}_{-\alpha} \end{aligned}$$

is the root space decomposition of $\underline{g}$ relative to the torus T, and

$$\Phi(T, G) = \{\alpha, -\alpha\} .$$

Write the elements of K^2 as column vectors, and denote the projection

$$K^2 - \{0\} \longrightarrow \mathbb{P}_1$$

by

$$\begin{pmatrix} a \\ b \end{pmatrix} \longrightarrow \begin{bmatrix} a \\ b \end{bmatrix} .$$

The action (by left multiplication) of $\mathbb{GL}_2$ on K^2 induces an action of $\mathbb{GL}_2$ on $\mathbb{P}_1$ so that the above projection is equivariant. Since S operates trivially on $\mathbb{P}_1$ we deduce an action of G on $\mathbb{P}_1$ by

$$\begin{bmatrix} a & b \\ c & d \end{bmatrix} \begin{bmatrix} x \\ y \end{bmatrix} = \begin{bmatrix} ax + by \\ cx + dy \end{bmatrix} .$$

Embed K into $\mathbb{P}_1$ by the identification

$$x \longmapsto \begin{bmatrix} 1 \\ x \end{bmatrix} ,$$

and write $\infty = \begin{bmatrix} 0 \\ 1 \end{bmatrix}$, so that

$$\mathbb{P}_1 = K \cup \{\infty\} .$$

We next introduce the open set

$$V = \{(x, y, z) \in (\mathbb{P}_1)^3 \mid x, y, \text{ and } z \text{ are distinct}\}$$

and define

$$\varphi : G \longrightarrow V \text{ by } \varphi(g) = (g(0), g(1), g(\infty)) .$$

Thus φ is just the G-orbit map for $(0, 1, \infty) \in V$.

CONTENTION. φ <u>is an isomorphism of varieties. In particular</u> G <u>operates simply transitively on triples of distinct points</u> in $\mathbb{P}_1$.

If $g = \begin{bmatrix} a & b \\ c & d \end{bmatrix}$ then

$$\varphi(g) = \left(\begin{bmatrix} a \\ c \end{bmatrix}, \begin{bmatrix} a+b \\ c+d \end{bmatrix}, \begin{bmatrix} b \\ d \end{bmatrix} \right) .$$

Thus

(4)
$$\begin{aligned} g(\infty) = \infty &\Longleftrightarrow b = 0 , \\ g(0) = 0 &\Longleftrightarrow c = 0, \text{ and} \\ g(1) = 1 &\Longleftrightarrow a + b = c + d . \end{aligned}$$

Therefore $\varphi(g) = (0, 1, \infty)$ implies $g = \begin{bmatrix} a & 0 \\ 0 & a \end{bmatrix} = e$, so

φ is injective.

To see that φ is surjective suppose we are given $(x, y, z) \in V$. Since $\mathbb{GL}_2$ is clearly doubly transitive on lines in K^2 we can first transform (x, y, z) into an element of the form $(0, \begin{bmatrix} a \\ d \end{bmatrix}, \infty)$. The fact that $\begin{bmatrix} a \\ d \end{bmatrix}$ is distinct from 0 and ∞ means that $a \neq 0 \neq d$. Therefore, we can transform $(0, \begin{bmatrix} a \\ d \end{bmatrix}, \infty)$ to $(0, 1, \infty)$ with $\begin{bmatrix} a & 0 \\ 0 & d \end{bmatrix}^{-1}$.

Finally we must show that $(d\varphi)_e : \underline{g} \longrightarrow T(V)_{(0,1,\infty)}$ is surjective. We have:

$$u_{-\alpha}(c)(0,1,\infty) = (c, 1 + c, \infty) \quad .$$

Since $du_{-\alpha}(1) = X_{-\alpha}$ this yields $(d\varphi)_e(X_{-\alpha}) = (1, 1, 0)$. By symmetry, we have $(d\varphi)_e(X_\alpha) = (0, 1, 1)$. Next we have

$$a^\lambda(0, 1, \infty) = (0, a^{-1}, \infty) \quad .$$

Since $d\lambda(1) = H$, it follows that $(d\varphi)_e(H) = (0, -1, 0)$. Q. E. D.

REMARK. If we worked with $\mathbb{SL}_2$ in place of $\mathbb{GL}_2$ it would still be true that $\mathbb{SL}_2 \longrightarrow \mathbb{PGL}_2$ is surjective. However, it is not separable in characteristic two. We would have to replace T by the image of the group T' of matrices of the form $\mathrm{diag}(a, a^{-1})$ in $\mathbb{SL}_2$. But $L(T')$ is spanned by $\begin{bmatrix} 1 & 0 \\ 0 & -1 \end{bmatrix}$, and $\begin{bmatrix} 1 & 0 \\ 0 & -1 \end{bmatrix}_L$ vanishes in characteristic two.

PROPOSITION. Let H be a k-group acting

k-morphically on $\mathbb{P}_1$. *Then this action is induced by a unique k-morphism* $\alpha : H \longrightarrow \mathbb{P}\mathbb{G}\mathbb{L}_2$.

PROOF. Define $\beta : H \longrightarrow V$ by $\beta(h) = (h(0), h(1), h(\infty))$, and let $\alpha = \varphi^{-1} \circ \beta$. Then $\alpha(h)(i) = h(i)$, $i = 0, 1, \infty$, and α is clearly a k-morphism. To show, finally, that $\alpha(h)$ and h yield the same automorphism of $\mathbb{P}_1$ it suffices to show that an automorphism g of $\mathbb{P}_1$ fixing 0, 1, and ∞ is the identity.

But $K(\mathbb{P}_1) = K(x)$ where x is the unique rational function on $\mathbb{P}_1$ with a zero of order one at 0, a pole of order one at ∞, and no other singularities, and $x(1) = 1$. Since $x \circ g$ must have the same properties we see that g induces the identity on $K(\mathbb{P}_1)$; hence g is the identity.

(10.9) THEOREM. *Let* G *be a connected affine group of dimension one. Then* G *is isomorphic to either* $\mathbb{G}\mathbb{L}_1$ *or to* $\mathbb{G}_a$.

PROOF. G is a dense open set in a unique complete smooth curve $\overline{G}$ (see (AG.18.5(d))). It follows from (AG.18.5(f)) that the action of G on itself by translation extends uniquely to an action of G on $\overline{G}$. Since $\overline{G} - G$ is a finite set stable under the connected group G it follows that G fixes the points of $\overline{G} - G$. Since G is affine the number, m, of such points is > 0. Hence it follows from (10.7) that $\overline{G} \cong \mathbb{P}_1$. Choose an identification of $\overline{G}$ with $\mathbb{P}_1$ so that $\infty \notin G$. Then we obtain from (10.8) an embedding of G into $\mathbb{PGL}_2$ so that G lies in the isotropy group $\left\{\begin{bmatrix} a & 0 \\ c & d \end{bmatrix}\right\}$ of ∞ (see (10.8)(4)). It further follows from (10.8) that G fixes at most two points of $\mathbb{P}_1$, i.e. that $m \leqq 2$.

Case 1. $m = 2$. Choose projective coordinates so that the fixed point other than ∞ is 0. Then G lies in the torus $T \cong \mathbb{GL}_1$ of elements $\left\{\begin{bmatrix} a & 0 \\ 0 & d \end{bmatrix}\right\}$. For dimension reasons $G = T$.

Case 2. $m = 1$. G acts on the affine line $K = \mathbb{P}_1 - \{\infty\}$ by transformations of the form $x \longmapsto ax + c$. These form a solvable group, so G is solvable. Since DG is connected and $\dim DG < \dim G = 1$ we conclude that G is abelian. Write $G = G_s \times G_u$ (see (4.7)). For dimension reasons again, we must have $G = G_s$ or $G = G_u$. If $G = G_s$, then (see (8.4) and (8.5)) G is a one dimensional torus, i.e. $G \cong \mathbb{GL}_1$. Let now $G = G_u$. If $g(x) = a_g x + c_g$ then $g \longmapsto a_g$ is a morphism $G \longrightarrow \mathbb{GL}_1$. It must be trivial because G is unipotent. Hence $g \longmapsto c_g$ gives an embedding $G \longrightarrow \mathbb{G}_a$, and dimension count again shows that this must be an isomorphism.

REMARK. In case $G \cong \mathbb{GL}_1$, it follows from (8.11) that such an isomorphism exists over k_s. Suppose, on the other hand, that $G \cong \mathbb{G}_a$. Let $\overline{G}$ be the complete non-singular curve defined over k containing G. The argument above shows that $\overline{G} - G$ consists of a single point, P, so P must be rational over $L = k^{p^{-\infty}}$. It is known then (see Serre, Corps locaux, Ch. X, §6, Ex. 1) that $\overline{G}$ is isomorphic over L to $\mathbb{P}_1$, and we can choose this isomorphism to carry P to ∞ in $\mathbb{P}_1$. This done, the isomorphism of G with $\mathbb{G}_a$ obtained above can be seen to be rational over L.

(10.10) Group actions on $\mathbb{G}_a$. The points of $\mathbb{G}_a$ and of its Lie algebra $\underline{g}_a$ both coincide with K. An endomorphism of $\mathbb{G}_a$ as a curve is given by an endomorphism of its affine algebra, K[T], and the latter is defined by a polynomial f(T). This will be a group morphism if and only if f is additive: $f(T + H) = f(T) + f(H)$. Let $p = \mathrm{char}(K)$.

(i) If $p = 0$ then $f(T) = cT$ for some $c \in K$.

(ii) If $p > 0$ then $f(T) = \Sigma_i c_i T^{p^i}$.

These follow by applying $\frac{d}{dT}$ to the addition formula to conclude that $f'(T)$ is a constant. Subtracting the linear term from f(T) one obtains, in case (ii), a polynomial $g(T^p)$ and g is additive of lower degree, so induction applies to establish (ii).

In either case it is easily seen that an automorphism of $\mathbb{G}_a$ corresponds to a polynomial $f(T) = cT$ $(c \in K^*)$, and that we thus obtain an isomorphism of $\mathbb{GL}_1$ with the automorphism group of $\mathbb{G}_a$.

If we view $\mathbb{G}_a$ as $\mathbb{P}_1 - \{\infty\}$ and note that group automorphisms fix $0 \in \mathbb{G}_a$, then we can also obtain the automorphism group as the intersection in $\mathbb{PGL}_2$ of the isotropy groups of 0 and ∞. This intersection is the torus $T = \left\{\begin{bmatrix} a & 0 \\ 0 & 1 \end{bmatrix}\right\}$ introduced in (10.8).

Let G be any group acting as automorphisms on $\mathbb{G}_a$. Then it follows from the above remarks that there is a character $\alpha : G \longrightarrow \mathbb{GL}_1$ through which G acts:

$$g(x) = g^{\alpha} x \qquad (g \in G,\ x \in \mathbb{G}_a) \ .$$

For such an action the induced action on $\underline{g}_a$ is clearly given by the same character:

$$g(X) = g^{\alpha} \cdot X, \qquad (g \in G,\ X \in \underline{g}_a) \ .$$

BIBLIOGRAPHICAL NOTE

(10.4) and (10.6) are proved in [1]. The original Lie theorem states that a connected linear solvable Lie group over the complex numbers can be put in triangular form. The generalization to algebraic groups in (10.5) is due to Kolchin [11]. The proof given here is taken from [1].

It seems somewhat surprising that the proof $G \cong \mathbb{GL}_1$, $\mathbb{G}_a$ if G is connected, one-dimensional (10.9) is not more elementary, or at any rate more self-contained. The result has been known for quite a while, of course. However, the author would be hard put to refer to a complete proof antedating the one given by Grothendieck in [8, Exp. 7]. The latter proof is quite different from the one described above, and is much more algebraic. It makes use of some results of §§10, 11, and will be sketched in (11.6).

CHAPTER IV

BOREL SUBGROUPS; REDUCTIVE GROUPS

Throughout this chapter G *denotes a connected affine group, and all algebraic groups are understood to be affine.*

§11. BOREL SUBGROUPS

(11.1) A *Borel subgroup* of G is one which is maximal among the connected solvable subgroups. They clearly exist, for dimension reasons.

THEOREM. *Let* B *be a Borel subgroup of* G. *Then all Borel subgroups are conjugate to* B, *and* G/B *is a projective variety*.

PROOF. Let R be a Borel subgroup of maximal dimension. Choose a faithful representation $\pi : G \longrightarrow GL(V)$ with a line $V_1 \subset V$ such that R is the stability group of V_1 in G and L(R) is the stability Lie algebra of V_1 in

L(G). (See Theorem (5.1).) Applying (10.5) to the induced representation of R on V/V_1, we obtain a flag $F = (V_1, V_2, \ldots, V_n)$ in V stabilized by R. Let $\mathcal{F}(V)$ denote the flag variety of V, on which G operates via π. Then the canonical map from G/R to the orbit, G(F), of F in $\mathcal{F}(V)$ is an isomorphism of varieties. This follows because the map from G/R to the orbit of V_1 in the projective space $\mathbb{P}(V)$ is already an isomorphism of varieties. (See Theorem (6.8) and proof.)

Suppose $F' \in \mathcal{F}(V)$ has stability group R' in G. Since R' leaves a flag invariant, it is solvable. The maximality of dim R therefore implies $\dim R' \leqq \dim R$, and hence $\dim G/R \leqq \dim G/R'$. Thus G(F) is a G-orbit in $\mathcal{F}(V)$ of minimal dimension, so the closed orbit lemma (1.8) implies that G(F) is closed. This proves that G/R is a projective variety.

Letting B operate on G/R, in the natural way, we see, using (10.4), that B has a fixed point, i.e. that $BxR \subset xR$ for some $x \in G$. But this means $x^{-1}BxR \subset R$, hence $x^{-1}Bx \subset R$. Since B is maximal connected solvable, this implies $x^{-1}Bx = R$.

(11.2) A <u>parabolic subgroup</u> P of G is a closed subgroup such that G/P is a complete variety. Since the homogeneous space G/P is always quasi-projective (see (5.7)), it is complete if and only if it is a projective variety.

COROLLARY. <u>A closed subgroup</u> P <u>of</u> G <u>is parabolic</u>

if and only if it contains a Borel subgroup.

PROOF. If P contains a Borel subgroup B then $G/B \longrightarrow G/P$ is a surjective morphism from a complete variety, so G/P is complete. Conversely, by (10.4), a Borel subgroup B has a fixed point in the complete variety G/P, so some conjugate of B lies in P.

(11.3) COROLLARY. (1) The maximal tori in G coincide with the maximal tori in the various Borel subgroups of G, and they are all conjugate.

(2) The maximal connected unipotent subgroups of G are each the unipotent part of a Borel subgroup, and they are all conjugate.

PROOF. (1) A maximal torus T is connected and solvable so it lies in some Borel subgroup B. Evidently it is a maximal torus in B, so (10.6)(4) implies that $B = T \cdot B_u$ (semi-direct), and that all maximal tori of B are conjugate to T. Since any two Borel subgroups are conjugate, part (1) follows.

(2) If U is connected and unipotent then U is nilpotent (see (4.8)), so U lies in a Borel subgroup B. According to (10.6)(2), B_u is a connected subgroup of B, evidently containing U, and hence $U = B_u$ if U is maximal. The conjugacy of the B_u's follows immediately from that of the B's.

(11.4) COROLLARY. (1) If an automorphism a of G fixes

the elements of a Borel subgroup B, *then* a *is the identity*.

(2) *If* $x \in G$ *centralizes* B *then* $x \in Z(G)$.

PROOF. Part (2) follows from (1) with $a = \text{Int}(x)$. To prove (1) consider the morphism $f : G \longrightarrow G$, $f(g) = a(g)g^{-1}$. Then f factors through $G \longrightarrow G/B$, so $f(G)$ is complete, and affine, hence a point (see (10.1)).

(11.5) COROLLARY. *Let* B *be a Borel subgroup of* G.

(1) *If* $B = B_s$, *then* G *is a torus*.

(2) *If* B *contains no torus* $\neq \{e\}$, *then* G *is unipotent*. *In either case* $G = B$.

(3) *The following conditions are equivalent:*

(a) G *has a unique maximal torus*.

(b) *Some maximal torus lies in* $Z(G)$.

(c) G *is nilpotent*.

(d) B *is nilpotent*.

PROOF. (1) Using (10.6)(4), we can write $B = T . B_u$, with T a maximal torus. If $B = B_s$ then $B = T$ is commutative, and hence, by (11.4), central in G. But then G/B is an affine connected group which is also a complete variety, hence $= \{e\}$.

(2) On the other hand, if $T = \{e\}$, so that $B = B_u$ is nilpotent, then $Z_B(B)^0 = H \neq \{e\}$. By (11.4), H is central in G. Since B/H is a unipotent Borel subgroup in G/H we conclude by induction on $\dim G$ that $G/H = B/H$, i.e. that $B = G$.

(3) (a) $\Longrightarrow$ (b). If T is the unique maximal torus, then T is normal in G, and the rigidity of tori (8.10) implies that T is central.

(b) $\Longrightarrow$ (c). If T is a central maximal torus, then let T' be the inverse image in G of a torus in G/T. Since T and T'/T both consist of semi-simple elements, so also does T'. Hence it follows from part (1) above that T' is a torus. (We have used the fact that T' is connected, which follows because T and T'/T are connected.) Now by maximality of T, we must have $T' = T$. In conclusion, this argument shows that G/T contains no non-trivial tori. Hence part (2) above implies that G/T is unipotent, and hence also nilpotent. Since T is central in G, the group G is also nilpotent.

(c) $\Longrightarrow$ (d) is obvious.

(d) $\Longrightarrow$ (a). If B is nilpotent then (10. 6)(3) implies that $B = T \times B_u$ with $T = B_s$, a maximal torus in G. Now $T \subset Z(B)$, and $Z(B) \subset Z(G)$ by (11. 4). Hence T has a unique conjugate (itself), and (a) follows from (11. 3) (1).

COROLLARY. *Suppose* G *contains a normal torus* T *such that* G/T *is also a torus. Then* G *is a torus.*

PROOF. The hypotheses clearly imply that $G = G_s$, so part (1) above implies G is a torus.

(11. 6) COROLLARY. *If* $\dim G \leqq 2$, *then* G *is solvable.*

PROOF. Write $B = T \cdot B_u$ as above. If $B \neq G$ then $\dim B \leqq 1$, so we must have $B = T$ or $B = B_u$. But (11.5) then implies that $G = B$; contradiction.

REMARK. We now sketch the proof of (10.9) given in [8, Exp. 7], alluded to at the end of §10. Let G be one-dimensional. The Corollary above implies that G is solvable. Then $\dim(G, G) < \dim G$, hence G is <u>commutative</u>. By (10.6)(4), we have $G = T \cdot G_u$ where T is a maximal torus. Dimension considerations then show that either $G = T$, in which case $G \cong \mathbb{GL}_1$, or $G = G_u$. It follows from the proof of (10.6)(2) (using an embedding of G in the unipotent part of some $\mathbb{T}_n$) that G admits a non-trivial morphism $\pi : G \longrightarrow \mathbb{G}_a$. Since $\mathbb{G}_a$ is connected of dimension one it follows that π is an isogeny, i.e. that π is surjective and that $N = \ker(\pi)$ is finite.

Let p be the characteristic exponent of K. Then every element of the unipotent group G has order a power of p. It follows that π is an isomorphism if $p = 1$ (i.e. if $\mathrm{char}(K) = 0$). If $p > 1$ then N is a finite group of order p^n for some $n \geqq 0$. One proves that $G \cong \mathbb{G}_a$ by induction on n.

If $n = 0$, i.e. if π is bijective, then, by (AG.18.2), K(G) is a purely inseparable extension of $K(\mathbb{G}_a) = K(x)$. Taking a high $p^{\underline{th}}$ power one concludes that K(G) is isomorphic to a subfield of K(x), so Lüroth's theorem (see e.g. van der Waerden, <u>Algebra</u>, vol. I) implies that K(G) is purely transcendental.

Thus G is, as a variety, isomorphic to an open subset of the projective line, and one concludes the proof by embedding G into $\mathbb{P}\mathbb{G}\mathbb{L}_2$ as in the proof of Theorem (10.9).

If $n > 0$ we can factor out a subgroup of index p in N and apply induction to reduce to the case $n = 1$. We can further use the case $n = 0$ to conclude that $G/N \cong \mathbb{G}_a$ and so arrange that π is separable. In this case $K(G)$ is a galois extension of degree p of $K(x)$, to which one can apply Artin-Schreier theory. (See [8, Exp. 7], Lemme 3, for details.)

(11.7) COROLLARY. Let T be a maximal torus of G. Then $C = Z_G(T)^0$ is nilpotent, and $C = N_G(C)^0$.

The conjugacy theorem (11.3) shows that T is the unique maximal torus of C, therefore (11.5), C is nilpotent. Moreover, T is normal in $N_G(C)$, and consequently by (8.10), T is centralized by $N_G(C)^0$.

(11.8) PROPOSITION. Let $X \in L(G)$. Then X is semi-simple if and only if it is tangent to a torus in G.

A torus is isomorphic to a diagonal group, hence its Lie algebra consists of semi-simple elements, which proves the "if" part of the proposition.

Assume now X to be semi-simple. By (9.1), the Lie algebra $\underline{h}$ of $H = Z_G(X)$ is equal to $\underline{z}_{\underline{g}}(X)$; in particular, it contains X. Let T be a maximal torus of H and $C = Z_H(T)^0$. Then $L(C) = \underline{z}(T)$ by (9.2, Cor.), hence $X \in L(C)$. By (11.7), C is nilpotent, hence $C = T \times C_u$, in view of (10.6). Since $L(C_u)$ consists of nilpotent elements, it follows that $X \in L(T)$.

(11.9) LEMMA. Let H be a closed subgroup of G, and put

$$X = {}^G H = \bigcup_{g \in G} gHg^{-1} .$$

(1) If G/H is complete, then X is closed.

(2) Assume there is an $h \in H$ having only finitely many fixed points in G/H, i.e. such that $\{x \in G \mid h \in xHx^{-1}\}$ constitutes a finite number of cosets of H. Then X contains a dense open set in G.

PROOF. Consider the morphisms

$$G \times G \xrightarrow{\alpha} G \times G \xrightarrow{\beta} (G/H) \times G$$

where $\alpha(x, y) = (x, xyx^{-1})$ and $\beta = \pi \times 1_G$, with $\pi : G \longrightarrow G/H$ the quotient morphism. Put $M = \beta(\alpha(G \times H)) = \{(\pi(x), z) \mid x \in G, x^{-1}zx \in H\}$.

(i) M is closed. If $x^{-1}zx \in H$, then $(xh)^{-1}z(xh) \in H$ for all $h \in H$, so it follows that $\beta^{-1}(M) = \alpha(G \times H)$. Since α is an isomorphism of varieties, and since $\beta : G \times G \longrightarrow (G \times G)/(H \times \{e\})$ is a quotient morphism, and hence open, we conclude that M is closed because $\beta^{-1}(M)$ is closed.

(ii) $X = pr_G(M)$, so X is closed if G/H is complete. For $pr_G(M) = \{y \mid x^{-1}yx \in H$ for some $x \in G\} = X$

(iii) $\dim M = \dim G$ at each point of M.

The fibre over $\pi(x)$ of the surjective morphism $pr_{G/H} : M \longrightarrow G/H$ is isomorphic to xHx^{-1}, so the dimension of each fibre is $\dim H$. Hence $\dim M = \dim G/H + \dim H = \dim G$ at each point.

The fibre of $pr_G : M \longrightarrow G$ over y is

$$\{\pi(x) \mid x^{-1}yx \in H\} = \{\pi(x) \mid y \in xHx^{-1}\} =$$

$$= \{\pi(x) \mid y\cdot\pi(x) = \pi(x)\} .$$

(In the latter, the dot refers to the natural action of G on G/H.) In view of this, the hypothesis of (2) says simply that the fibre of $pr_G : M \longrightarrow G$ over some $h \in H$ is finite (and $\neq \phi$). Therefore, if N is an irreducible component of M such that $h \in pr_G(N)$, the fibres of pr_G in N are "generically finite," i.e. they are each finite over some dense open set in $\overline{pr_G(N)}$ (see (AG.10.1)). Since $\dim N = \dim G$ and G is connected it follows that $pr_G : N \longrightarrow G$ is dominant. Thus X, which contains $pr_G(N)$, contains a dense open set in G.

(11.10) THEOREM. <u>Let</u> B <u>be a Borel subgroup of</u> G, T <u>a maximal torus of</u> G, <u>and</u> $C = Z_G(T)^0$. <u>Then the union of the conjugates of</u> B (<u>resp.</u> B_u, <u>resp.</u> T, <u>resp.</u> C) <u>is</u> G (<u>resp.</u> G_u, <u>resp.</u> G_s, <u>resp. contains a dense open set of</u> G).

By (11.7), C is nilpotent. Since T is a maximal torus, it follows then from (10.6) that $C = T \times C_u$. By

(8.8), there exists $t \in T$ such that $Z(t)^0 = Z(T)^0 = C$. Let $g \in G$ be such that $gtg^{-1} \in C$. Then $gtg^{-1} \in T$, and $Z(gtg^{-1}) \supset Z(T)$. For dimension reasons, we have then $Z(gtg^{-1})^0 = C$, hence $g \in N(C)$. Since $N(C)^0 = C$, by (11.7), it follows that the set of conjugates of t contained in C is finite. This is condition (2) of (11.9), taking C to be the subgroup H, hence ${}^G C$ contains a dense open subset of G. Since C is nilpotent, it is contained in some Borel subgroup B' of G. Then ${}^G B'$ contains a dense open set. But G/B' is complete (11.1), hence (11.9) ${}^G B'$ is closed. Consequently $G = {}^G B'$. By the conjugacy of Borel subgroups, we have also $G = {}^G B$. The remaining part of the theorem then follows from (10.6).

(11.11) COROLLARY. $Z(G)$ <u>is the center of each Borel subgroup</u>. $Z(G)_s$ <u>is the intersection of all maximal tori in</u> G.

PROOF. Let $g \in Z(G)$ and let B be a Borel subgroup. Some conjugate of g lies in B, so $g \in B$, i.e. $Z(G) \subset Z(B)$. The reverse inclusion follows from (11.4).

If $g \in Z(G)_s$ then $g \in B$, as we saw above, and (10.6)(5) implies that g belongs to a maximal torus T in B. Now part (1) of (11.3) implies g belongs to every maximal torus. Thus $Z(G)_s \subset H$, the intersection of all maximal tori. Since H is a closed subgroup of a torus it is a diagonalizable group, and it is clearly normal in G. Hence by rigidity (8.10), H is central in G. With the inclusion proved above this shows that $H = Z(G)_s$, as claimed.

(11.12) COROLLARY. Let S be a subtorus of G and $a \in Z_G(S)$. Then $\{a_s\} \cup S$ is contained in a torus of G. The group $Z_G(S)$ is connected. For any $g \in G$, the element g belongs to $Z_G(g_s)^0$.

PROOF. We show first that $\{a\} \cup S$ is contained in a Borel subgroup of G. Let B be such a group and F the fixed point set of a in G/B, under the natural action. By (11.10), a is contained in a conjugate of B, hence F is not empty. Since S centralizes a, it leaves F stable. By (10.4), S has a fixed point in F, say x. The stability group B' of x is then a Borel subgroup of G containing $\{a\} \cup S$.

This reduces the proof of the first assertion to the case where G is solvable, in which case it follows from (10.6)(5). By (10.6)(5), also, the group $Z_{B'}(S)$ is connected, whence $a \in Z_G(S)^0$, and the second assertion. Let now $g \in G$. By (11.10), g belongs to a Borel subgroup B of G. Then $g \in Z_B(g_s)$. But the latter group is connected (10.6)(5), hence $g \in Z_G(g_s)^0$.

(11.13) DEFINITION. A Cartan subgroup of G is the centralizer of a maximal torus.

The Cartan subgroups of G are connected by (11.12), nilpotent by (11.7), and conjugate to each other by

(11.3). In view of (10.6), the map $T \mapsto Z_G(T)$ is a bijection of the set of maximal tori onto the set of Cartan subgroups, and $Z_G(T) = T \times Z_G(T)_u$. Finally, by (11.10), the union ${}^G C$ of the conjugates of a Cartan subgroup contains a dense open set of G.

(11.14) PROPOSITION. (1) *Let* $\alpha : G \longrightarrow G'$ *be a surjective morphism of algebraic groups, and let* $B = T \cdot B_u$ *be a Borel subgroup of* G, *with* T *a maximal torus. Then* $\alpha(B) = \alpha(T) \cdot \alpha(B_u)$ *is a Borel subgroup of* G', *and every such subgroup is obtained in this way. Moreover* $\alpha(T)$ *is a maximal torus in* G' *and* $\alpha(B_u) = \alpha(B)_u$.

(2) *Let* H *be a connected subgroup of* G *and let* B_0 *be a Borel subgroup of* H. *Then* $B_0 = (H \cap B)^0$ *for some Borel subgroup* B *of* G. *If* H *is normal, the Borel subgroups of* H *are the groups* $(B \cap H)^0$, *where* B *ranges over all Borel subgroups of* G.

The analogous assertions hold for maximal tori and for maximal connected unipotent subgroups.

PROOF. The composite $G \longrightarrow G' \longrightarrow G'/\alpha(B)$ induces a surjective morphism $G/B \longrightarrow G'/\alpha(B)$, so the latter is complete, i.e. $\alpha(B)$ is parabolic. Therefore $\alpha(B)$ contains a Borel subgroup (11.2). But $\alpha(B)$ is connected and solvable, so $\alpha(B)$ is itself a Borel subgroup. The semi-direct product decomposition $\alpha(B) = \alpha(T) \cdot \alpha(B_u)$ and the fact that $\alpha(B_u) = \alpha(B)_u$ follow from the conservation of Jordan decomposition. In particular $\alpha(T)$ is a maximal torus in $\alpha(B)$, and hence also in G'. The conjugacy theorem in G' implies that all Borel subgroups, all maximal tori, and all maximal connected unipotent subgroups of G' are obtained in this way.

(2) Extend the connected solvable group B_0 to a Borel subgroup B of G. Then $B_0 \subset (H \cap B)^0$, and the latter is a connected solvable subgroup of H. Hence it coincides with B_0. The argument for tori and connected unipotent groups is similar.

COROLLARY. _Let_ S _be a torus and_ $f : G \longrightarrow S$ _a surjective morphism. Then any maximal torus_ T _of_ G _contains a torus_ S' _such that_ $f : S' \longrightarrow S$ _is an isogeny._

By the proposition, $f : T \longrightarrow S$ is surjective. By (8.5), Cor., the identity component of $\ker f|_T$ is a direct factor in T, whence the corollary.

(11.15) THEOREM (Chevalley). _If_ P _is a parabolic subgroup, then_ $P = N_G(P)$.

We begin with a group-theoretic lemma.

LEMMA. _Let_ $H \supset M \supset L$ _be groups such that the_ H-_conjugates of_ L _in_ M _coincide with the_ M-_conjugates of_ L. _Then_ $N_H(M) \subset M \cdot N_H(L)$.

PROOF. If $h \in N_H(M)$ then ${}^hL = {}^mL$ for some $m \in M$, so $m^{-1}h \in N_H(L)$, and $h = m(m^{-1}h)$.

First we reduce the theorem to the case of Borel subgroups. For suppose we know it for a Borel subgroup $B \subset P$. By the conjugacy theorem (11.1) in G and P we can apply the lemma to $B \subset P \subset G$ to conclude that $N_G(P) \subset P \cdot N_G(B) = P \cdot B = P$.

Now let B be a Borel subgroup with normalizer N. We can assume B to contain a Cartan subgroup $C = Z_G(T)$ for some maximal torus T (see (11.12)). By the conjugacy theorem for maximal tori (in B and G) we can apply the lemma to $T \subset B \subset G$ to conclude that $N \subset B \cdot N_G(T)$. By rigidity of tori and (11.12) we have $N_G(T)^0 = C \subset B$, so $B \cdot N_G(T)$ is a *finite* union of cosets of B. Hence $N^0 \subset B$, so we have

$$(*) \qquad B = N^0 .$$

The rest of the proof will be based on the following lemma:

LEMMA. *Suppose we are given closed subgroups*

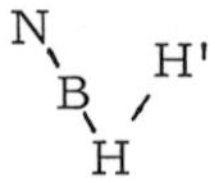

of G, *and an element* $a \in N$, *such that*

(i) H *and* H' *are connected and solvable*;

(ii) *the set of commutators* (a^{-1}, H') *is contained in* H;

(iii) B *is a Borel subgroup and* $N = N_G(B)$.

Then there exists a Borel subgroup B' *containing* H', *whose normalizer* N' *contains* a, *and such that* $a \in B'$ *only if* $a \in B$.

PROOF. Set $D = \{d \in G \mid d^{-1}ad \in N\}$; D is the inverse image of the fixed point set in G/N of a. (See diagram below.) Let D_0 denote the connected component of e in D. Let $\pi : G \longrightarrow G/B$ be the quotient morphism, write $E = \pi(D)$, and let E_0 be the connected component of $\pi(e)$ in E.

$$\begin{array}{ccccc} G & \xrightarrow{\pi} & G/B & \longrightarrow & G/N \\ \cup & & \cup & & \cup \\ D & \longrightarrow & E & \longrightarrow & (G/N)^a \\ \cup & & \cup & & \\ D_0 & \longrightarrow & E_0 & & \end{array}$$

We first claim:

E and E_0 are closed, and $E_0 = \pi(D_0)$.

Since D is the inverse image in G of a closed set in G/N, it follows that $E = \pi(D)$ is the inverse image in G/B of the same set, and hence is closed. Therefore E_0 is also closed. $\pi(D_0) \subset E_0$ because $\pi(D_0)$ is connected. Since B is connected, $d \in D_0 \Longrightarrow dB \subset D_0$, so $D_0 = \pi^{-1}(\pi(D_0)) \subset \pi^{-1}(E_0)$. Since $\pi : \pi^{-1}(E_0) \longrightarrow E_0$ has connected fibres ($\cong B$) it follows that $\pi^{-1}(E_0)$ is connected, and it therefore is contained in D_0. Thus $D_0 = \pi^{-1}(E_0)$, so $\pi(D_0) = \pi(\pi^{-1}E_0) = E_0$.

Now suppose $h \in H'$. Since $a^{-1}hah^{-1} \in H$ we have $hah^{-1} \in aH \subset N \cdot B \subset N$, i.e. $h \in D$. Since H' is connected this implies $H' \subset D_0$. Thus $\pi(H') \subset E_0$, and, since E_0 is closed, $\overline{\pi(H')} \subset E_0$. Since $\overline{\pi(H')}$ is the closure of the orbit $H' \cdot \pi(e)$, it is stable under H', and it is complete because G/B is complete. Since H' is connected and solvable, it has a fixed point in E_0. Since $E_0 = \pi(D_0)$ we can write this fixed point in the form $\pi(d)$, $d \in D_0$. Then we claim that $B' = dBd^{-1}$ answers the requirements of the lemma.

(1) $\pi(d)$ fixed by $H' \Longrightarrow H'dB = dB \Longrightarrow d^{-1}H'd \subset B$
$\Longrightarrow H' \subset dBd^{-1} = B'$.

(2) $d \in D \Longrightarrow d^{-1}ad \in N \Longrightarrow a \in dNd^{-1} = dN_G(B)d^{-1}$
$= N_G(dBd^{-1}) = N_G(B') = N'$.

(3) If $a \in B'$ then $d^{-1}ad \in B$ so the map $D_0 \longrightarrow N$, $g \longmapsto g^{-1}ag$, has a connected image that meets B (because D_0 is connected and $d \in D_0$). Since $B = N^0$ (see (*) above) it follows that the image lies in B. In particular, since $e \in D_0$, $a = e^{-1}ae \in B$.

The above three conclusions verify the conditions of the lemma.

PROOF OF (11.15). B is a Borel subgroup, and we claim that $B = N$, where $N = N_G(B)$. If $a \in N$ then a_s, $a_u \in N$, so it suffices to prove $a \in B$ when a is either semi-simple or unipotent. In either case we can, by the density theorem (11.10), find a connected nilpotent group H containing a. (If $a = a_s$ we can take H to be a maximal torus and, if $a = a_u$, a maximal connected unipotent subgroup.) There is a chain, $\{e\} = H_0 \subset H_1 \subset \dots \subset H_n = H$, of connected normal subgroups of H such that

$(H, H_i) \subset H_{i-1} (1 \leqq i \leqq n)$; in particular
$(a^{-1}, H_i) \subset H_{i-1} (1 \leqq i \leqq n)$.

Put $B_0 = B$ and $N_0 = N$. Then for each $i = 1, 2, \ldots, n$ we can find a Borel subgroup B_i containing H_i, whose normalizer N_i contains a, and such that $a \in B_i$ only if $a \in B_{i-1}$. This follows by induction on i from the lemma above.

At the last step we have $a \in H = H_n \subset B_n$. Hence $a \in B_{n-1}$; hence $a \in B_{n-2}$; ...; hence $a \in B_0 = B$. Q. E. D.

(11.16) <u>The "variety"</u> $\mathcal{B} = \mathcal{B}(G)$ <u>of all Borel subgroups of</u> G. It is first of all a set on which G operates by conjugation. The conjugacy theorem says G acts transitively. The stability group of $B \in \mathcal{B}$ is $N_G(B)$ which, by the normalizer theorem, is just B.

If H is a subgroup of G then its fixed point set in $\mathcal{B}$ is

$$\mathcal{B}^H = \{B \in \mathcal{B} | H \subset B\} ,$$

again because of the normalizer theorem.

Fix $B_0 \in \mathcal{B}$ and let $\pi : G \longrightarrow G/B_0$ be the quotient morphism. If $x = \pi(g)$ then the stability group of x is

$$G_x = \{h | hgB_0 = gB_0\} = \{h | g^{-1}hg \in B_0\} = {}^gB_0 \in \mathcal{B} .$$

Thus we can define

$$\varphi : G/B_0 \longrightarrow \mathcal{B}, \qquad \varphi(x) = G_x .$$

Since $\varphi(\pi(g)) = {}^gB_0$ it follows from the conjugacy theorem that φ is surjective. Moreover $\varphi(\pi(g)) = \varphi(\pi(h)) \Longleftrightarrow {}^gB_0 = {}^hB_0 \Longleftrightarrow g^{-1}h \in N_G(B_0) = B_0$ (normalizer theorem) $\Longleftrightarrow \pi(g) = \pi(h)$. Thus φ is also injective. With the aid of the bijection φ one can therefore give $\mathcal{B}$ the variety structure of G/B_0. Moreover the conjugacy theorem implies that this structure does not depend on the choice of B_0. This follows from the fact that φ is G-equivariant.

For if $g, h \in G$ we have $\varphi(h\cdot \pi(g)) = \varphi(\pi(hg)) = {}^{hg}B_0 = {}^h({}^gB_0) = {}^h\varphi(\pi(g))$. A further consequence of this is that: If H is a subgroup of G then φ induces a bijection

$$(G/B_0)^H \longrightarrow \mathcal{B}^H .$$

Thus the fixed points of H in G/B_0 correspond bijectively to the set of Borel subgroups containing H.

(11.17) COROLLARY. A Borel subgroup B is maximal among the solvable (not necessarily closed or connected) subgroups of G.

PROOF. Suppose $B \subset H \subset G$ with H a solvable subgroup. Then $\bar{H}$ is solvable (see (2.4)) so we can assume H is closed. It then follows that $B = H^0$. Hence $H \subset N_G(B) = B$, by (11.15).

CAUTION. A maximal solvable subgroup need not be a Borel subgroup. For instance, if $G = SO(n)$ and $p \neq 2$, the group of diagonal matrices in G is isomorphic to $(\mathbb{Z}/2\mathbb{Z})^{n-1}$ and not contained in any Borel subgroup.

(11.18) The action of G^T on $(G/B)^T$.

PROPOSITION. Suppose G acts transitively on a variety D with stability groups in $\mathcal{B}$. Let T be a torus in G. Then G^T stabilizes, and acts transitively on, each irreducible component of D^T. If $B \in \mathcal{B}^T$ then B^T is a Borel subgroup of G^T, and the resulting map $\mathcal{B}^T \longrightarrow \mathcal{B}(G^T)$ is surjective.

PROOF. Clearly G^T stabilizes D^T, and hence also each irreducible component of D^T since G^T is connected (11.12). Let X be an irreducible component of D^T and let $B_0 = G_{x_0} \in \mathcal{B}$ be the stability group of some $x_0 \in X$. The orbit map $\pi : G \longrightarrow D$, $\pi(g) = gx_0$, induces a bijective morphism $G/B_0 \longrightarrow D$ so D is complete.

We must show that the inclusion $G^T x_0 \subset X$ is an equality. Since X is connected and since π has connected fibres ($\cong B_0$) it follows that $Y = \pi^{-1}(X)$ is connected. If $y \in Y$ then $\pi(y) \in D^T$ so $y^{-1}Ty \subset B_0$. Let $\alpha : Y \times T \longrightarrow B_0/(B_0)_u$ be the composite of $(y, t) \longmapsto y^{-1}ty$ with the projection $B_0 \longrightarrow B_0/(B_0)_u$. The rigidity of tori (8.10) implies now that $\alpha(y, t)$ is independent of y. Since $T \subset B_0$ we have $e \in Y$ and hence for $y \in Y$ we have $y^{-1}ty \equiv t \bmod (B_0)_u$ for all $t \in T$. Thus $y^{-1}Ty \subset T \cdot (B_0)_u$. The latter is connected so the conjugacy of its maximal tori implies that $y^{-1}Ty = g^{-1}Tg$ for some $g = tb \in T\cdot(B_0)_u$, and we can replace g by b. If $s \in T$ then, modulo $(B_0)_u$, we have $y^{-1}sy \equiv s \equiv b^{-1}sb$. But $y^{-1}Ty \longrightarrow B_0/(B_0)_u$ is injective, so the congruence implies $y^{-1}sy = b^{-1}sb$, i.e. that $yb^{-1} \in G^T$. Thus $\pi(y) = yx_0 = yb^{-1}x_0 \in G^T x_0$ (because $b \in B_0 = G_{x_0}$). Thus $G^T x_0$ contains $\pi(Y) = X$, as claimed. Since X is complete (being a closed set in D), it follows from (AG.18.3) that $G^T/B_0{}^T$ is complete, for we have a bijective morphism $G^T/B_0{}^T \longrightarrow X$. But $B_0{}^T$ is connected and solvable, so $B_0{}^T \in \mathcal{B}(G^T)$. It follows from (11.14) that every Borel subgroup of G^T has this form.

COROLLARY. <u>If</u> G^T <u>is solvable then</u> $\mathcal{B}^T$ <u>is finite, and every</u> $B \in \mathcal{B}^T$ <u>contains</u> G^T. <u>This occurs, for example, if</u> T <u>is a maximal torus</u>.

PROOF. Let $D = G/B$ for some $B \in \mathcal{B}$. The orbits of G^T on the complete variety D^T are the irreducible components, by the proposition. But if G^T is solvable then the fixed point theorem (10.4) implies G^T has a fixed point in each component, so each of the latter reduces to a point, and D^T is finite. Now $x \longmapsto G_x$ is a bijection $D^T \longrightarrow \mathcal{B}^T$, and each such G_x contains G^T. The last assertion follows from (11.13)(2).

(11.19) <u>Simple transitivity of the Weyl group</u>. If T is a torus in G then

$$W = W(T, G) = N_G(T)/Z_G(T) ,$$

is called the Weyl group of G relative to T. The Weyl groups of maximal tori are isomorphic, by virtue of the conjugacy of maximal tori, and they are called, simply, "Weyl groups of G."

We know from the rigidity of tori that $Z_G(T) = N_G(T)^0$, so W is a finite group.

PROPOSITION. Assume T is a maximal torus in G.

(a) A Borel subgroup containing T also contains $Z_G(T)$.

(b) Via conjugation by $N_G(T)$, the Weyl group W acts simply transitively on the set $\mathcal{B}^T$ of Borel subgroups containing T. In particular card $\mathcal{B}^T = [W : 1]$ is finite.

PROOF. (a) follows from (11.18) Corollary.

(b) $N_G(T)$ operates by conjugation on $\mathcal{B}^T$, and part (a) implies that G^T operates trivially; therefore W operates. Suppose $B, B' \in \mathcal{B}^T$. We can write $B = {}^gB'$ for some $g \in G$. Then T and ${}^gT$ are maximal tori in B, so ${}^gT = {}^bT$ for some $b \in B$. Thus $g = bn^{-1}$ with $n = g^{-1}b \in N_G(T)$. Now $B' = {}^{g^{-1}}B = {}^{nb^{-1}}B = {}^nB$. This proves that $N_G(T)$ (and hence W) acts transitively on $\mathcal{B}^T$.

Suppose now that $n \in N_G(T)$ and ${}^nB = B$, i.e. $n \in N_B(T)$. Simple transitivity of W then requires that we show that $n \in G^T$. Since $n \in B$ this follows from (10.6)(5).

REMARK. We shall see in §13 that the Borel subgroups containing T generate G.

(11.20) PROPOSITION. *Let* $\alpha : G \longrightarrow G'$ *be a surjective morphism of algebraic groups, and let* T *be a maximal torus in* G. *Then* $T' = \alpha(T)$ *is a maximal torus in* G', *and* α *induces surjective maps*

$$(1) \qquad \mathcal{B}^{T} \longrightarrow \mathcal{B}'^{T'}, \qquad (\mathcal{B}' = \mathcal{B}(G')) ,$$

$$(2) \qquad W(T, G) \longrightarrow W(T', G') .$$

If the kernel of α *lies in every Borel subgroup of* G, *then* (1) *and* (2) *are bijective.*

PROOF. It follows from (11.14) that T' is a maximal torus in G', and that $\mathcal{B} \longrightarrow \mathcal{B}'$ is surjective. If $B' \in \mathcal{B}'^{T'}$ then every Borel subgroup of $\alpha^{-1}(B')^0$ is a Borel subgroup of G mapping onto B', and one of them contains the maximal torus $T \subset \alpha^{-1}(B')^0$. This shows that (1) is surjective.

Choose $B \in \mathcal{B}^T$ and put $B' = \alpha(B)$. Writing W and W' for the two Weyl groups we obtain a commutative square

$$(3) \qquad \begin{array}{ccc} W & \xrightarrow{(2)} & W' \\ \downarrow & & \downarrow \\ \mathcal{B}^{T} & \xrightarrow[(1)]{} & \mathcal{B}'^{T'} \end{array} ,$$

where the verticals are the orbit maps $w \longmapsto {}^{w}B$ and

$w' \mapsto {}^{w'}B'$, respectively. According to (11.18) the latter are bijective, so the surjectivity of (2) follows from that of (1).

Finally, if $\ker(\alpha)$ is contained in every Borel subgroup then $\mathcal{B} \longrightarrow \mathcal{B}'$ is injective, and hence (1) is injective. The argument above with diagram (3) then shows that (2) is also injective.

(11.21) The radicals; reductive and semi-simple groups. The group

$$R(G) = \Big(\bigcap_{B \in \mathcal{B}} B\Big)^0$$

is called the radical of G. It is evidently a connected solvable normal subgroup of G, and it contains all other such subgroups. Its unipotent part

$$R(G)_u \quad \text{(sometimes denoted } R_u(G)) \quad ,$$

is called the unipotent radical of G. It is a connected unipotent normal subgroup of G, and it contains all other such subgroups. This follows from the analogous property of R(G).

One says that G is semi-simple if $R(G) = \{e\}$, and reductive if $R_u(G) = \{e\}$. Evidently $G/R(G)$ is semi-simple, and $G/R_u(G)$ is reductive, and these are the largest quotient groups of G with these properties.

By considering the derived series in R(G) and the descending central series in $R_u(G)$ we see that: G is semi-simple (resp., reductive) if and only if G has no connected abelian (resp., unipotent abelian) normal subgroups $\neq \{e\}$.

PROPOSITION. _If_ G _is reductive then_ $R(G) = Z(G)^0$, _and this group is a torus._

PROOF. Evidently $R(G) \supset Z(G)^0$. Since G is reductive we have $R(G) = R(G)_s$, so (10.6) implies that R(G) is a torus. By rigidity of tori, a normal torus in a connected group is central, and so $R(G) \subset Z(G)^0$. Q.E.D.

BIBLIOGRAPHICAL NOTE

Up to (11.14), and except for (11.8), the results of this paragraph are proved in [1]. The terminology, however, was introduced later in [8], and was kindly used by the note-taker. Most of the other results of this paragraph are due to Chevalley [8]. In particular, the proof of (11.15) is essentially the one of [8, Exp. 9]. The variety $\mathcal{B}$ of (11.16) can be introduced in an intrinsic way, and can be defined over k, even if it has no element defined over k, (see [3, §7] or [9, Exp. 12]).

§12. CARTAN SUBGROUPS; REGULAR ELEMENTS

(12.1) _Properties of Cartan subgroups._ Recall from (11.13) that a _Cartan subgroup_ of G is the centralizer of a maximal torus in G.

THEOREM. (a) The Cartan subgroups are all conjugate.

(b) Their union contains a dense open set in G.

Let C be a Cartan subgroup.

(c) $C = N_G(C)^0$.

(d) $C = C_s \times C_u$, where $T = C_s$ is a maximal torus in G, the unique one contained in C, and $C = G^T$.

(e) C is a connected nilpotent group, and it is maximal among such subgroups of G.

PROOF. (a) to (d) have already been proved in (11.7), (11.13).

It remains to show that C is maximal connected nilpotent in G. By virtue of (c) this follows from the following lemma, reminiscent of its analogue for finite groups.

LEMMA. If G is nilpotent and H is a proper closed subgroup then $\dim H < \dim N_G(H)$.

For the application above take $H = C$ and, for G, a connected nilpotent subgroup properly containing C.

PROOF. Let $Z = Z(G)^0$. If $Z \not\subset H$ then the conclusion follows because $ZH \subset N_G(H)$. If not we apply induction on dimension to H/Z in G/Z, the inverse image of whose normalizer is $N_G(H)$.

(12.2) Regular elements; rank. The dimension of a Cartan subgroup of G is called the rank of G. If $g \in G$ then g_s

belongs to a maximal torus T so $\dim Z_G(g_s) \geqq \dim G^T = $ = rank G, and we call g <u>regular</u> if the former is an equality. Thus g is regular if and only if g_s is regular.

The set of regular elements of G will be denoted G_{reg}. An element in $G - G_{reg}$ is called <u>singular</u>.

LEMMA. *Let T be a maximal torus in G. The following conditions on a $t \in T$ are equivalent:*

(a) t *is regular*; (b) $Z_G(t)^0 = G^T$; (c) $t^\alpha \neq 1$ *for all roots* $\alpha \in \Phi(T, G)$.

PROOF. Since G^T is a connected subgroup of $Z_G(t)$ the equivalence of (a) and (b) follows by dimension count. The equivalence of (b) and (c) follows from (9.4).

It follows from (c) that *the regular elements in* T *form a dense open set in* T. In particular regular elements exist.

PROPOSITION. *The following conditions on a semi-simple element* $g \in G$ *are equivalent:*

(1) g *is regular.*

(2) $Z(g)^0$ *is a Cartan subgroup.*

(3) $Z(g)^0$ *is nilpotent.*

(4) g *belongs to a unique maximal torus.*

(5) g *belongs to only finitely many maximal tori.*

PROOF. Let T be a maximal torus containing g. Then (1) $\Longleftrightarrow$ (2) follows from (a) $\Longleftrightarrow$ (b) in the Lemma, and (2) $\Longrightarrow$ (3) is (12.1)(e).

Since a connected nilpotent group contains a unique maximal torus ((10.6)(3)), it follows that (3) $\Longrightarrow$ (4). Moreover (4) $\Longrightarrow$ (5) is obvious.

Let $H = Z_G(g)^0$ Condition (5) implies, by virtue of the conjugacy of maximal tori in H, that $H/N_H(T)$ is a finite connected variety, hence a single point. Thus T is normal in the connected group H. By rigidity (8.10), T is central in H, i.e. $H \subset G^T$. But $G^T \subset Z_G(g)^0$ so $G^T = H$. This proves that (5) implies (2), and hence completes the proof.

(12.3) THEOREM. (1) An element $g \in G$ is regular if and only if it belongs to a unique Cartan subgroup.

(2) G_{reg} contains a dense open set in G.

PROOF. (1) Suppose g is regular. Then g_s belongs to a unique Cartan subgroup $C = Z_G(g_s)^0$ (see (12.2)), and (11.12) implies $g \in C$. If C' is a Cartan subgroup containing g then $g_s \in C'_s$ so $C' = Z_G(C'_s)$ (see (12.1)(d)) is contained in $Z_G(g_s)$, and hence equals C.

Suppose, conversely, that g belongs to a unique Cartan subgroup C. Since $g_s \in C_s \subset Z(C)$ it follows that $H = Z_G(g_s)^0$ contains C, and C is clearly then a Cartan subgroup of H. The others are conjugate in H to C and hence contain $g_s \in Z(H)$. Since g lies in a unique one, the same is therefore true of $g_u = g_s^{-1}g$. Now the regularity of g_s, and hence of g, follows, in view of (12.2), from the:

LEMMA. Suppose a connected group H has a unipotent element h belonging to a unique Cartan subgroup C. Then H is nilpotent.

PROOF. Write $C = H^T$ with T a maximal torus, and embed C in a Borel subgroup $B = T \cdot B_u$. It suffices, by (11.5)(3), to show that B is nilpotent. This will follow by showing that $B \subset C$, which, in turn, results if $B_u \subset C$. Let $B_u = N_m \supset N_{m-1} \supset \dots \supset N_0 = \{e\}$ be the descending central series of B_u. We will show, by induction on i, that $N_i \subset C$, and we may assume $i > 0$, clearly. If $x \in N_i$ then $h^{-1}xhx^{-1} \in N_{i-1}$ because $h \in B_u$, so $xhx^{-1} \in hN_{i-1} \subset C$, by induction. Thus $N_i \subset N_H(C)$, so $N_i \subset N_H(C)^0 = C$ because N_i is connected. This completes the proof of the lemma.

(2) Let $C = G^T = T \times C_u$ be a Cartan subgroup, and let $T_0 = \{t \in T \mid t^\alpha \neq 1$ for all $\alpha \in \Phi(T, G)\}$. Then $C_0 = T_0 \times C_u$ is open dense in C, and the Lemma of (12.2) implies that $C_0 = C \cap G_{reg}$. Since every regular element belongs to a Cartan subgroup it follows that G_{reg} is the image of the morphism

$$f : G \times C_0 \longrightarrow G, \quad f(g, c) = gcg^{-1} .$$

Since $C_0 \subset \text{im}(f) = G_{reg}$ it follows that $C = \bar{C}_0 \subset \bar{G}_{reg}$. Since $\bar{G}_{reg}$ is stable under conjugation it therefore contains ${}^G C$, and (12.1)(b) implies the latter is dense in G. Since $G \times C_0$ is irreducible it follows that f is dominant. Thus $G_{reg} = im(f)$ contains a dense open set.

(12.4) PROPOSITION. Let $\alpha : G \longrightarrow G'$ be a surjective morphism of algebraic groups.

(1) The Cartan subgroups of G' are the images of those in G.

(2) $\alpha(G_{reg}) \subset G'_{reg}$.

PROOF. (1) Let $C = G^T$ be a Cartan subgroup of G. By conjugacy, it suffices to show that $\alpha(C)$ is a Cartan subgroup of G'. But $T' = \alpha(T)$ is a maximal torus (11.14) and it follows from (9.6) and (11.12) that $G^T \longrightarrow G'^{T'}$ is surjective.

(2) If $g \in G_{reg}$ and $t = g_s$ then $\alpha(t) = \alpha(g)_s$, and (9.6) implies that $Z_G(t)^0 \longrightarrow Z_{G'}(\alpha(t))^0$ is surjective. Since $Z_G(t)^0$ is a Cartan subgroup, part (1) implies that $Z_{G'}(\alpha(t))^0$ is one also, so $\alpha(g)$ is regular.

(12.5) PROPOSITION. Let H be a not necessarily connected nilpotent algebraic group, and let $T = (H^0)_s$ be the maximal torus in H^0 (cf. (10.6)(3)). Then T is central in H.

PROOF. Since $H^0 = T \times (H^0)_u$ (see (10.6)(3)) it follows that T is central in H^0 and normal in H. Consider the isomorphism,

$$X_* : \mathrm{End}_{\text{alg.grp.}}(T) \longrightarrow \mathrm{End}_{\mathbb{Z}\text{-mod}}(X_*(T)) \quad ,$$

of endomorphism rings (see (8.3) and (8.6)). If $h \in H$

write $I(h)$ for $Int(h)$ on T, and $x(h)$ for $X_*(I(h))$. If we think of T additively, then commutating with h, i.e. $t \longmapsto (h, t) = hth^{-1}t^{-1}$, is the endomorphism $I(h) - id$. Since H is nilpotent, it follows that $I(h) - id$, and hence $x(h) - id$, are nilpotent, i.e. $x(h)$ is unipotent. Thus $x(H)$, being an image of H/H^0, is a finite unipotent group in $Aut_{\mathbb{Z}\text{-mod}}(X_*(T)) \cong \mathbb{GL}_n(\mathbb{Z})$ for some $n \geq 0$. But in characteristic zero, there are no non-trivial unipotents of finite order (see, e.g., (7.2)). Thus $x(H) = \{id\}$, and this implies that H centralizes T.

(12.6) Chevalley's definition of a Cartan subgroup. It is condition (2) of the following theorem. Its interest is that it makes sense for an abstract group.

THEOREM. *The following conditions on a (not necessarily closed) subgroup C of G are equivalent:*

(1) *C is a Cartan subgroup.*

(2) (a) *C is a maximal nilpotent subgroup; and*

(b) *every subgroup of finite index in C has finite index in its normalizer (in G).*

(3) *C is a closed connected nilpotent subgroup, and* $C = N_G(C)^0$.

PROOF. (1) $\Longrightarrow$ (2). If H is a nilpotent group containing $C = Z_G(T)$, we can assume H to be closed. Since T is a maximal torus in G it is also one in H^0, so (12.5) implies that $T \subset Z(H)$, i.e. $H \subset Z_G(T) = C$.

If H is a subgroup of finite index in C then H is dense in C, because C is connected. Hence $N_G(H) \subset N_G(C)$. But $N_G(C)^0 = C$, by (12.1), hence the chain $H \subset C \subset N_G(C)$ shows that H has finite index in $N_G(H)$.

(1) $\Longrightarrow$ (3) is contained in (12.1).

(3) $\Longrightarrow$ (1). Write $C = S \times C_u$ with $S = C_s$. Embed C in a Borel subgroup B, and let T be a maximal torus in B containing S; then $B = T \cdot B_u$. Put $M = Z_B(S)$. Then M is connected (11.12) and $M = T \cdot M_u$, clearly. Now S is central in M, so $S \cdot M_u$ is connected nilpotent, and contains C. Since, by hypothesis, $C = N_G(C)^0$, it follows from the lemma in (12.1) that $S \cdot M_u = C$. Since M is connected and solvable we have $(M, M) \subset M_u \subset C$, so C is normal in M. But $C = N_G(C)^0$ and M is connected, so $C = M$. Thus $C \supset T$, hence $S = T$, and $C = Z_B(T)$ is a Cartan subgroup of B, therefore also of G.

(2) $\Longrightarrow$ (1). Suppose $C \subset G$ satisfies (a) and (b). Since $\overline{C}$ is nilpotent whenever C is, (a) implies that C is closed. Now (b) implies that C^0 has finite index in $N_G(C^0)$, so we have $C^0 = N_G(C^0)^0$. Since C^0 is nilpotent it follows from (3) $\Longrightarrow$ (1) that C^0 is a Cartan subgroup of G. But then (1) $\Longrightarrow$ (2) implies C^0 to be maximal nilpotent, so $C^0 = C$.

BIBLIOGRAPHICAL NOTE

Chevalley's "abstract group theoretic" definition

of Cartan subgroups is given in [7b], where Cartan subgroups are studied in characteristic zero. For the results of this section, see [1].

§13. THE BOREL SUBGROUPS CONTAINING A GIVEN TORUS

If H is a closed connected subgroup of G then the set $\mathcal{B}^H$ of Borel subgroups containing H is empty unless H is solvable. When it is not empty we shall write

$$I(H) = I_G(H) = (\bigcap_{B \in \mathcal{B}^H} B)^0 .$$

If T is a maximal torus then, since $I(T)$ is connected solvable, we can write $I(T) = T \cdot I(T)_u$. The main objective of this paragraph is to prove that $I(T)_u$ is the unipotent radical $R_u(G)$ (see (13.16)) of G.

This fact has several important consequences for reductive groups. Together with some information on groups of "semi-simple rank 1" in (13.14), it goes a long way toward showing (in (13.18)) that $\Phi(T, G)$ is a root system when G is reductive. The final proof of this fact in (14.8) requires further information about actions of tori on unipotent groups.

A further consequence is the construction of the "big cell" associated with a pair of "opposite" Borel subgroups (see (14.1)).

(13.1) Regular, semi-regular, and singular tori. Let S be a torus in G.

S is regular if S contains a regular element. Thus maximal tori are regular (see proof of (12.3)).

S is semi-regular if $\mathcal{B}^S$ is finite.

S is singular if $\mathcal{B}^S$ is infinite.

Let S be regular. Then, if $s \in S$ is regular, $\dim Z_G(s) \leqq \dim Z_G(t)$ for any $t \in S$. On the other hand (8.18), there exists $t \in S$ such that $Z_G(t) = Z_G(S)$. Since the centralizer of S is connected (11.12), it follows that $Z_G(S) = Z_G(s)^0$ if and only if $s \in S$ is regular. In particular G^S is then a Cartan subgroup, and is nilpotent. The proposition below implies therefore that regular tori are semi-regular.

If $\lambda : \mathbf{GL}_1 \longrightarrow G$ is a one-parameter subgroup then we shall call λ a regular, semi-regular, or singular parameter if the torus $S = \mathrm{im}(\lambda)$ has the corresponding property.

In the next proposition S is a torus in G and $X = G/B$ for some $B \in \mathcal{B}$. We know then (see (11.16)) that there is a natural bijection between $\mathcal{B}^S$ and X^S.

PROPOSITION. The following conditions are equivalent:

(1) S is semi-regular.

(2) S has an isolated fixed point in X. (I.e. X^S has a connected component with one point).

(3) G^S is solvable.

(4) $G^S \subset I(S)$.

PROOF. (1) $\Longrightarrow$ (2) is obvious since X^S is finite and non-empty.

(2) $\Longrightarrow$ (3). G^S is connected (11.12) and leaves X^S stable, so it stabilizes the connected components of X^S. If one of these components is reduced to a point then that point is fixed by G^S. The corresponding Borel subgroup contains G^S, so G^S is solvable.

(3) $\Longrightarrow$ (1) and (4) follows from ((11.18), Cor.).

(4) $\Longrightarrow$ (3) is clear because $I(S)$ is solvable.

COROLLARY. Let H be a connected subgroup of G containing S. If S is regular (resp., semi-regular) in G then it is likewise in H.

PROOF. H^S is nilpotent (resp., solvable) as soon as the larger group G^S is nilpotent (resp., solvable).

(13.2) Singular subtori, and roots. We fix a semi-regular torus T. If $\alpha \in X(T)$ is not zero, then $T_\alpha = (\ker \alpha)^0$ is a subtorus of codimension 1.

We shall denote the roots of G relative to T by Φ in place of the usual $\Phi(T, G)$. Thus

$$\underline{g} = \underline{g}^T \oplus \coprod_{\alpha \in \Phi} \underline{g}_\alpha .$$

Consider also the subset $\Psi = \Phi(T, G/I(T))$. Recall from (8.16) that, if one writes $\underline{g}_\alpha = L(I(T))_\alpha \oplus \underline{g}'_\alpha$, then Ψ is the set of α for which $\underline{g}'_\alpha \neq 0$. These are the "roots of G outside of $I(T)$." Moreover, since

$G^T \subset I(T)$, and hence $\underline{g}^T \subset L(I(T))$, we have

$$\underline{g} = L(I(T)) \oplus \coprod_{\alpha \in \Psi} \underline{g}'_\alpha .$$

PROPOSITION. (1) The following conditions on a subtorus S of T are equivalent: (a) S is singular; (b) $S \subset T_\alpha$ for some $\alpha \in \Psi$; (c) $G^S \not\subset I(T)$.

(2) If $\lambda \in X_*(T)$, then λ is semi-regular if and only if $\langle \alpha, \lambda \rangle \neq 0$ for all $\alpha \in \Psi$.

An immediate consequence of (1) is:

COROLLARY. A singular subtorus of T is contained in a singular subtorus of codimension 1.

PROOF. (1) (a) $\Longleftrightarrow$ (c). If S is semi-regular then $G^S \subset I(S)$ (condition (4) of (13.1)) and clearly $I(S) \subset I(T)$. Conversely if $G^S \subset I(T)$ then, G^S is solvable (condition (3) of (13.1)), so S is semi-regular.

Now the equivalence of (b) and (c) is just the equivalence of 2(a) and 2(c) in Proposition (9.4). We take $I(T)$ for the H in that proposition, and use the fact that G^S is connected (11.12).

(2) is just the equivalence of (a) and (b) applied to $S = \mathrm{im}(\lambda)$.

(13.3) Actions of one-parameter groups at 0 and ∞. We shall write

$$\mathbb{P}_1 = \mathbb{GL}_1 \cup \{0\} \cup \{\infty\}, \quad \text{(disjoint union)}$$

with the following convention: The coordinate ring of $\mathbb{GL}_1$ is $K[\chi, \chi^{-1}]$, and $\mathbb{P}_1$ is covered by the affine lines with coordinate rings $K[\chi]$ and $K[\chi^{-1}]$. The points 0 and ∞ correspond to the loci "$\chi = 0$" and "$\chi^{-1} = 0$," respectively, in these open sets. The character χ is the identity map of $\mathbb{GL}_1 = K^*$.

Suppose $f : \mathbb{GL}_1 \longrightarrow Y$ is a morphism into a complete variety. Then it follows from (AG. 18. 5(f)) that f extends uniquely to a morphism $f : \mathbb{P}_1 \longrightarrow Y$. Thus we may speak of $f(0)$ and $f(\infty)$.

Now suppose we have a linear representation of G on a vector space V, and let $\lambda : \mathbb{GL}_1 \longrightarrow T$ be a one-parameter group in a torus T in G. Then G, and hence $\mathbb{GL}_1$, operates on the projective space $\mathbb{P}(V)$. If $x \in \mathbb{P}(V)$ then $f : \mathbb{GL}_1 \longrightarrow \mathbb{P}(V)$, $f(t) = \lambda(t)x$, extends as above to $\mathbb{P}_1$. In place of $f(0)$ and $f(\infty)$, in this case, we shall write

$$\lambda(0)x \quad \text{and} \quad \lambda(\infty)x \ .$$

To determine these points, choose a basis $e_1, \ldots, e_n$ of V such that e_i is an eigenvector, say with character α_i, for T; let $\langle \alpha_i, \lambda \rangle = m_i$ (see (8. 6)). Then if $v = \Sigma a_i e_i \in V$ and if $t \in \mathbb{GL}_1$ we have

$$\lambda(t)v = \Sigma a_i t^{m_i} e_i \ .$$

Assume $v \neq 0$, and let $I = \{i \mid a_i \neq 0\}$. Let $\underline{J}$ be the set of $i \in I$ such that m_i takes the minimal value, $m = \min m_i (i \in I)$. Similarly let $\bar{J}$ be the set of $i \in I$ such that m_i takes the maximum value $M = \max m_i (i \in I)$. If $[v] \in \mathbb{P}(V)$ denotes the image of v under the projection $\pi : V - \{0\} \longrightarrow \mathbb{P}(V)$ then we have, for any $t \in \mathbb{GL}_1$, $[v] = [t^{-m}v] = [t^{-M} v]$. Define morphisms

$$g_m : \mathbb{GL}_1 \cup \{0\} \longrightarrow V - \{0\}$$

by

$$g_m(t) = \Sigma_i a_i t^{m_i - m} e_i ,$$

$$g_M : \mathbb{GL}_1 \cup \{\infty\} \longrightarrow V - \{0\}$$

by

$$g_M(t) = \sum_{i \in I} a_i t^{m_i - M} e_i .$$

Since $m_i - M \leqq 0 \leqq m_i - m$ for all $i \in I$, both formulas make sense (at 0 and ∞, resp.) and they give non-zero vectors of V. If $t \in \mathbb{GL}_1$, then $g_m(t) = t^{-m} \lambda(t)v$ and $g_M(t) = t^{-M} \lambda(t)v$. Thus the morphism $f : t \longmapsto [\lambda(t)v]$ coincides with both $\pi \circ g_m$ and $\pi \circ g_M$. The former of these two gives the extension of f to $t = 0$, and the latter to $t = \infty$. Explicitly, we have

$$\lambda(0)[v] = [\Sigma_{j \in \underline{J}} a_j e_j]$$

$$\lambda(\infty)[v] = [\Sigma_{j \in \bar{J}} a_j e_j] .$$

It is clear from these formulas that:

$$\lambda(0)[v] = \lambda(\infty)[v]$$

$\Longleftrightarrow \underline{J} = \bar{J}$

$\Longleftrightarrow m = M$ (i.e. all $m_i (i \in I)$ are equal)

$\Longleftrightarrow v$ is an eigenvector of $\mathbb{G}\mathbb{L}_1$ under λ

$\Longleftrightarrow [v]$ is a fixed point of $\mathbb{G}\mathbb{L}_1$ under the action induced by λ.

In case λ is such that $m_i = \langle \alpha_i, \lambda \rangle$ are distinct for distinct $\alpha_i (1 \leqq i \leqq n)$, then the eigenvectors of $\mathbb{G}\mathbb{L}_1$ (under λ) coincide with the eigenvectors of T. In this case, therefore, $\lambda(0)[v] = \lambda(\infty)[v]$ if and only if $[v]$ is a fixed point of T.

(13.4) PROPOSITION. Let T be a torus with a linear representation on a vector space V. Let Y be a closed set of dimension $\geqq 1$ in $\mathbb{P}(V)$, which is stable under T. Then T has at least two fixed points in Y.

PROOF. Let $\alpha_1, \ldots, \alpha_n$ be the distinct characters of T in V. We can choose $\lambda \in X_*(T) \cong \text{Hom}(X(T), \mathbb{Z})$ (see (8.6)) so that the $m_i = \langle \alpha_i, \lambda \rangle$ are all distinct. Then $\mathbb{G}\mathbb{L}_1$ (via λ) and T have the same eigenvectors in V, and hence the same fixed points in $\mathbb{P}(V)$. Thus we may, without loss, assume that $T = \mathbb{G}\mathbb{L}_1$.

If $Y^T = Y$ then Y^T is infinite since $\dim Y \geqq 1$. If not choose a $v \in V - \{0\}$ which projects under $\pi : V - \{0\} \longrightarrow \mathbb{P}(V)$ to a point x of Y not fixed by T.

Since Y is closed it contains the points $\lambda(0)x$ and $\lambda(\infty)x$ which are fixed by T (see (13.3)). Moreover, since x is not fixed by T it follows also from (13.3) that these fixed points are distinct. Q.E.D.

(13.5) COROLLARY. If $P \subsetneq G$ is a parabolic subgroup, and if T is a torus in G, then T has at least two fixed points on G/P.

PROOF. According to (5.1) (cf. also the proof of (6.8)) we can choose a linear representation $G \longrightarrow GL(V)$ and an $x \in \mathbb{P}(V)$ so that $g \longmapsto gx$ induces an isomorphism of G/P onto the orbit $Y = Gx$. The hypotheses imply that Y is closed and that $\dim Y \geqq 1$, so the corollary follows from (13.4).

(13.6) PROPOSITION. Let T be a maximal torus of G. Then G is generated by all $B \in \mathcal{B}^T$.

PROOF. Let P be the subgroup generated by the $B \in \mathcal{B}^T$. It is closed, connected (2.2). Fix $B \in \mathcal{B}^T$, and consider the quotient morphisms

$$G \xrightarrow{\pi} G/B \xrightarrow{p} G/P \ .$$

Suppose $P \neq G$. Since P is clearly parabolic, (13.5) implies that T has a fixed point in G/P distinct from $p(\pi(e))$. The inverse image Y in G/B of that fixed point is closed and stable under T. Thus T has a fixed point

$\pi(y) \in Y$, and, by construction,

$$p(\pi(y)) \neq p(\pi(e)) \quad .$$

Now $Ty \subset yB$, i.e. $y^{-1} \cdot T \cdot y \subset B$. By the conjugacy of maximal tori in B we can write ${}^{y^{-1}}T = {}^{b}T$ for some $b \in B$, in which case $yb \in N_G(T)$. But it is clear from the definition of P that $N_G(T)$ normalizes P. By the normalizer theorem (11.15) we therefore have $N_G(T) \subset N_G(P) = P$, so $y = (yb)b^{-1} \in PB = P$, and hence $p(\pi(y)) = p(\pi(e))$. Contradiction.

REMARK. We shall see later (14.1, Cor. 1) that any connected k-group is in fact generated by <u>two</u> suitably chosen Borel subgroups.

(13.7) LEMMA. <u>Let</u> W <u>be a hyperplane in a vector space</u> V, <u>let</u> Y <u>be a closed subvariety of</u> $\mathbb{P}(V)$, <u>and let</u> $H = \mathbb{P}(W) \subset \mathbb{P}(V)$.

(a) <u>If</u> $\dim Y \geq 1$ <u>then</u> $Y \cap H \neq \phi$.

(b) <u>If</u> Y <u>is irreducible and not contained in</u> H <u>then each irreducible component of</u> $Y \cap H$ <u>has dimension</u> $\dim Y - 1$.

PROOF. (a) If $Y \cap H = \phi$, then Y is a complete variety in the affine variety $\mathbb{P}(V) - H$, so Y is finite (see (10.1)(2)).

(b) Locally on $\mathbb{P}(V)$, the hyperplane H is defined by a single (linear) equation, and hence likewise for

$Y \cap H$ on Y. Therefore part (b) follows from (AG. 9. 2).

(13. 8) We fix a semi-regular torus T in G and write $X_*(T)_{sr}$ for the set of semi-regular one-parameter subgroups in T. According to (13. 2)(2) this set is not empty. More precisely (see (13. 2)),

$$X_*(T)_{sr} = \{\lambda \in X_*(T) \mid \langle \alpha, \lambda \rangle \neq 0 \text{ for all } \alpha \in \Psi\} .$$

Fix a $B_0 \in \mathcal{B}$ and put $X = G/B_0$. If $\lambda \in X_*(T)_{sr}$ then the set of fixed points of $\mathrm{im}(\lambda)$ in X is finite, and hence coincides with X^T.

PROPOSITION. Let $\lambda \in X_*(T)_{sr}$. (1) There is a unique point $x(\lambda) \in X$ such that $\lambda(\infty)x = x(\lambda)$ for all x in some neighborhood of $x(\lambda)$. The corresponding Borel subgroup, $B(\lambda)$, contains T.

(2) $U = \{x \in X \mid \lambda(\infty)x = x(\lambda)\}$ is the complement of a of a T-invariant hyperplane section (in some $\mathbb{P}(V)$) of X. In particular, $\dim(X - U) = \dim X - 1$.

(3) There is a set $\{\beta_i\}$ of non-trivial characters of T, with trivial restrictions to $T \cap R(G)$, such that, for $\lambda' \in X_*(T)_{sr}$, we have $B(\lambda) = B(\lambda')$ if and only if $\langle \beta_i, \lambda' \rangle > 0$ for each i.

REMARK. Conversely, the existence of an $x(\lambda)$ as above implies that λ is semi-regular, because (see (13. 1)(2)) $x(\lambda)$ must then be an isolated fixed point of $\mathrm{im}(\lambda)$. The group $B(\lambda)$ will be said to be associated to λ.

PROOF. Since X is irreducible any two non-empty open sets meet, and this clearly implies the uniqueness of $x(\lambda)$.

Since $X = G/B_0 \cong (G/R(G))/(B_0/R(G))$ we can choose a linear representation of $G/R(G)$, and hence of G, on a vector space V so that X can be identified with the G-orbit of a point in $\mathbb{P}(V)$. Let $\pi : V - \{0\} \longrightarrow \mathbb{P}(V)$, $v \longmapsto [v]$ be the canonical morphism. Replacing V by the subspace spanned by $\pi^{-1}(X)$, if necessary, we can further arrange that X lies in no hyperplane in $\mathbb{P}(V)$.

Let $e_1, \ldots, e_n$ be a basis of V such that each e_i is an eigenvector, say with character α_i, of T. Put $m_i = \langle \alpha_i, \lambda \rangle$ and assume the basis ordered so that $m_1 \geqq \ldots \geqq m_n$. Say $m_1 = \ldots = m_r$ and $m_r > m_i$ for $i > r$. Let W be the hyperplane in V spanned by $e_2, \ldots, e_n$, and suppose $v = \Sigma a_i e_i \notin W$ (i.e. $a_1 \neq 0$). Then the calculation of (13.3) shows that:

$$(*) \qquad \lambda(\infty)[v] = [a_1 e_1 + \ldots + a_r e_r] \; .$$

Let H be the hyperplane $\mathbb{P}(W)$ in $\mathbb{P}(V)$. We propose to show that $r = 1$, and that $x(\lambda) = [e_1]$ has the property required by part (1). Moreover we will prove that the U of part (2) is $X - (X \cap H)$, and this, by virtue of (13.7), will yield (2).

Suppose $r > 1$. We can find infinitely many $b \in K$ and v of the form $v = e_1 + be_2 + \ldots$ such that $[v] \in X$. Otherwise X would lie in the union of H and of a finite number of hyperplanes, "$a_2 = ba_1$." This is impossible since X is irreducible and lies in no hyperplane. Since $r > 1$ it follows from (*) that, for $v = e_1 + be_2 + \ldots$ as above, the $\lambda(\infty)[v]$ are distinct for distinct b. Thus we obtain infinitely many fixed points of $\mathrm{im}(\lambda)$ in X, contradicting the assumption that λ is semi-regular. Thus indeed $r = 1$.

Now that $r = 1$ it follows further from (*) that $\lambda(\infty)[v] = [e_1]$ if and only if $v \notin W$. Thus

$$\{x \in X \mid \lambda(\infty)x = [e_1]\} = X - (X \cap H) \ .$$

This completes the proof of (1) and (2).

To prove (3), suppose we are given $\lambda' \in X_*(T)_{sr}$. Let $m_i' = \langle \alpha_i, \lambda' \rangle$. The proof above shows that, for some j, m_j' is strictly larger than m_i' for all $i \neq j$, and that $x(\lambda') = [e_j]$. Thus $x(\lambda') = x(\lambda) \Longleftrightarrow m_1' > m_i'$ for all $i > 1 \Longleftrightarrow \langle \alpha_1, \lambda' \rangle > \langle \alpha_i, \lambda' \rangle$ for all $i > 1 \Longleftrightarrow \langle \beta_i, \lambda' \rangle > 0$ for all $i > 1$, where $\beta_i = \alpha_1 - \alpha_i$. Since α_i are characters of T, trivial on $T \cap R(G)$, this proves (3).

Let $f : G \longrightarrow G'$ be an <u>isomorphism</u> of algebraic groups, and put $T' = f(T)$. If $\lambda \in X_*(T)_{sr}$ then $f \circ \lambda \in X_*(T')_{sr}$, clearly, and $B(f \circ \lambda) = f(B(\lambda))$. Now suppose $n \in N_G(T)$ and $f = \mathrm{Int}(n)$. Then $T' = T$ and, if we write ${}^n\lambda = \mathrm{Int}(n) \circ \lambda$, we have

$$B({}^n\lambda) = {}^nB(\lambda) \quad \text{for} \quad n \in N_G(T) \ .$$

(13.9) COROLLARY. *Let* T *be a maximal torus,*

$W = W(T, G)$ and $X = G/B_0$ as above.

(1) If $\dim X \geqq 1$ then $\operatorname{card} W \geqq 2$.

(2) If $\dim X \geqq 2$ then $\operatorname{card} W \geqq 3$.

PROOF. Recall ((11.16), (11.19)) that W acts simply transitively on X^T; hence $\operatorname{card} W = \operatorname{card} X^T$. Thus (1) follows from (13.4). Let now $\dim X \geqq 2$. Choose $\lambda \in X_*(T)_{sr}$ and put $S = \operatorname{im}(\lambda)$. Then X^S is finite and T-stable so $X^S = X^T$, and it suffices to show that card $X^S \geqq 3$.

Let Y be the T-invariant hyperplane section of X such that $\lambda(\infty)$ projects the neighborhood $X-Y$ of $x(\lambda)$ onto $x(\lambda)$. (See (13.8).) Then Y is closed and $\dim Y = \dim X - 1 \geqq 1$. Now (13.4) implies S has two fixed points in Y, and $x(\lambda) \notin Y$ makes three in X.

(13.10) Weyl chambers. Let T be a maximal torus, and $W = W(T, G)$. If $\lambda \in X_*(T)_{sr}$ we have the associated $B(\lambda) \in \mathcal{B}^T$ constructed above in (13.8). Given $B \in \mathcal{B}^T$,

$$WC(B) = \{\lambda \in X_*(T)_{sr} \mid B(\lambda) = B\}$$

is called the Weyl chamber of B (with respect to T in G).

PROPOSITION. (1) There is a set $\{\beta_i\}$ of non-trivial characters of T, which are trivial on $T \cap R(G)$, such that

$$WC(B) = \{\lambda \in X_*(T)_{sr} \mid \langle \beta_i, \lambda \rangle > 0 \text{ \underline{for each} } i\} .$$

(2) The Weyl group W acts simply transitively on the set of Weyl chambers $WC(B)$ of $B \in \mathcal{B}^T$.

PROOF. Part (2) will imply each Weyl chamber is non-empty, whereupon (1) reduces to part (3) of (13.8).

If $n \in N_G(T)$ and $\lambda \in WC(B)$ then (see end of (13.8)) we have $B({}^n\lambda) = {}^nB(\lambda)$, so ${}^nWC(B) = WC({}^nB)$. If $n \in G^T$ then ${}^n\lambda = \lambda$ so $W = N_G(T)/G^T$ acts on the set of Weyl chambers in such a way that $f : B \longmapsto WC(B)$ is W-equivariant. Since W is transitive on the B's it follows that each $WC(B)$ is not empty (since at least one of them is not empty). In that case $WC(B)$ determines B, clearly, so f is bijective. The simple transitivity of W on the $WC(B)$'s now follows from the simple transitivity of W on $\mathcal{B}^T$ (11.19).

(13.11) Centralizers of singular subtori of codimension 1. Let S be a singular subtorus of codimension 1 in the maximal torus T, and let $B \in \mathcal{B}^T$. Then T is a maximal torus in G^S, and we know from (11.18) that B^S is a Borel subgroup of G^S. Indeed, the map $B \longmapsto B^S$ is a surjection from $\mathcal{B}(G)^T$ to $\mathcal{B}(G^S)^T$. When we write $WC(B^S)$, it is understood with reference to B^S as an element of $\mathcal{B}(G^S)^T$.

PROPOSITION. (1) The Weyl group $W(T, G^S)$ has order 2.

(2) In $X_*(T)$ we have $WC(B) \subset WC(B^S)$.

(3) If C is one of the two elements of $\mathcal{B}(G^S)^T$, then there is a non-trivial $\alpha \in X(T/S) \subset X(T)$ such that, for any $B \in \mathcal{B}^T$, we have

$$B^S = C \Longleftrightarrow \langle \alpha, \lambda \rangle > 0 \text{ for all } \lambda \in WC(B) .$$

If C' is the other element of $\mathcal{B}(G^S)^T$ then

$$B^S = C' \Longleftrightarrow \langle \alpha, \lambda \rangle < 0 \text{ for all } \lambda \in WC(B) .$$

PROOF. (1) Put $H = G^S$ and let $\pi : H \longrightarrow H' = H/R(H)$ be the quotient morphism. Then $T' = \pi(T)$ is a maximal torus in H', and (11.20) implies that $W(T, H) \longrightarrow W' = W(T', H')$ is an isomorphism. We shall show that $\dim T' = 1$, and then deduce from this that $\operatorname{card} W' = 2$, thus proving (1).

Since $S \subset R(H)$, and S has codimension 1 in T, we have $\dim T' = \dim(T/T \cap R(H)) \leqq 1$. On the other hand, since S is singular, $H = G^S$ is not solvable, hence H' is not solvable, and $T' \neq \{e\}$ by (11.5). Thus $\dim T' = 1$.

We just observed that H' is not solvable, so (13.9)(1) implies that $\operatorname{card} W' \geqq 2$. On the other hand $W' = N_{H'}(T')/Z_{H'}(T')$ acts faithfully on T', and, since $T' \cong \mathbb{GL}_1$, it follows from (8.3) and (8.4) that $\operatorname{Aut}(T') \cong \mathbb{GL}_1(\mathbb{Z})$ has order 2. Thus $\operatorname{card} W' \leqq 2$.

(2) Consider the commutative square

$$\begin{array}{ccc} G & \xrightarrow{\pi} & G/B \\ \cup & & \uparrow j \\ G^S & \xrightarrow[\pi^S]{} & G^S/B^S \end{array} ,$$

where π and π^S are the quotient morphisms, and $j(\pi^S(g)) = g \cdot \pi(e)$. Then j is injective. If $\lambda \in WC(B)$, then $\pi(e) = x(\lambda)$, so $\lambda(\infty)$ projects an open set onto $\pi(e)$. Hence, with respect to the corresponding action in G^S/B^S, $\lambda(\infty)$ projects an open set onto $\pi^S(e)$, i.e. B^S is associated to λ in G^S, as was to be shown.

(3) It follows from (1) and (13.10)(2) that there are two Weyl chambers of T as a torus in G^S. According to (13.10)(1), each one is of the form $\{\lambda \in X_*(T)_{sr} | \langle \beta_i, \lambda \rangle > 0 \text{ for each } i\}$. Here $X_*(T)_{sr}$ refers to the set of λ which are semi-regular in G^S, and the β_i are non-trivial characters of T/S. Since $\dim T/S = 1$ we have $X(T/S) \cong \mathbb{Z}$. Since there are two Weyl chambers, each non-empty, they must be of the form

$$\{\lambda \in X_*(T)_{sr} | \langle \alpha, \lambda \rangle > 0\}$$

where α varies over the two generators of $X(T/S)$. In particular $WC(C)$ has this form for some α, so that (3) follows immediately from (2).

(13.12) COROLLARY. *Let* Q *be a singular subtorus of codimension* 1 *in* T, *distinct from* S. *Then there is a*

$B' \in \mathcal{B}^T$ such that

$$B'^S = B^S \text{ and } B'^Q \neq B^Q .$$

PROOF. Using part (3) above, we can find non-trivial $\alpha \in X(T/S)$ and $\beta \in X(T/Q)$ such that, for $B' \in \mathcal{B}^T$ and $\lambda' \in WC(B')$, we have

$$B'^S = B^S \Longleftrightarrow \langle \alpha, \lambda' \rangle > 0$$

$$B'^Q = B^Q \Longleftrightarrow \langle \beta, \lambda' \rangle > 0 .$$

Since $S \neq Q$ it follows that α and β are linearly independent in $X(T)$ (their kernels have distinct connected components) so we can find a $\lambda' \in X_*(T)_{sr}$ such that $\langle \alpha, \lambda' \rangle > 0$ and $\langle \beta, \lambda' \rangle < 0$. Then $B' = B(\lambda')$ solves our problem.

(13.13) Groups of semi-simple rank 1, and $\mathbb{PGL}_2$. In the following T denotes a maximal torus in G, and $W = W(T, G)$. The semi-simple rank of G is defined to be $\dim(T/(T \cap R(G)))$, i.e. the dimension of a maximal torus in $G/R(G)$. The conjugacy of maximal tori shows that this depends only on G. For example $\mathbb{PGL}_2$ is not solvable and it has a maximal torus of dimension 1 (see (10.8)); hence its semi-simple rank is 1.

PROPOSITION. The following conditions are equivalent:

(1) G has semi-simple rank 1.

(2) card $W = 2$.

(3) $\dim G/B = 1$ (where $B \in \mathcal{B}$).

(4) G/B is isomorphic to $\mathbb{P}_1$.

(5) There is a surjective morphism $\varphi : G \longrightarrow \mathbb{PGL}_2$ such that $\ker \varphi = \bigcap_{B' \in \mathcal{B}} B'$ (and so $(\ker \varphi)^0 = R(G)$).

PROOF. The implication (1) $\Longrightarrow$ (2) is contained in the proof of part (1) of (13.11).

(2) $\Longrightarrow$ (3). Since card W = card $\mathcal{B}^T > 1$, G is not solvable, so $\dim G/B \geqq 1$. Since card $W < 3$ it follows from (13.9)(2) that $\dim G/B < 2$.

(3) $\Longrightarrow$ (4). Let $\lambda \in X_*(T)$ be a regular one-parameter subgroup. Then $\mathbb{GL}_1$ (via λ) does not act trivially on G/B because T does not. Since G/B is irreducible of dimension 1 it follows that, for $x \in G/B$ and not fixed by T, the orbit map $\mathbb{GL}_1 \longrightarrow G/B$, $t \longmapsto \lambda(t)x$, is dominant. Therefore we obtain an inclusion of function fields $K(G/B) \subset K(\mathbb{GL}_1)$. Since $K(\mathbb{GL}_1)$ is a pure function field in one variable it follows from Lüroth's theorem that $K(G/B)$ is likewise. Since G/B is a complete non-singular curve, it must therefore be isomorphic to $\mathbb{P}_1$.

(4) $\Longrightarrow$ (5). Since $G/B \cong \mathbb{P}_1$ it follows from (10.8) that the action of G on G/B is given by a morphism $\varphi : G \longrightarrow \mathbb{PGL}_2$ (= $\mathrm{Aut}(\mathbb{P}_1)$). Clearly the kernel is $\bigcap B'(B' \in \mathcal{B})$, so $(\ker \varphi)^0 = R(G)$. Since G is not solvable (because $B \neq G$) it follows from (11.6) that $\dim \varphi(G) > 2$. However $\mathbb{PGL}_2$ is connected and has dimension 3. Hence φ is surjective.

(5) $\Longrightarrow$ (1). The existence of φ clearly implies that the semi-simple rank of G coincides with that of $\mathbb{P}\mathbb{G}\mathbb{L}_2$, which is 1.

COROLLARY. Suppose G has semi-simple rank 1, and let B_0, B_1, B_∞ be distinct Borel subgroups of G. Put $I = \bigcap B(B \in \mathcal{B})$. Then $(B_0 \cap B_1)/I \cong \mathbb{G}\mathbb{L}_1$ and $B_0 \cap B_1 \cap B_\infty = I$.

PROOF. We have a surjection $\varphi : G \longrightarrow \mathbb{P}\mathbb{G}\mathbb{L}_2$, with kernel I, such that the B_i are stability groups of distinct points of $\mathbb{P}_1$. (With the aid of an automorphism of $\mathbb{P}_1$ we can even assume B_i is the stability group of $i (i = 0, 1, \infty)$ (see (10.8)).) The assertions of the corollary follow from the fact that $\mathbb{P}\mathbb{G}\mathbb{L}_2$ acts simply transitively on triples of distinct points in $\mathbb{P}_1$, and that the subgroup fixing a pair of points is isomorphic to $\mathbb{G}\mathbb{L}_1$ (see (10.8)).

(13.14) Reductive groups of semi-simple rank 1. In the following proposition we assume G to be a reductive group of semi-simple rank 1, and T a maximal torus in G. We put

$$I = \bigcap_{B \in \mathcal{B}} B \quad \text{and} \quad \mathcal{B}^T = \{B, B'\} .$$

The Lie algebras are denoted:

$$\underline{g} = L(G), \quad \underline{b} = L(B), \quad \underline{b}' = L(B') .$$

PROPOSITION. (1) $I(T) = B \cap B' = T$, and $I = Z(G)$.

(2) $B_u \cong \mathbb{G}_a$ <u>and the action of</u> T <u>on</u> B_u <u>is given by a generator</u>, α, <u>of</u> $X(T/(T \cap I))$. $\Phi(T, B) = \{\alpha\}$, <u>and</u> $\underline{b} = L(T) \oplus \underline{g}_\alpha$. <u>Moreover</u> B_u <u>is the unique</u> T-<u>invariant connected subgroup of</u> G <u>such that</u> $L(B_u) = \underline{g}_\alpha$. <u>Similar conclusions apply to</u> B' <u>with</u> $-\alpha$ <u>in place of</u> α.

(3) $\underline{b} \cap \underline{b}' = L(T)$.

$\underline{b} + \underline{b}' = \underline{g} = L(T) \oplus \underline{g}_\alpha \oplus \underline{g}_{-\alpha}$.

$\Phi(T, G) = \{\alpha, -\alpha\}$.

(4) $WC(B) = \{\lambda \in X_*(T) \mid \langle \alpha, \lambda \rangle > 0\}$

$WC(B') = \{\lambda \in X_*(T) \mid \langle \alpha, \lambda \rangle < 0\}$.

PROOF. From (13.13), we have a surjective morphism $\varphi : G \longrightarrow \mathbb{PGL}_2$ with kernel I. Since $R_u(G) = \{e\}$ it follows that $\varphi : B_u \longrightarrow \varphi(B_u) \cong \mathbb{G}_a$ has finite kernel. Thus B_u is connected, unipotent, and one dimensional, so (10.9) implies there is an isomorphism $\theta : \mathbb{G}_a \longrightarrow B_u$. Similarly we have an isomorphism $\theta' : \mathbb{G}_a \longrightarrow B'_u$. If $t \in T$ and $b \in \mathbb{G}_a$ we have

$$t\theta(b)t^{-1} = \theta(t^\alpha b)$$

for some $\alpha \in X(T)$ (see (10.10)). Passing to $\mathbb{PGL}_2$, we see that α generates $X(\varphi(T)) = X(T/(T \cap I))$ and that the action of T on B'_u is given by $-\alpha$ (see (10.8)).

Now $B_u \cap B'_u$ corresponds to a proper subgroup of $\mathbb{G}_a$ stable under the non-trivial linear action of T given by α, so $B_u \cap B'_u = \{e\}$. Since $B = T \cdot B_u$ it follows that $B \cap B' = T \cdot (B_u \cap B') = T \cdot (B_u \cap B'_u) = T$. Since

$T \subset I(T) = (B \cap B')^0$ this proves the first part of (1). It further implies that $I \subset T$, so I is a normal and diagonalizable subgroup of G. By rigidity it follows that $I \subset Z(G)$. The reverse inclusion follows from (11.11), thus proving (1).

We have $B = T \cdot B_u$ so that $\underline{b} = L(T) \oplus L(B_u)$, and the remarks above show that $L(B_u)$ is a one dimensional subspace of $\underline{g}_\alpha$. Similarly $\underline{b}' = L(T) \oplus L(B'_u)$ with $L(B'_u)$ a one dimensional subspace of $\underline{g}_{-\alpha}$. Hence $\underline{b} \cap \underline{b}' = L(T)$, and $\underline{b} + \underline{b}' = \underline{g}$ by dimension count, for $\dim(\underline{b} + \underline{b}') = 2 + \dim T$, $\dim G = \dim I + \dim \mathbb{P}\mathbb{G}\mathbb{L}_2 = \dim I + 3$, and $\dim T = \dim I + \dim \varphi(T) = \dim I + 1$.

This proves all of (2) and (3) except for the assertion: If H is a connected T-invariant subgroup such that $L(H) = \underline{g}_\alpha$, then $H = B_u$.

Since $\dim H = 1$ it follows that H is either a torus or unipotent. If H were a torus T would have to centralize H, by rigidity. But T acts non-trivially on $L(H)$, so we must have $H = H_u$. Next note that $T \cdot H$ is a connected solvable subgroup containing T, hence contained in B or B'. Since $\Phi(T, B') = \{-\alpha\}$ and $\Phi(T, T \cdot H) = \{\alpha\}$ we must have $T \cdot H \subset B$, and hence $H \subset B_u$. Dimension count now implies that $H = B_u$.

Finally we prove (4). Let $\pi : G \longrightarrow G/B$ be the quotient morphism and put $x_0 = \pi(e)$. Since B is the stability group of x_0 and $B'_u \cap B = \{e\}$, it follows that the points $\theta'(c)x_0 (c \in \mathbb{G}_a)$ cover a neighborhood of x_0 in

$G/B \cong \mathbb{P}_1$. Suppose $\lambda \in X_*(T)$ is such that $m = \langle \alpha, \lambda \rangle > 0$. For $c \in \mathbb{G}_a$ and $t \in \mathbb{GL}_1$ we have

$$\lambda(t)\theta'(c)x_0 = \lambda(t)\theta'(c)\lambda(t)^{-1}x_0 \qquad (T \text{ fixes } x_0)$$

$$= \theta'(t^{\langle -\alpha, \lambda \rangle} c)x_0 = \theta'(t^{-m}c)x_0 \quad .$$

Specializing t^{-1} to 0 (i.e. t to ∞) we obtain

$$\lambda(\infty)\theta'(c)x_0 = \theta'(0)x_0 = x_0 \quad .$$

If follows that λ is semi-regular and that $x(\lambda) = x_0$. This proves:

$$\langle \alpha, \lambda \rangle > 0 \Longrightarrow \begin{cases} \lambda \text{ is semi-regular} \\ \text{and } x(\lambda) = x_0 \quad (\text{i.e. } B(\lambda) = B) \end{cases} .$$

According to (13.11)(3) the condition, "$\langle \alpha, \lambda \rangle > 0$," defines a Weyl chamber in $X_*(T)_{sr}$, so we must have

$$WC(B) = \{\lambda \in X_*(T) \mid \langle \alpha, \lambda \rangle > 0\} \quad .$$

The analogue for B' follows similarly. Q.E.D.

(13.15) From now on we return to the general setting, i.e. G is no longer assumed to be of semi-simple rank 1, unless otherwise stated.

LEMMA. <u>Let</u> S <u>and</u> Q <u>be distinct singular tori of co-dimension</u> 1 <u>in the maximal torus</u> T, <u>and let</u> $B \in \mathcal{B}^T$.

(1) $\dim(B_u^S / (B_u^S \cap I(T)_u)) \leqq 1$.

(2) $I(B^S)^Q \subset I(T)$.

PROOF. (1) Thanks to (13.11)(1) and (13.13), we have a surjective morphism $\varphi : G^S \longrightarrow \mathbf{PGL}_2$ such that $(\ker \varphi)^0 = R(G^S)$ and $\varphi(B_u^S) \cong \mathbb{G}_a$. It follows that $\dim(B_u^S/(B_u^S \cap R_u(G^S))) = 1$. Now (1) follows because $R(G^S) \subset I(S) \subset I(T)$ (see (11.18)).

(2) Choose B' as in (13.12). Then since $B^Q \neq B'^Q$ it follows from the Corollary of (13.13) that $B^Q \cap B'^Q = T \cdot R_u(G^Q)$, and (11.18) again implies this lies in $I(T)$. Since $B'^S = B^S$ we have $I(B^S) \subset B \cap B'$, and hence $I(B^S)^Q \subset B^Q \cap B'^Q \subset I(T)$.

(13.16) THEOREM. Let T be a maximal torus in G. Then

$$I(T)_u = R_u(G) .$$

PROOF. Clearly $R_u(G) \subset I(T)_u$, and the latter is connected and unipotent. Hence we need only show that $I(T)_u$ is a normal subgroup of G.

According to (13.6) G is generated by the $B \in \mathcal{B}^T$. Combined with (9.5)(2), this shows that G is generated by groups B^S, for $B \in \mathcal{B}^T$, and variable subtori S of co-dimension 1 in T. Since $B^S = T \cdot B_u^S$, it suffices to show that B_u^S normalizes $I(T)_u$. Note first:

(*) If S is semi-regular, then, by (13.1), we have $B^S \subset G^S \subset I(S) \subset I(T)$, so $B_u^S \subset I(T)_u$.

Now assume S is singular. Then B_u^S is contained in

$$H = (I(B^S) \cap B_u)^0 ,$$

so it suffices to show that H normalizes $I(T)_u$. Note that $I(T)_u \subset H$ and that H is a connected unipotent group, which is normalized by T (because B^S and B_u are). Hence it will follow from (12.1) Lemma that H normalizes $I(T)_u$ if we show that $\dim H \leqq \dim I(T)_u + 1$.

As above, we know from (9.5)(2) that H is generated by the H^Q where Q varies over subtori of codimension 1 in T. If $Q = S$ then evidently $H^S = B_u^S$, and it follows from (13.15)(1) that $\dim(H^S/(H^S \cap I(T)_u)) \leqq 1$. If $Q \neq S$ and Q is semi-regular then we have $H^Q \subset B_u^Q \subset I(T)_u$, as pointed out in (*) above. Finally suppose Q is singular and $\neq S$. Then $H^Q \subset I(B^S)^Q$, clearly, and the latter lies in $I(T)$, by (13.15)(2). Hence $H^Q \subset I(T)_u$ for all $Q \neq S$, so the natural morphism

$$H^S/(H^S \cap I(T)_u) \longrightarrow H/I(T)_u$$

is surjective. Since we observed already that the left side has dimension $\leqq 1$, the proof is now complete.

(13.17) In the following important corollaries T denotes a maximal torus in G, S a subtorus of G.

COROLLARY 1. (a) $R_u(G^S) = R_u(G)^S$.

(b) If S is semi-regular then $(G^S)_u = R_u(G)^S$.

(c) $G^T = T \cdot R_u(G)^T$.

PROOF. (c) is a special case of (b), and (b) follows from (a) because $R_u(H) = H_u$ when H is a connected solvable group (see (10.6)).

To prove (a) we may assume $S \subset T$ (11.5). The group $R_u(G)^S$ is a connected unipotent normal subgroup of G^S, hence contained in $R_u(G^S)$. On the other hand, $R_u(G^S)$ lies in every Borel subgroup of G^S, among which are all B^S, $B \in \mathcal{B}^T$. In particular $R_u(G^S) \subset I(T) = T \cdot R_u(G)$, by (13.16) so $R_u(G^S) \subset R_u(G)^S$.

COROLLARY 2. Suppose G is reductive, $S \subset T$.

(a) G^S is reductive.

(b) If S is semi-regular, then $G^S = T$. In particular, S is regular.

(c) $G^T = T$. The Cartan subgroups of G coincide with the maximal tori.

(d) The intersection, Z, of all maximal tori is $Z(G)$.

Parts (a), (b), and (c) follow immediately from the corresponding parts of Corollary 1. Since Z is a normal diagonalizable subgroup of G, it is central by rigidity. Conversely part (c) implies $Z(G)$ lies in every maximal torus. This proves (d).

(13.18) Roots in reductive groups. T still denotes a

maximal torus in G. An automorphism of X(T) will be called a reflection if it has order 2 and induces the identity on a subgroup of corank 1.

Recall from (13.2) that $\Psi = \Phi(T, G/I(T))$; we also write Φ for $\Phi(T, G)$.

The next theorem summarizes much of the information we have accumulated about reductive groups.

THEOREM. Suppose G is reductive.

(1) $\Psi = \Phi$, $L(T) = \underline{g}^T$, and $\underline{g} = \underline{g}^T \oplus \coprod_{\alpha\in\Phi} \underline{g}_\alpha$.

(2) The singular tori of codimension 1 in T are the $T_\alpha = (\ker \alpha)^0$ $(\alpha \in \Phi)$, and $(\bigcap_{\alpha\in\Phi} T_\alpha)^0 = Z(G)^0$.

(3) Φ generates a subgroup of finite index in $X(T/Z(G)^0) \subset X(T)$. If α and β in Φ are linearly dependent, then $\beta = \pm\alpha$.

(4) Let $\alpha \in \Phi$, and put $G_\alpha = Z_G(T_\alpha)$. Then G_α is a reductive group of semi-simple rank 1, and:

(a) $-\alpha \in \Phi$, and $L(G_\alpha) = \underline{g}^T \oplus \underline{g}_\alpha \oplus \underline{g}_{-\alpha}$.

(b) $\dim \underline{g}_\alpha = 1$.

(c) The subgroup $W(T, G_\alpha)$ of $W(T, G)$ is generated by a reflection, r_α, such that $r_\alpha(\alpha) = -\alpha$.

(d) There is a unique connected T-stable subgroup U_α of G such that $L(U_\alpha) = \underline{g}_\alpha$. It is the unipotent part of a Borel subgroup of G_α containing T.

(5) Let $B \in \mathcal{B}^T$.

(a) <u>For each</u> $\alpha \in \Phi$, $\Phi(T, B) = \Phi(B) \cap \{\alpha, -\alpha\} = \Phi(T, B^{T_\alpha})$ <u>has precisely one element. Hence</u> Φ <u>is the disjoint union of</u> $\Phi(B)$ <u>and</u> $-\Phi(B)$.

(b) $WC(B) = \{\lambda \in X(T) \mid \langle \alpha, \lambda \rangle > 0$ <u>for all</u> $\alpha \in \Phi(B)\}$.

(c) <u>If</u> $\lambda \in WC(B)$ <u>then</u> $\Phi(B) = \{\alpha \in \Phi \mid \langle \alpha, \lambda \rangle > 0\}$.

(d) <u>One can give</u> $X(T)$ <u>the structure of a totally ordered abelian group so that</u> $\Phi(B)$ <u>is the set of positive elements in</u> Φ.

(e) $L(B) = \underline{g}^T \oplus \coprod_{\alpha \in \Phi(B)} \underline{g}_\alpha$.

PROOF. (1) It follows from (13.16) and from the assumption G reductive, that $I(T) = T$. Clearly $\Phi(T, G/T) = \Phi$. One always has

$$\underline{g} = \underline{g}^T \oplus \coprod_{\alpha \in \Phi} \underline{g}_\alpha ,$$

(see (8.16)). By (9.4), $\underline{g}^T = L(G^T)$, and Corollary 2 of (13.17) tells us that $G^T = T$.

(2) The first assertion follows from (13.2)(1) since $\Psi = \Phi$. We know from (13.17), Corollary 2, that $Z(G)^0$ is a subtorus of T. If S is a subtorus of T, then we know, by (9.4), that $G^S = G \Longleftrightarrow \underline{g}^S = \underline{g} \Longleftrightarrow S \subset T_\alpha$ for each $\alpha \in \Phi$. Thus $Z(G)^0 = (\bigcap T_\alpha)^0$.

(3) The equality just proved is equivalent to the condition that Φ generate a subgroup of finite index in $X(T/Z(G)^0)$, clearly. If $\alpha, \beta \in X(T)$, then it is clear that α and β are linearly dependent, i.e. $n\alpha = m\beta$ for

some $n, m \in \mathbb{Z}$, not both zero, if and only if $T_\alpha = (\ker \alpha)^0$ and $T_\beta = (\ker \beta)^0$ coincide. In this case we have $\beta \in \Phi(G_\alpha)$ so the last assertion of (3) will follow from (4)(a), which implies that $\Phi(T, G_\alpha) = \{\alpha, -\alpha\}$.

(4) We have $L(G_\alpha) = \underline{g}^T \oplus \coprod_{T_\alpha \subset T_\beta} \underline{g}_\beta$. From (13.11) we know that G_α has semi-simple rank 1, and from (13.17) that it is reductive; hence we can apply (13.14). Since $\alpha \in \Phi(G_\alpha)$, it follows from (13.14) that $\Phi(G_\alpha) = \{\alpha, -\alpha\}$ and that $\dim \underline{g}_\alpha = 1$. In particular $\underline{g}^{T_\alpha} = \underline{g}^T \oplus \underline{g}_\alpha \oplus \underline{g}_{-\alpha}$ so that $T_\alpha \subset T_\beta$ (for $\beta \in \Phi$) $\Longleftrightarrow \beta = \pm\alpha$. This proves (a) and (b).

As already remarked, $W(T, G_\alpha)$ has order 2, say with generator r_α represented by $n \in N_{G_\alpha}(T)$. The automorphism of T induced by n has order 2 and fixes pointwise the subtorus T_α of codimension 1. Hence the set of commutators (n, T) is a subtorus of dimension 1 (being a non-trivial image of $T/T_\alpha \cong \mathbb{GL}_1$). If $\beta \in X(T)$, then $\beta(ntn^{-1}) = \beta(t)$ for all $t \in T \Longleftrightarrow \beta((n, T)) = \{1\}$ $\Longleftrightarrow (n, T) \subset \ker \beta$. The set of such β is a subgroup of corank 1 in $X(T)$, not containing α. Since $\Phi(G_\alpha) = \{\alpha, -\alpha\}$ is stable under r_α, we must have $r_\alpha(\alpha) = -\alpha$, for otherwise r_α would fix a subgroup of finite index in $X(T)$, and hence be the identity. This proves (c).

Finally, to prove (d), let H be a connected T-stable subgroup of G such that $L(H) = \underline{g}_\alpha$. Since dim H = 1, H is either a torus or unipotent. If it were a torus it would be centralized by T, by rigidity of tori, contradicting the non-triviality of the action of T on L(H). Hence, by (10.9), there is an isomorphism $\theta : \mathbb{G}_a \longrightarrow H$, and we have $t\theta(b)t^{-1} = \theta(t^{\alpha}b)$ for $t \in T$, $b \in \mathbb{G}_a$. It follows that $H \subset G_\alpha$. At this point the uniqueness, as well as the existence, of U_α follow from the corresponding assertion in G_α (see (13.14)).

(5) (a) follows from (13.14) because $B^{T_\alpha} \in \mathcal{B}(G_\alpha)^T$ and $\Phi(G_\alpha) = \{\alpha, -\alpha\}$, as noted above.

Moreover, it follows from (13.11) that

$$WC(B) \subset WC(B^{T_\alpha}) = \{\lambda \in X_*(T) \mid \langle \alpha, \lambda \rangle > 0\}$$

for each $\alpha \in \Phi(B)$. To prove (b) we claim, conversely, that any $\lambda \in \bigcap_{\alpha \in \Phi(B)} WC(B^{T_\alpha})$ lies in WC(B).

If λ were not semi-regular then, by (2), we would have $S = \mathrm{im}(\lambda) \subset T_\alpha$ for some α, so that $G_\alpha \subset G^S$, contradicting the fact that λ is semi-regular in G_α. Thus $B' = B(\lambda)$ is defined, and we must show that $B' = B$. The hypothesis implies that $B'^{T_\alpha} = B^{T_\alpha}$ for all $\alpha \in \Phi$. But (9.5(2)) says B is generated by these B^{T_α}, and similarly for B'; hence B = B' as claimed.

Part (c) is clearly a consequence of parts (a) and (b).

To prove (d), let $\lambda_1, \ldots, \lambda_r$ be a basis for $X_*(T)$ such that $B = B(\lambda_1)$. For a non-zero character α write $\alpha > 0$ if the first non-zero term among the

$\langle \alpha, \lambda_i \rangle$ $(1 \leqq i \leqq r)$ is positive. This defines a total ordering of $X(T)$. If $\alpha \in \Phi(B)$ then $\langle \alpha, \lambda_1 \rangle > 0$ so $\alpha > 0$. If $\alpha \in \Phi$, $\alpha \notin \Phi(B)$ then, by part (a), $-\alpha \in \Phi(B)$, so $\alpha < 0$.

(e) By definition, if $\underline{b} = L(B)$, we have $\underline{b} = \underline{b}^T \oplus \coprod_{\alpha \in \Phi(B)} \underline{b}_\alpha$. But clearly $\underline{b}^T = L(T) = \underline{g}^T$, and, if $\alpha \in \Phi(B)$, $\underline{b}_\alpha = \underline{g}_\alpha$ because $\dim \underline{g}_\alpha = 1$ (part (4)(b)). Q.E.D.

(13.19) PROPOSITION. Let G be connected, reductive, and X a semi-simple element of $\underline{g}$. Then $Z_G(X)^0$ is reductive.

PROOF. We keep the notation of (13.18), and let $H = Z_G(X)^0$. By (11.8), we may assume $X \in \underline{t}$. We have

$$\underline{z}(X) = \underline{t} + \Sigma_{\alpha \in \Psi} \underline{g}_\alpha \qquad (\Psi = \{\alpha \in \Phi \text{ , } d\alpha(X) = 0\}) \text{ .}$$

By (9.1), $\underline{z}(X) = L(H)$. In particular, if $\alpha \in \Psi$, then $G_\alpha \subset H$. We have to show that $R_u(H)$ is reduced to $\{e\}$. By (9.5), $R_u(H)$ is generated by centralizers of singular tori in T, i.e. by its intersections with some G_α, i.e. finally by some U_α, with α necessarily in Ψ. But if $U_\alpha \subset R_u(H)$, then U_α belongs to the unipotent radical of G_α. The latter group being reductive ((13.17), Cor. 2) this is a contradiction.

BIBLIOGRAPHICAL NOTE

The results of this section (except for (13.19)) are all due to Chevalley (see [8], in particular Exp. 10, 11, 12).

§14. ROOT SYSTEMS AND THE BRUHAT DECOMPOSITION IN REDUCTIVE GROUPS

In this section the connected affine group G is assumed to be reductive. T denotes a maximal torus in G, and we shall write Φ for $\Phi(T, G)$. For each $\alpha \in \Phi$, we put $T_\alpha = (\ker \alpha)^0$ and $G_\alpha = Z_G(T_\alpha)$.

The Weyl group $W = W(T, G)$ operates on $X(T)$ and leaves Φ stable. We propose to show that Φ is a reduced root system in a suitable subspace of $X(T)_{\mathbb{Q}} = X(T) \otimes_{\mathbb{Z}} \mathbb{Q}$, with Weyl group W (14.8). In view of §13, what remains to be shown is mainly the integrality condition $r_\alpha(\beta) - \beta \in \mathbb{Z}\cdot\alpha$, to be proved in (14.6), after some preliminary work in (14.3) to (14.5).

Let $B \in \mathcal{B}^T$, and let $\pi : G \longrightarrow G/B$ be the quotient morphism and put $o = \pi(e)$. The Bruhat decomposition (14.11) refers to the following: Let $U = B_u$. Then $w \longmapsto Uw(o)$ is a bijection from W to the set of U-orbits in G/B. Moreover, for $w \in W$, $Uw(o)$ is isomorphic to an affine space (a cell) and $w(o)$ is the unique fixed point of T in $Uw(o)$.

(14.1) THEOREM. Let $\lambda \in WC(B)$. For $B, B' \in \mathcal{B}^T$, the following conditions are equivalent:

(I) $B \cap B' = T$; (i) $\underline{b} \cap \underline{b}' = L(T)$ ($\underline{b} = L(B)$, $\underline{b}' = L(B')$).

(II) The product morphism $B \times B' \longrightarrow G$ is dominant and separable; (ii) $\underline{b} + \underline{b}' = \underline{g}$.

(III) $B' = B(-\lambda)$; (iii) $\Phi(B') = -\Phi(B)$.

In view of condition (III) we see that there exists a unique B' satisfying the above conditions. It is called the opposite Borel subgroup to B. The "big cell" associated with T and B is B·B', which contains a dense open set in G, by (II).

PROOF. We know from (13.18) that:

$$\underline{g} = \underline{g}^T \oplus \coprod_{\alpha\in\Phi} \underline{g}_\alpha, \quad \underline{g}^T = L(T),$$
$$\underline{b} = \underline{g}^T \oplus \coprod_{\alpha\in\Phi(B)} \underline{g}_\alpha,$$
$$\underline{b}' = \underline{g}^T \oplus \coprod_{\alpha\in\Phi(B')} \underline{g}_\alpha,$$

and Φ is the disjoint union of $\Phi(B)$ and $-\Phi(B) = \Phi(B(-\lambda))$. From these facts the equivalence of (i), (ii), (iii), and (III) is clear.

The equivalence of (II) and (ii) is also clear (see (AG.17.3)).

(I) $\Longrightarrow$ (iii). Suppose, on the contrary, that $B \cap B' = T$ but that there is an $\alpha \in \Phi(B) \cap \Phi(B')$. Then we must have $B^{T_\alpha} = B'^{T_\alpha} \subset B \cap B'$; contradiction.

(i) $\Longrightarrow$ (I). Since $T \subset B \cap B'$ and $L(B\cap B') \subset \underline{b} \cap \underline{b}'$ we see that (i) implies $T = (B \cap B')^0$. Since $B = T\cdot B_u$ we have $B \cap B' = T\cdot C$ where $C = B_u \cap B' = B_u \cap B'_u$. Now C is a finite group normalized, and hence centralized by (the connected group) T. Thus $C \subset G^T \cap B_u = T \cap B_u = \{e\}$ (see (13.17) Corollary 2).

COROLLARY 1. Let H be a connected k-group, T a

maximal torus of H, and B a Borel subgroup of H containing T. There exists one and only one Borel subgroup B' of H verifying the following three conditions, which are equivalent:

$$B \cap B' = T \cdot R_u(H); \quad \underline{b} \cap \underline{b}' = \underline{t} + L(R_u(H)); \quad \underline{b} + \underline{b}' = \underline{h} \; .$$

Let $\pi : H \longrightarrow H' = H/R_u(H)$ be the canonical projection. The group H' is reductive (11.21) and $\pi(B)$ (resp. $\pi(T)$) is a Borel subgroup (resp. a maximal torus) of H' (11.14). Moreover, the Borel subgroups of H all contain $R_u(H)$ and are the inverse images of the Borel subgroups of H'. This reduces the corollary to the theorem.

COROLLARY 2. Let H be a connected k-group and P a parabolic subgroup of H. Then P is equal to the normalizer in G of L(P).

Let $Q = N_G(L(P))$. Then Q contains P, hence is parabolic, and therefore connected (11.15). Let B be a Borel subgroup of G contained in P. If B' is a Borel subgroup of Q, then it is conjugate to B by an element of Q, hence $L(B') \subset L(P)$. On the other hand, by Cor. 1, there exists such a B' verifying $L(B') + L(B) = L(Q)$. Therefore $L(Q) = L(P)$ and $Q = P$.

(14.2) The center and derived group. Write $C = Z(G)^0$ for the "connected center" of G. Since G is reductive,

C coincides with R(G) (see (11.21)), so that G/C is semi-simple.

PROPOSITION. (1) $C = (\bigcap_{\alpha \in \Phi} T_\alpha)^0 = (T^W)^0$.

(2) DG <u>is semi-simple</u>.

(3) $G = C \cdot DG$ <u>and</u> $C \cap DG$ <u>is finite</u>.

PROOF. (1) That $C = (\bigcap_{\alpha \in \Phi} T_\alpha)^0$ follows from (13.18)(2), and clearly $C \subset T^W$. It remains to be shown that $(T^W)^0 \subset T_\alpha$ for each $\alpha \in \Phi$. According to (13.18)(3)(c) there is a $w \in W$ such that $w(\alpha) = -\alpha$. Now if $t \in T^W$ we have ${}^w t = t$ so $t^\alpha = ({}^w t)^\alpha = t^{w(\alpha)} = t^{-\alpha}$. Thus $T^W \subset \ker(2\alpha)$, and $(\ker(2\alpha))^0 = (\ker \alpha)^0 = T_\alpha$.

(3) To prove that $G = C \cdot DG$ we first recall (10.8) that $\mathbf{PGL}_2$ is its own derived group. Since G_α / T_α is isogenous to $\mathbf{PGL}_2$ it follows that $G_\alpha = T_\alpha \cdot DG_\alpha$ for each $\alpha \in \Phi$. We know (cf. (13.18)) that the $G_\alpha (\alpha \in \Phi)$ generate G, so it remains to show that $T \subset C \cdot DG$. Put $D = (N_G(T), T)^0 \subset (DG \cap T)$. It will suffice to prove that $T = C \cdot D$, or that $T'_{\mathbb{Q}} = C'_{\mathbb{Q}} + D'_{\mathbb{Q}}$, where $T' = X_*(T)$, $C' = X_*(C)$, $D' = X_*(D)$. But $C' = T'^W$, by (1), and by construction all $(1-w)\lambda$ $(w \in W, \lambda \in T')$ lie in D'. Now the subspace these span in $T'_{\mathbb{Q}}$ has complement $(T'_{\mathbb{Q}})^W = (T'^W)_{\mathbb{Q}}$, since the group algebra $\mathbb{Q}[W]$ is semi-simple. This proves that $G = C \cdot DG$.

Once we show that $C \cap DG$ is finite the semi-simplicity of DG will follow because $DG \longrightarrow G/C = G/R(G)$ is surjective with finite kernel. Thus the proof is completed by the:

LEMMA. Let C be a central torus in a connected group H. Then $C \cap DH$ is finite.

PROOF. Using a faithful linear representation we may assume $H \subset GL(V)$. Write $V = \coprod V_i (1 \leq i \leq n)$, where $V_i = V_{\alpha_i}$, α_i ranging over the weights of C in V. Then $H \subset GL(V)^C = GL(V_1) \times \ldots \times GL(V_n)$. If $t \in C$ then $t = (t^{\alpha_1} \text{Id.}, \ldots, t^{\alpha_n} \text{Id.})$ in these coordinates. If further $t \in DH$ then each $t^{\alpha_i} \text{Id.}$ has determinant 1, so $(t^{\alpha_i})^{m_i} = 1$, where $m_i = \dim V_i$. Thus $C \cap DH$ lies in a group of the form $C_1 \times \ldots \times C_n$, where C_i is cyclic of order dividing m_i.

COROLLARY. The following three conditions are equivalent: G is semi-simple; $G = DG$; and $Z(G)$ is finite. Let H be a closed connected normal subgroup of G. Then H is reductive, $Z(H)^0 = (Z(G) \cap H)^0$, and $DH = DG \cap H$.

The first assertion is an obvious consequence of the proposition. Let H be as in the statement. Then $R_u(H) \subset R_u(G)$, hence $R_u(H) = \{e\}$ and H is reductive. The group $Z(H)^0$ is a torus, normal in G, hence central ((8.10), Cor.) and contained in $Z(G)^0 \cap H$. The other inclusion is obvious. That $DH \subset DG \cap H$ is clear. That it is no bigger follows from $Z(H)^0 \subset Z(G)$ and the proposition.

(14.3) Direct spanning. Let $(H_i)_{i \in I}$ be a finite family of closed connected subgroups of a connected group H. We shall say that H is directly spanned by the H_i if, for some ordering $i_1, \ldots, i_n$ of I, the product morphism

$$H_{i_1} \times \ldots \times H_{i_n} \longrightarrow H$$

is an isomorphism of varieties. We shall denote this circumstance by writing

$$H_{i_1} \cdot H_{i_2} \cdot \ldots \cdot H_{i_n} .$$

In case $n = 2$ and one of the groups normalizes the other we have, as a special case, just a semi-direct product decomposition.

(14.4) Certain actions of T on unipotent groups. We consider an action of T on a connected unipotent group U, subject to the following assumptions, where $\Phi(U)$ stands for $\Phi(T, U)$:

(i) Each weight α of T in $\underline{u} = L(U)$ is not zero, so that

$$\underline{u} = \coprod_{\alpha \in \Phi(U)} \underline{u}_{\alpha} ,$$

and $\dim \underline{u}_{\alpha} = 1$ for each $\alpha \in \Phi(U)$.

(ii) If $\alpha, \beta \in \Phi(U)$ are distinct, then they are linearly independent, i.e. the subtori $T_{\alpha} = (\ker \alpha)^0$ and $T_{\beta} = (\ker \beta)^0$ are distinct.

PROPOSITION. (1) If $\alpha \in \Phi(U)$ then $U_\alpha = U^{T_\alpha}$ is the unique T-stable closed subgroup of U with Lie algebra $\underline{u}_\alpha$.

(2) Let Λ denote the set of T-stable closed subgroups of U.

(a) If $H \in \Lambda$ then H is connected and H is directly spanned by

$$\{U_\alpha \mid \alpha \in \Phi(H)\} = \{U_\alpha \mid \underline{u}_\alpha \subset \underline{h}\} ,$$

in any order.

(b) $H \longmapsto \underline{h}$ is a lattice monomorphism from Λ to the lattice of T-stable subalgebras of $\underline{u}$.

(c) If $H, {}^xH \in \Lambda$ for some $x \in U$, then $H = {}^xH$.

PROOF. We know from (9.4) that for a subtorus S of T, the group U^S is connected, and $L(U^S) = \underline{u}^S = \coprod \underline{u}_\beta (S \subset T_\beta)$. Taking $S = T$ we see that $U^T = \{e\}$. Taking $S = T_\alpha$ for some $\alpha \in \Phi(U)$, we see that U_α is connected and, thanks to assumption (ii), that $L(U_\alpha) = \underline{u}_\alpha$. The uniqueness of U_α follows from (2)(a), which we now prove.

Let $H \in \Lambda$. We assume first H to be connected. From (9.4) again we know that H is generated by the subgroups $H^{T_\alpha} (\alpha \in \Phi(U))$. Now $H^{T_\alpha} \subset U_\alpha$ and, if $\underline{h} = L(H)$, we have $L(H^{T_\alpha}) = \underline{h}^{T_\alpha} = \underline{h}_\alpha \subset \underline{u}_\alpha$. From assumption (i) we have $\dim U_\alpha = \dim \underline{u}_\alpha = 1$. Thus either

$$H^{T_\alpha} = \{e\},\ \underline{h}_\alpha = 0, \text{ and } \alpha \notin \Phi(H)$$

or

$$H^{T_\alpha} = U_\alpha, \quad \underline{h}_{-\alpha} = \underline{u}_{-\alpha}, \quad \text{and} \quad \alpha \in \Phi(H) \, .$$

Let $\alpha_1, \ldots, \alpha_n$ be some ordering of $\Phi(H)$ and let

$$f : P = U_{\alpha_1} \times \ldots \times U_{\alpha_n} \longrightarrow H$$

be the product map. To prove (2)(a) we must show that f is an isomorphism of varieties. Clearly $(df)_e$ is an isomorphism, so f is dominant and separable.

There is no loss in generality in assuming that the ordering is chosen so that the U_{α_i} which lie in $Z(H)$ occur last; say $U_{\alpha_1}, \ldots, U_{\alpha_m}$ are those not contained in $Z(H)$. We distinguish two cases:

(i) $m = 0$; i.e. H is commutative. Then P is a group on which T acts subject to the analogues of the assumptions made on U, and f is a dominant T-equivariant homomorphism with finite kernel. But then, since T is connected, $\ker f \subset P^T$, and we saw above that the assumptions (i) and (ii) imply $P^T = \{e\}$. Thus f is an isomorphism.

(ii) General case. Let $\pi : H \longrightarrow H/Z(H)^0$ be the quotient morphism. If $i \leq m$ then $U_{\alpha_i} \longrightarrow \pi(U_{\alpha_i})$ is bijective, and we have $\pi(H) = \pi(U_{\alpha_1}) \cdot \ldots \cdot \pi(U_{\alpha_m})$, by induction on $\dim H$. Therefore $H = U_{\alpha_1} \cdot \ldots \cdot U_{\alpha_m} \cdot Z(H)^0$. By (i) $Z(H)^0 = U_{\alpha_{m+1}} \cdot \ldots \cdot U_{\alpha_n}$.

In case $H \in \Lambda$ is not connected we apply the conclusion above to H^0 and to U to write U in the form $U = H^0 \cdot V$, where say $V = U_{\beta_1} \cdot \ldots \cdot U_{\beta_q}$. Then H is the set theoretic cartesian product of H^0 and $F = H \cap V$. Since F is a finite T-stable subset of U we have $F \subset U^T = \{e\}$.

This completes the proof of (1) and of (2)(a). Part (2)(b) is an immediate consequence of (2)(a).

There remains the proof of (2)(c), so suppose $H, {}^xH \in \Lambda$ for some $x \in U$. We will show, by induction on $\dim U$, that $H = {}^xH$.

Choose a $U_\gamma \subset Z(U)$ and let $\pi : U \longrightarrow U' = U/U_\gamma$ be the quotient morphism. By induction we have $\pi(H) = \pi({}^xH)$. If $U_\gamma \subset H$ then $U_\gamma = {}^xU_\gamma \subset {}^xH$ also, and we see that $H = {}^xH$. If not, then at least $M = H \cdot U_\gamma$ coincides with ${}^xH \cdot U_\gamma$. Thus $L(M) = L(H) \oplus \underline{u}_{-\gamma} = L({}^xH) \oplus \underline{u}_{-\gamma}$. Since $L(H)$ and $L({}^xH)$ are T-stable, and since the weights of T in $\underline{u}$ have multiplicity 1, it follows that $L(H) = L({}^xH)$. Hence, by (2)(a) (or (2)(b)) we have $H = {}^xH$.

REMARK. Each U_α above is isomorphic to $\mathbb{G}_a$. Thus the product map

$$f : U_{\alpha_1} \times \ldots \times U_{\alpha_n} \longrightarrow H$$

in the proof above gives rise to a T-equivariant isomorphism of H (as a variety) with the affine space K^n on which T acts diagonally via $\alpha_1, \ldots, \alpha_n$. This also shows the existence of a T-equivariant isomorphism of varieties of L(H) onto H. In characteristic zero, it is given by the exponential map.

(14.5) Special sets of roots. Recall first that, if $\alpha \in \Phi$ then (see (13.18)(4)(d)) there is a unique connected T-stable subgroup U_α with Lie algebra $\underline{g}_\alpha$.

If $\alpha, \beta \in \Phi$ we denote by (α, β) the set of roots $\gamma \in \Phi$ of the form $\gamma = r\alpha + s\beta$, where r, s are strictly-positive integers. If Ψ and Ψ' are subsets of Φ write

$$(\Psi, \Psi') = \bigcup(\alpha, \beta) \qquad (\alpha \in \Psi, \beta \in \Psi') .$$

We shall call Ψ special if

(a) $(\Psi, \Psi) \subset \Psi$, and

(b) there is a $\lambda \in X_*(T)$ such that $\langle\alpha, \lambda\rangle > 0$ for all $\alpha \in \Psi$.

There is no loss, in (b), in assuming that λ is regular, i.e. that $\langle\alpha, \lambda\rangle \neq 0$ for all $\alpha \in \Phi$. For let λ' be any regular one-parameter subgroup. Since Φ is finite we can choose a large positive integer N so that, if $\lambda'' = N\lambda + \lambda'$, we have $\langle\alpha, \lambda''\rangle > 0$ whenever $\alpha \in \Phi$ and $\langle\alpha, \lambda\rangle > 0$. Then λ'' is evidently regular, and serves as well as λ in (b).

PROPOSITION. (1) *If* $\alpha, \beta \in \Phi$, *and if* $\beta \neq \pm\alpha$, *then*

$$[\alpha, \beta) = \{\gamma \in \Phi \mid \gamma = r\alpha + s\beta \text{ for } r, s \in \mathbb{Z} \text{ with } s > 0\}$$

is special.

Let $\Psi \subset \Phi$ be special.

(2) The set $\{U_\alpha \mid \alpha \in \Psi\}$ directly spans, in any order, a T-stable subgroup U_Ψ of G.

(3) If $\alpha \in \Phi$ and $(\alpha, \Psi) \subset \Psi$ then U_α normalizes U_Ψ.

PROOF. Suppose $\alpha, \beta \in \Phi$ and $\beta \neq \pm\alpha$. Condition (a) above is obviously satisfied by $[\alpha, \beta)$. To establish (b) recall from (13.18)(3) that $\beta \neq \pm\alpha$ implies α and β to be linearly independent. Hence there is a $\lambda \in X_*(T)$ such that $\langle\alpha, \lambda\rangle = 0$ and $\langle\beta, \lambda\rangle > 0$. This λ is clearly positive on $[\alpha, \beta)$, so we have proved (1).

Note that $(\alpha, \beta) \subset [\alpha, \beta)$. Since condition (a) is obvious for (α, β) we see that (α, β) is also special. We claim the following:

(*) Let $U_{(\alpha,\beta)}$ denote the product, in some order, of $\{U_\gamma \mid \gamma \in (\alpha, \beta)\}$. Then $(U_\alpha, U_\beta) \subset U_{(\alpha,\beta)}$.

(In case $(\alpha, \beta) = \phi$ we take $U_{(\alpha,\beta)} = \{e\}$.)

We shall now give the proof of (2) and (3), using (*), and then prove (*) at the end.

We are given a special $\Psi \subset \Phi$. The remark preceding the proposition shows that we can choose a regular $\lambda \in X_*(T)$ such that $\langle\alpha, \lambda\rangle > 0$ for all $\alpha \in \Psi$. Put $B = B(\lambda)$, $U = B_u$, and $\Phi^+ = \Phi(U) = \Phi(B)$. Then it follows from (13.18) that the action of T on U satisfies hypotheses (i) and (ii) of (14.4). If $\alpha \in \Phi^+$, moreover, the group U_α here coincides with the group so denoted (w.r.t. T and U) in (14.4). Suppose that the product, in some order, of $\{U_\alpha \mid \alpha \in \Psi\}$ is a subgroup, call it U_Ψ. Then U_Ψ is clearly a closed T-stable subgroup of U with Lie algebra $\sum_{\alpha \in \Psi} \mathfrak{g}_\alpha$. It follows therefore from (14.4) that $\Psi = \Phi(U_\Psi)$ and that U_Ψ is directly spanned, in any order, by $\{U_\alpha \mid \alpha \in \Psi\}$.

Now we shall prove (2) and (3) by induction on card Ψ. If card $\Psi = 0$ both assertions are clear, with $U_\Psi = \{e\}$. Otherwise write $\Psi = \{\beta\} \cup \Psi'$ where $\beta \notin \Psi'$ and $\langle \beta, \lambda \rangle \leqq \langle \gamma, \lambda \rangle$ for all $\gamma \in \Psi'$. Then it is easy to see that Ψ' is special and that $(\beta, \Psi') \subset \Psi'$. By induction, therefore, we have the group $U_{\Psi'}$ directly spanned by $\{U_\gamma \mid \gamma \in \Psi'\}$. In view of (*) $U_{\Psi'}$ is normalized by U_β (see the proof of (3) below). In particular $U_\beta \cdot U_{\Psi'}$ is a subgroup, U_Ψ of U, and the paragraph above shows that U_Ψ is directly spanned, in any order, by $\{U_\gamma \mid \gamma \in \Psi\}$. This proves (2).

To prove (3), suppose $(\alpha, \Psi) \subset \Psi$. To show that U_α normalizes U_Ψ it suffices to show that, for $x \in U_\alpha$ and $\gamma \in \Psi$, we have ${}^x U_\gamma \subset U_\Psi$. Suppose $y \in U_\gamma$. Then ${}^x y = (xyx^{-1})(y^{-1}y) = (x, y)y \in (U_\alpha, U_\gamma)U_\gamma$. Thus it suffices to see that $(U_\alpha, U_\gamma) \subset U_\Psi$. But, according to (*), $(U_\alpha, U_\gamma) \subset U_{(\alpha, \gamma)}$, where $U_{(\alpha,\gamma)}$ is the product, in some order, of $\{U_\delta \mid \delta \in (\alpha, \gamma)\}$. Since $(\alpha, \gamma) \subset \Psi$ we have $U_{(\alpha, \gamma)} \subset U_\Psi$, and this completes the proof, modulo the:

Proof of (*). Put $\Psi = (\alpha, \beta) \cup \{\alpha, \beta\}$. It is clear (see proof of (1) above) that Ψ is special. Hence we can choose λ, $B = B(\lambda)$, $U = B_u$, and $\Phi^+ = \Phi(U)$, as above, so that $\Psi \subset \Phi^+$.

If $\gamma \in \Phi^+$, let $\theta_\gamma : \mathbb{G}_a \longrightarrow U_\gamma$ be an isomorphism. Then,

$$^t\theta_\gamma(x) = \theta_\gamma(t^\gamma x) \quad (\text{for } t \in T,\ x \in \mathbb{G}_a) \ .$$

Let $\alpha_1, \ldots, \alpha_n$ be the elements of Φ^+, in any fixed order. According to (14.4) the product morphism

$$U_{\alpha_1} \times \ldots \times U_{\alpha_n} \longrightarrow U$$

is an isomorphism of varieties. Define

$$f : \mathbb{G}_a \times \mathbb{G}_a \longrightarrow U, \ f(x, y) = (\theta_\alpha(x), \ \theta_\beta(y)) \ .$$

Then the isomorphism above shows that

$$f(x, y) = \prod_{1 \leqq i \leqq n} \theta_{\alpha_i}(P_i(x, y))$$

(product in ascending order), where the P_i are polynomials in two variables. Say

$$P_i(x, y) = \sum_{r, s \geqq 0} c_{i, r, s} x^r y^s \ .$$

Since $f(0, y) = e = f(x, 0)$ we see that each monomial in P_i involves both x and y, i.e. the summation is actually over $r, s > 0$.

For $t \in T$ and $x, y \in \mathbb{G}_a$ we see that $^t f(x, y)$ is equal to

$$(\theta_\alpha(t^\alpha x),\ \theta_\beta(t^\beta y)) = \prod_i \theta_{\alpha_i}(P_i(t^\alpha x,\ t^\beta y))$$

as well as to

$$\prod_i \theta_{\alpha_i}(t^{\alpha_i} P_i(x,\ y)) \ .$$

This yields, for each $i = 1, \ldots, n$,

$$\Sigma_{r,\, s>0} c_{i,\, r,\, s}(t^\alpha x)^r (t^\beta y)^s = \Sigma_{r,\, s>0} c_{i,\, r,\, s} t^{\alpha_i} x^r y^s \ .$$

It follows that

$$c_{i,\, r,\, s} = 0 \ \text{ unless } \ \alpha_i = r\alpha + s\beta \ .$$

Since, as already observed, $c_{i,\, r,\, s} = 0$ unless $r,\ s > 0$, we therefore have $c_{i,\, r,\, s} = 0$ unless $\alpha_i \in (\alpha,\ \beta)$. Thus,

$$P_i = 0 \ \text{ unless } \ \alpha_i \in (\alpha,\ \beta) \ .$$

The latter is precisely what we sought to prove. It asserts, for $x, y \in \mathbb{G}_a$, that $(\theta_\alpha(x),\ \theta_\beta(y))$ lies in the product (in the above order) of those U_{α_i} for which $\alpha_i \in (\alpha,\ \beta)$.

REMARKS. (1) Since α and β are linearly independent there is at most one expression for an α_i in the form $r\alpha + s\beta$. Hence the proof above shows that <u>each P_i is a monomial</u>, zero unless $\alpha_i \in (\alpha,\ \beta)$.

(2) The statement just proved is a weak analogue of the corresponding fact, $[\underline{g}_\alpha,\ \underline{g}_\beta] = \underline{g}_{\alpha+\beta}$, in the theory of complex semi-simple Lie algebras.

(3) In characteristic $p > 0$ it may happen that

$\alpha, \beta, \alpha + \beta \in \Phi$, but nevertheless $(U_\alpha, U_\beta) = \{e\}$.

(14.6) COROLLARY. Let $\alpha \in \Phi$, and let $r_\alpha \in W$ be the generator of the subgroup $W(T, G_\alpha)$. Then if $\beta \in \Phi$ we have

$$r_\alpha(\beta) = \beta - n_{\beta,\alpha}\alpha$$

with $n_{\beta,\alpha} \in \mathbb{Z}$. Moreover $n_{\alpha,\alpha} = 2$.

PROOF. We know from (13.18)(4)(c) that $r_\alpha(\alpha) = -\alpha = \alpha - 2\alpha$, and that r_α fixes the elements of a subgroup of corank 1 in $X(T)$. Passing to $X(T)_{\mathbb{Q}}$, and extending α to a basis whose remaining members are in the fixed hyperplane of r_α (extended to $X(T)_{\mathbb{Q}}$), we see that, for any $\gamma \in X(T)_{\mathbb{Q}}$, $\gamma - r_\alpha(\gamma)$ is a (rational) multiple of α. In particular, $r_\alpha(\beta) = \beta - n_{\beta,\alpha}\alpha$ for some $n_{\beta,\alpha} \in \mathbb{Q}$, moreover $n_{\alpha,\alpha} = 2$ and $n_{\alpha,-\alpha} = -2$. Therefore, to prove $n_{\beta,\alpha} \in \mathbb{Z}$, we may assume $\beta \neq \pm\alpha$.

We apply the proposition above, which says that $[\alpha, \beta)$ is special, and hence that the $U_\gamma (\gamma \in [\alpha, \beta))$ directly span a T-stable subgroup $H = U_{[\alpha,\beta)}$. Evidently $(\alpha, [\alpha, \beta)) \subset [\alpha, \beta)$ and $(-\alpha, [\alpha, \beta)) \subset [\alpha, \beta)$, so the proposition implies that U_α and $U_{-\alpha}$ normalize H. Since U_α, $U_{-\alpha}$ and T generate G_α it follows that G_α normalizes H. Now r_α arises from conjugation by an $n \in N_{G_\alpha}(T)$, and we have just seen that this n normalizes H. Since $\beta \in [\alpha, \beta)$ and $nU_\beta n^{-1} = {}^{r_\alpha}U_\beta = U_{r_\alpha(\beta)}$ it follows that $r_\alpha(\beta) \in [\alpha, \beta)$, i.e. that $r_\alpha(\beta) = r\alpha + s\beta$ for suitable $r, s \in \mathbb{Z}$, $s > 0$. Thus $s = 1$ and $n_{\beta,\alpha} = -r \in \mathbb{Z}$. Q.E.D.

(14.7) Review of root systems. The facts to be reviewed here can all be found in ([20], Chap. V and p. VII-13), or in [10].

Let R be a subfield of $\mathbb{R}$. If V is a vector space over R we write $V^* = \mathrm{Hom}_R(V, R)$. Let α be a non-zero vector in V. We call $r \in GL(V)$ a reflection with respect to α if $r(\alpha) = -\alpha$ and if r fixes the points of a hyperplane H in V. Thus $r(\beta) = \beta - \langle\beta, \lambda\rangle\alpha$, for $\beta \in V$, where $\lambda \in V^*$ has kernel H, and $\langle\alpha, \lambda\rangle = 2$.

If Φ is a finite spanning set of V, there is at most one reflection with respect to α leaving Φ stable.

A root system is a pair (V, Φ) where V is a vector space over R, and where Φ is a subset of V satisfying:

(1) Φ is finite, spans V, and does not contain zero.

(2) For each $\alpha \in \Phi$ there is a reflection r_α with respect to α which leaves Φ stable (and which is therefore unique, by the remark above).

(3) If $\alpha, \beta \in \Phi$ then $r_\alpha(\beta) = \beta - n_{\beta,\alpha}\alpha$ with $n_{\beta,\alpha} \in \mathbb{Z}$. The elements of Φ are called roots.

The notion of isomorphism of root systems is evident. We will usually denote the root system by Φ, and say that "Φ is a root system in V." In particular we have $\mathrm{Aut}(\Phi) \subset GL(V)$. The subgroup $W(\Phi)$ of $\mathrm{Aut}(\Phi)$

generated by the r_α ($\alpha \in \Phi$) is called the Weyl group of Φ.

Let $\alpha \in \Phi$ be such that the only roots, $a\alpha$, proportional to α are such that $|a| \leqq 1$. If $a\alpha$ is one such then $-a\alpha = r_\alpha(a\alpha) = a\alpha - n_{a\alpha,\alpha}\alpha$, so that $2a = n_{a\alpha,\alpha} \in \mathbf{Z}$. Thus the roots proportional to α are either $\{-\alpha, \alpha\}$ or $\{-\alpha, -\alpha/2, \alpha/2, \alpha\}$. If the latter case never occurs, i.e. if, whenever α and β are proportional roots we have $\beta = \pm\alpha$, then the root system Φ is said to be reduced.

Fix a root system Φ in V. A basis of Φ is a subset S of Φ, which is a basis of V such that each root β is a linear combination, $\beta = \Sigma_{\alpha\in S} m_\alpha \alpha$, with the m_α integers all of the same sign. We then define the positive roots Φ^+ (with respect to S) to be those β for which all m_α are $\geqq 0$. Thus Φ is the disjoint union of Φ^+ and $\Phi^- = -\Phi^+$. We call

$$WC(S) = \{\lambda \in V^* \mid \langle\alpha, \lambda\rangle > 0 \text{ for all } \alpha \in S\}$$

the Weyl chamber of S (or of Φ^+. One can clearly replace S by Φ^+ in the definition without essentially altering it.)

Call $\lambda \in V^*$ regular if $\langle\alpha, \lambda\rangle \neq 0$ for all $\alpha \in \Phi$. For example, a Weyl chamber clearly consists of regular elements. If λ is regular we shall write

$$\Phi^+(\lambda) = \{\alpha \in \Phi \mid \langle\alpha, \lambda\rangle > 0\}$$

and

$$S(\lambda) = \{\alpha \in \Phi^+(\lambda) \mid \alpha \text{ is not the sum of two elements of } \Phi^+(\lambda)\}.$$

THEOREM. Let Φ be a root system in V.

(1) If $\lambda \in V^*$ is regular then $S(\lambda)$ is a basis of Φ. It is the unique basis contained in $\Phi^+(\lambda)$. Thus, $S \longmapsto WC(S)$ is a bijection from the set of bases to the set of Weyl chambers.

Now suppose Φ is reduced.

(2) $W(\Phi)$ acts simply transitively on the set of bases of Φ, and (equivalently) on the set of Weyl chambers.

Let S be a basis of Φ.

(3) The r_α $(\alpha \in S)$ generate $W(\Phi)$.

(4) $\Phi = \bigcup_{w \in W(\Phi)} wS$.

One associates to a basis S of Φ the so-called Dynkin diagram $\mathrm{Dyn}(\Phi, S)$ which is a finite graph having S as its set of vertices, supplied with suitable "weights," and in which α and β in S are joined by $n_{\alpha,\beta} n_{\beta,\alpha}$ edges. The Dynkin diagrams give a complete classification of root systems. Moreover $\mathrm{Dyn}(\Phi, S)$ is functorial in (Φ, S), and the automorphism group of Φ is the semi-direct product of W and of $\mathrm{Aut}(\mathrm{Dyn}(\Phi, S))$, the latter being the stability group of S in $\mathrm{Aut}(\Phi)$.

The root system (V, Φ) is said to be irreducible if one cannot write $V = V_1 \oplus V_2$ as a non-trivial direct sum so that $\Phi = (\Phi \cap V_1) \cup (\Phi \cap V_2)$.

(14.8) THEOREM. Let $V = X(T/Z(G)^0)_{\mathbb{Q}}$, identified canonically with a subspace of $X(T)_{\mathbb{Q}}$. Then Φ is a reduced root system in V, with Weyl group W.

PROOF. From (13.18)(3) we conclude that Φ is a finite set of non-zero vectors spanning V, and that, if α and β in Φ are proportional, then $\beta = \pm\alpha$. For the rest we can, without loss, assume $Z(G)^0 = \{e\}$, by passing to $G/Z(G)^0$.

From (13.18)(4)(c) we obtain a reflection r_α of $X(T)$ with respect to α which leaves Φ stable. The extension of r_α to V (which we shall also denote by r_α) verifies condition (2) in the definition of a root system.

The (integrality) condition (3) is established by (14.6).

This shows that Φ is a reduced root system in V, and that $W(\Phi) \subset W$.

If we identify V^* with $X_*(T)_{\mathbb{Q}}$ then it is clear from (14.7) and from (13.18)(5) that the Weyl chambers in V^* of bases of Φ coincide with the subsets of V^* obtained from Weyl chambers in $X_*(T)$ of Borel subgroups $B \in \mathcal{B}^T$. (The Weyl chamber in V^* corresponding to $B \in \mathcal{B}^T$ is $\{\lambda \in V^* \mid \langle\alpha, \lambda\rangle > 0$ for $\alpha \in \Phi(T, B)\}$.) According to (13.10)(2), W acts simply transitively on these Weyl chambers. But (14.7) asserts $W(\Phi)$ does likewise, and hence the inclusion $W(\Phi) \subset W$ is an equality.

COROLLARY. Let $B \in \mathcal{B}^T$ and let $S = S(B)$ be the set of $\alpha \in \Phi(B)$ which are not sums of two elements in $\Phi(B)$.

(1) S is a basis of Φ. (We call S the set of simple roots associated with B (and T).)

(2) G is generated by $\{G_\alpha \mid \alpha \in S\}$.

PROOF. (1) follows from (14.6) in view of the fact (see (13.18)(5)) that $\Phi(B) = \{\alpha \in \Phi \mid \langle \alpha, \lambda \rangle > 0$ for $\lambda \in WC(B)\}$, and, for such a λ, $\langle \alpha, \lambda \rangle \neq 0$ for all $\alpha \in \Phi$, i.e. λ is regular.

(2) We know from (13.6) that G is generated by the set of $B \in \mathcal{B}^T$. If $B \in \mathcal{B}^T$ then $B = T \cdot B_u$ and (14.4) implies that B_u is generated (even directly spanned) by the set of U_α $(\alpha \in \Phi(B))$. Thus G is generated by T together with the U_α $(\alpha \in \Phi)$.

Let H be the subgroup generated by G_α $(\alpha \in S)$. G_α contains U_α as well as a representative, $n_\alpha \in N_{G_\alpha}(T)$, of $r_\alpha \in W$. Hence it follows from (14.7) that H contains a representative, $n = n(w) \in N_G(T)$, of each $w \in W$. If $\beta \in \Phi$ then ${}^n U_\beta = U_{w(\beta)}$. Thus H contains all U_β for which β is a W-transform of some $\alpha \in S$. According to (14.7) these β's exhaust Φ. Since, clearly, $T \subset H$, this shows that $H = G$.

(14.9) Automorphisms of semi-simple groups. Assume G is semi-simple, and fix a $B \in \mathcal{B}^T$. In

$$A = \mathrm{Aut}_{\mathrm{alg.\,grp.}}(G)$$

let $\mathrm{Int}(G)$ be the group of inner automorphisms. Also write $A_{(B, T)}$ for the subgroup of A stabilizing both B and T.

According to (14.8) $\Phi(B)$ is the set of positive roots with respect to a basis $S(B)$ of Φ. We shall write $\mathrm{Dyn}(\Phi, B)$ for the corresponding Dynkin diagram (see (14.7)), and $\mathrm{Aut}(\mathrm{Dyn}(\Phi, B))$ for its automorphism group.

If $a \in A_{(B, T)}$ then, since $a.T = T$, a induces an automorphism of the root system Φ. Since $a.B = B$ it follows that a leaves $S(B)$ stable and hence defines an element $a' \in \mathrm{Aut}(\mathrm{Dyn}(\Phi, B))$.

PROPOSITION. (1) $A = \mathrm{Int}(G) \cdot A_{(B, T)}$.

(2) $\mathrm{Int}(G) \cap A_{(B, T)}$ _is the kernel of the homomorphism_ $A_{(B, T)} \longrightarrow \mathrm{Aut}(\mathrm{Dyn}(\Phi, B))(a \longmapsto a')$ _described above._

(3) _There is a natural injection_ $A/\mathrm{Int}(G) \longrightarrow \mathrm{Aut}(\mathrm{Dyn}(\Phi, B))$. _In particular_ $\mathrm{Int}(G)$ _has finite index in_ A.

PROOF. Clearly (3) follows from (1) and (2).

(1) Let $a \in A$. By the conjugacy of Borel subgroups of G we have $cB = B$ where $c = \mathrm{Int}(g) \circ a$ for some $g \in G$. By the conjugacy of maximal tori in B we have $dT = T$ where $d = \mathrm{Int}(b) \circ c$ for some $b \in B$. Thus we have $d = \mathrm{Int}(b) \circ \mathrm{Int}(g) \circ a \in A_{(B, T)}$, as required.

(2) Suppose $a \in A_{(B, T)}$. If $a = \mathrm{Int}(g)$ for some $g \in G$ then by (10.6), (11.15), $g \in N_G(B) \cap N_G(T) = B \cap N_G(T) = N_B(T) = T$, so a induces the identity automorphism of Φ.

Suppose, conversely, that $a' \in \mathrm{Aut}(\mathrm{Dyn}(\Phi, B))$ is the identity. We must show that a is inner. For each $\alpha \in S(B)$ we have an isomorphism $\theta_\alpha : \mathbb{G}_a \longrightarrow U_\alpha$. Since a leaves U_α stable we have $a\theta_\alpha(x) = \theta_\alpha(c_\alpha x)$ for some $c_\alpha \in K^*$. Since the elements of $S(B)$ are linearly independent we can find a $t \in T$ such that $t^\alpha = c_\alpha$ for each $\alpha \in S(B)$. Then $\mathrm{Int}(t)$ has the same effect as a on each $U_\alpha (\alpha \in S(B))$ so we can replace a by $\mathrm{Int}(t)^{-1} \circ a$ and assume each $c_\alpha = 1$. In that case a fixes the elements of each $U_\alpha (\alpha \in S(B))$.

We claim a also fixes the elements of T. For if $t \in T$ then $t^\alpha = a(t)^\alpha$ for each $\alpha \in S(B)$. Since G is semi-simple, $S(B)$ spans a subgroup of finite index in $X(T)$ (14.8). Hence $t = a(t)$ as claimed.

Evidently a stabilizes $G_\alpha = G^{T_\alpha}$ and it fixes the elements of the Borel subgroup $T \cdot U_\alpha$. Hence (11.4)(1) implies $a|G_\alpha$ is the identity. Finally (14.8) asserts that the $G_\alpha (\alpha \in S(B))$ generate G, so a is the identity.

(14.10) PROPOSITION. <u>Assume</u> G <u>is semi-simple and</u> $\neq \{e\}$.

(1) <u>Let</u> H <u>be a connected normal subgroup of</u> G, <u>and let</u> $H' = (G^H)^0$.

(a) H <u>is semi-simple</u>.

(b) $G = H \cdot H'$ <u>and</u> $H \cap H'$ <u>is contained in the finite group</u> $Z(G)$.

(2) <u>Let</u> $\{G_i | i \in I\}$ <u>be the minimal elements among the connected normal subgroups of dimension</u> $\geqq 1$.

(a) If $i \neq j$ then $(G_i, G_j) = \{e\}$.

(b) I is finite; say $I = \{1, \ldots, n\}$.

The product morphism

$$G_1 \times \ldots \times G_n \longrightarrow G$$

is an isogeny.

(c) If H is a connected normal subgroup of G, then H is generated by $\{G_i \mid G_i \subset H\}$.

(3) G is "almost simple," i.e. $G/Z(G)$ is simple, if and only if the root system Φ is irreducible.

PROOF. (1) Assertion (a) follows from ((14.2), Cor.). G^H is the kernel of the conjugation homomorphism:

$$G \xrightarrow{\text{Int}|H} \text{Aut}_{\text{alg. grp.}}(H)$$

and, by (14.9), the image of H is a subgroup of finite index. Hence $H \cdot G^H$ has finite index in G. Therefore, by connectivity, $G = H \cdot (G^H)^0 = H \cdot H'$. Moreover $(H \cap H')^0 \subset Z(H)^0 \subset R(H) = \{e\}$ so $H \cap H'$ is a finite normal, and hence central, subgroup of G.

(2) Let H be as above and let $i \in I$. Then (G_i, H) is a connected normal subgroup of G contained in $G_i \cap H$. Hence, by minimality of G_i, it equals $\{e\}$ or G_i. In other words, $G_i \subset (G^H)^0$ or $G_i \subset H$. In particular $(G_i, G_j) = \{e\}$ for $i \neq j$.

Let $J = \{i_1, \ldots, i_r\} \subset I$ and let G_J denote the image of the morphism

$$f_J : G_{i_1} \times \ldots \times G_{i_r} \longrightarrow G \; .$$

With the aid of the remarks above an induction on $r = \text{card } J$ shows that $G_J \cap G_h$ is finite if $h \notin J$, and hence that $\ker(f_J)$ is finite. Therefore $\dim G \geqq \dim G_J = \Sigma_{j \in J} \dim G_j \geqq \text{card } J$, so I must be finite. Moreover,

$$f_J : G_{i_1} \times \ldots \times G_{i_r} \longrightarrow G_J \text{ is an isogeny.}$$

With H and H' as in (1) we see also that $I = J \cup J'$ (disjoint) where $J = \{j \in I \,|\, G_j \subset H\}$ and $J' = \{j \in I \,|\, G_j \subset H'\}$. It follows then, since $G = G_J \cdot G_{J'} = H \cdot H'$ and $H \cap H'$ is finite, that $H = G_J$.

(3) If $G = H \cdot H'$ as above then it is clear that the root system Φ of G decomposes into the direct sum of those of H and of H', respectively. Thus, if both H and H' have dimension $\geqq 1$, Φ is reducible.

Conversely, suppose Φ is reducible; say $\Phi = \Phi_1 \cup \Phi_2$ is a non-trivial decomposition into a sum of two root systems. Let G_i denote the subgroup generated by all $U_\alpha (\alpha \in \Phi_i)$. Then, since Φ_1 and Φ_2 are both not empty, $\dim G_i \geqq 1 (i = 1, 2)$.

We claim first that G_1 and G_2 generate G. For let H be the group they generate. Then $H_\alpha = H \cap G_\alpha$ projects onto the semi-simple quotient PGL_2 of G_α (see (10.8)) so H_α contains a complementary torus T'_α to T_α in T. Since $(\cap T_\alpha)^0 = \{e\}$ (G is semi-simple) it follows that the tori T'_α are independent and generate T. Thus H contains T, and hence each G_α, and hence

$H = G$ (see (14.8), Cor.).

Next we claim that G_1 centralizes G_2. For if $\alpha \in \Phi_1$ and $\beta \in \Phi_2$ there are no roots of the form $r\alpha + s\beta$ with $r, s > 0$. Hence the assertion (*) in the proof of (14.5) shows that U_α and U_β commute.

Finally, therefore, $G_1 \cap G_2$ commutes with the group generated by G_1 and G_2, which is G, so $G_1 \cap G_2 (\subset Z(G))$ is finite. This completes the proof of (3), and hence of the proposition.

(14.11) <u>The Bruhat decomposition</u>. We fix a $B \in \mathcal{B}^T$ and write $U = B_u$, $\Phi^+ = \Phi(B)$, and $S =$ the basis of Φ in $\Phi^+ =$ the set of "simple roots associated with B."

Let $B^- \in \mathcal{B}^T$ be the opposite Borel subgroup (see (14.1)). We put $U^- = B^-_u$ and $\Phi^- = \Phi(B^-) = -\Phi^+$. For $\alpha \in \Phi$ we shall write $\alpha > 0$ if $\alpha \in \Phi^+$ and $\alpha < 0$ if $\alpha \in \Phi^-$.

If $w \in W$ we shall allow ourselves to confuse w with a representing element in $N_G(T)$, whenever the use is unaffected by the choice of representative.

We shall consider the groups

$$U_w = U \cap {}^wU \quad \text{and} \quad U^-_w = U \cap {}^wU^- .$$

These are both T-stable closed subgroups of U, so it follows from (14.4) that they are directly spanned, in any order, by the $U_\gamma (\gamma > 0)$ that they contain. The sets of such γ are, respectively,

$$\Phi^+_w = \Phi(U_w) = \{\gamma > 0 \mid \gamma^w > 0\} ,$$

and

$$\Phi_w^- = \Phi(U_w^-) = \{\gamma > 0 \mid \gamma^w < 0\} \ ,$$

where $\gamma^w = \gamma \circ \mathrm{Int}(n)$ for any $n \in N_G(T)$ representing w. Since these sets partition Φ^+ it follows also from (14.4) that

$$U = U_w \cdot U_w^- = U_w^- \cdot U_w \ .$$

Let x_0 denote the fixed point of B in G/B.

THEOREM. (a) (<u>Bruhat decomposition of</u> G). G <u>is the disjoint union of the double cosets</u> $BwB (w \in W)$. <u>If</u> $w \in W$ <u>then the morphism</u> $U_w^- \times B \longrightarrow BwB ((x, y) \longmapsto xwy)$ <u>is an isomorphism of varieties.</u>

(b) (<u>Cellular decomposition of</u> G/B). G/B <u>is the disjoint union of the</u> U-<u>orbits</u> $Uwx_0 (w \in W)$. <u>If</u> $w \in W$ <u>then the morphism</u> $U_w^- \longrightarrow Uwx_0 (u \longmapsto uwx_0)$ <u>is an isomorphism of varieties.</u>

REMARKS. (1) The fixed points $(G/B)^T$ correspond to $\mathcal{B}^T$, and we know from (11.19) that W acts simply transitively on this set. In particular, $Wx_0 = (G/B)^T$, and this set has the same cardinality as W. Part (b) above therefore asserts that each U-orbit in G/B meets $(G/B)^T$ in precisely one point.

(2) Since $B = U \cdot T$ and W normalizes T it follows that, for $w \in W$, we have $BwB = UwB$ and $Bwx_0 = Uwx_0$. Thus it is clear that (a) and (b) are equivalent.

(3) It follows from (14.4) that each U_w^- is isomorphic, as a variety, to an affine space. Thus, if $K = \mathbb{C}$, each of the U-orbits is a cell; and (b) gives rise to a cell decomposition of G/B in the sense of algebraic topology. Since these cells are complex varieties they occur only in even (real) dimensions. Hence the $2i^{\underline{th}}$ Betti number of G/B is the number of cells of (complex) dimension i. The latter is the number of $w \in W$ for which $\dim U_w^- = \operatorname{card}\{\gamma > 0 \mid w^{-1}(\gamma) < 0\}$ is equal to i.

PROOF. In view of remark (2) above, the theorem will follow once we establish the following three assertions:

(1) _If_ $w, w' \in W$, _then_ $Uwx_0 = Uw'x_0 \Longrightarrow w = w'$.

(2) $G = BWB$.

(3) _If_ $w \in W$ _then the map_ $U_w^- \times B \longrightarrow BwB$ _given by_ $(x, y) \longmapsto xwy$ _is an isomorphism of varieties._

Proof of (1). Say $w'x_0 = uwx_0$ with $u \in U$. Then the stability group in U of $w'x_0$, i.e. $U \cap {}^{w'}B = U_{w'}$, coincides with that of uwx_0, i.e. with $U_{uw} = U \cap {}^{uw}B = {}^{u}(U \cap {}^{w}B) = {}^{u}U_w$. Thus U_w and ${}^{u}U_w = U_{w'}$ are each closed T-stable subgroups of U. Therefore (14.4)(2)(c) implies $U_w = U_{w'}$. In particular $\Phi_w^+ = \Phi(U_w)$ and $\Phi_{w'}^+ = \Phi(U_{w'})$ coincide, where $\Phi_w^+ = \{\gamma \in \Phi^+ \mid \gamma^w > 0\}$, and similarly for $\Phi_{w'}^+$. Therefore the proof is completed by the:

LEMMA. _If_ $w, w' \in W$ _and if_ $\Phi_w^+ = \Phi_{w'}^+$ _then_ $w = w'$.

PROOF. Suppose $n \in N_G(T)$ represents w. We then have the actions of w on $\lambda \in X_*(T)$ and on $\alpha \in X(T)$ given by ${}^w\lambda = \mathrm{Int}(n) \circ \lambda$ and $\alpha^w = \alpha \circ \mathrm{Int}(n)$. Thus $\alpha^w \circ \lambda = \alpha \circ {}^w\lambda$, or, equivalently, $\langle \alpha^w, \lambda \rangle = \langle \alpha, {}^w\lambda \rangle$.

If λ is semi-regular then the Weyl chamber to which λ belongs is determined by the signs of the numbers $\langle \alpha, \lambda \rangle$, where α varies over Φ^+. This follows from (13.18)(5). Suppose $\lambda \in WC(B)$, i.e. $\langle \alpha, \lambda \rangle > 0$ for all $\alpha > 0$. Then for $\alpha > 0$ we have $\langle \alpha, {}^w\lambda \rangle = \langle \alpha^w, \lambda \rangle$ which is > 0 if $\alpha \in \Phi^+_w$ and < 0 otherwise. It follows from the hypothesis, therefore, that ${}^w\lambda$ and ${}^{w'}\lambda$ lie in the same Weyl chamber. Therefore $w = w'$ since W acts simply transitively on the Weyl chambers (13.10).

Proof of (2). It will be carried out in several steps.

(i) If G has semi-simple rank 1 then (2) holds.

In this case W has order 2. so part (1) implies that BWx_0 consists of 2 U-orbits. Hence it suffices to show that G/B consists of at most 2 U-orbits. Consider the morphism $U \longrightarrow G/B (u \longmapsto uy)$, where y is not a fixed point of U. We can identify $U \cong \mathbb{G}_a$ with $\mathbb{P}_1$ minus a point, and then extend the morphism to $\mathbb{P}_1 \longrightarrow G/B$. The image is closed and one-dimensional, and hence equals G/B. On the other hand this image consists of a one-dimensional U-orbit together with a single fixed point.

(ii) If $\alpha \in \Phi$ and $x \in G/B$, then

$$G_\alpha x = (U_\alpha x) \cup (U_\alpha r_\alpha x) \quad .$$

Put $C = (G_\alpha)_x = G_\alpha \cap B_x$. This is a Borel subgroup of G_α (11.18), and we have a G_α-equivariant and bijective morphism $G_\alpha / C \longrightarrow G_\alpha x$. Since G_α has semi-simple rank 1 (13.18) and Weyl group $\{e, r_\alpha\}$ (with respect to T), (ii) now follows from (i).

(iii) Suppose α is a simple root (i.e. $\alpha \in S$) and let $\Psi = \Phi^+ - \{\alpha\}$. Then, in the terminology and notation of (14.5), Ψ is special, and so the $U_\beta (\beta \in \Psi)$ directly span a group U_Ψ. Moreover U_Ψ is normalized by G_α, and $U = U_\alpha U_\Psi = U_\Psi U_\alpha$.

It is clear from the properties of root systems (see (14.7)) that Ψ is special and that $(\alpha, \Psi) \subset \Psi$. Furthermore $(-\alpha, \Psi) \subset \Psi$. For suppose $\gamma = r(-\alpha) + s\beta \in \Phi$ where $\beta \in \Psi$ and $r, s > 0$. Then $\beta = \sum_{\delta \in S} m_\delta \delta$ with $m_{\delta_0} > 0$ for some $\delta_0 \neq \alpha$, because Φ is reduced. Hence the δ_0-coordinate of γ is $sm_{\delta_0} > 0$, so $\gamma \in \Phi^+$. Clearly $\gamma \neq \alpha$ so $\gamma \in \Psi$.

Now it follows from (14.5) that $\{U_\beta | \beta \in \Psi\}$ directly span (in any order) a group U_Ψ, and that U_Ψ is normalized by U_α and $U_{-\alpha}$, as well as, of course, by T. Thus U_Ψ is normalized by G_α, the latter being generated by U_α, $U_{-\alpha}$, and T. The equalities $U = U_\alpha U_\Psi = U_\Psi U_\alpha$ are now clear.

(iv) If $a \in S$ and $x \in (G/B)^T$ then $G_\alpha Bx = (Ux) \cup (Ur_\alpha x)$.

We have $B = UT = U_\alpha U_\Psi T$ (as in (iii)), so

$$
\begin{aligned}
G_\alpha Bx &= G_\alpha U_\alpha U_\Psi Tx \\
&= G_\alpha U_\Psi x && (Tx = x \text{ and } U_\alpha \subset G_\alpha) \\
&= U_\Psi G_\alpha x && (G_\alpha \text{ normalizes } U_\Psi;\ \text{(iii)}) \\
&= U_\Psi ((U_\alpha x) \cup (U_\alpha r_\alpha x)) && \text{(part (ii))} \\
&= (Ux) \cup (Ur_\alpha x)
\end{aligned}
$$

(v) *If* $\alpha \in S$ *then* $G_\alpha(BwB) \subset BwB \cup Br_\alpha wB$.

For if $w \in W$ then, by (iv), we have

$$G_\alpha BwB = (UwB) \cup (Ur_\alpha wB) \subset (BwB) \subset (Br_\alpha wB) \ .$$

According to the corollary of (14.8), C is generated by the $G_\alpha (\alpha \in S)$. Hence (v) implies $G(BWB) \subset (BWB)$, thus proving (2).

Proof of (3). Since $U_w = U \cap {}^wB = U \cap wBw^{-1} = U \cap wUw^{-1}$ we have $U_w w \subset wU$. Similarly, $U_w^- w \subset wU^-$. Writing $B = UT = U_w^- U_w T$ we see that $BwB = U_w^- U_w wB = U_w^- wB$, so

$$f : U_w^- \times B \longrightarrow BwB \quad ((x, y) \longmapsto xwy)$$

is surjective. Since $U_w^- w \subset wU^-$ and $U^- \cap B = \{e\}$ it follows that f is injective also. Moreover since $L(U^-) = \sum_{\alpha<0} \underline{g}_\alpha$ has trivial intersection with $L(B) = \underline{g}^T \oplus \sum_{\alpha>0} \underline{g}_\alpha$, it follows that f is separable, and hence an isomorphism.

(14.12) COROLLARY. If $B, B', B'' \in \mathcal{B}$ then $B \cap B'$ contains a maximal torus of G. If B' and B'' are opposite to B, then they are conjugate by an element of B.

PROOF. B' has a fixed point on $G/B = \bigcup_{w \in W} Uwx_0$ (in the notation of (14.11)). Say B' fixes $x = uwx_0$, where $w \in W$ and $u \in U$. Then $B' = {}^{uw}B$. Since $T \subset {}^{w}B$ we have ${}^{u}T \subset {}^{uw}B \cap B = B' \cap B$.

Let T', T'' be maximal tori in $B \cap B'$ and $B \cap B''$ respectively. If B' (resp. B'') is opposite to B, then it is the unique Borel subgroup of G opposite to B containing T' (resp. T'') by (14.1). Then an element $b \in B$ such that ${}^{b}T' = T''$ (see (10.6)) will conjugate B' onto B''.

(14.13) COROLLARY. Let $B, B' \in \mathcal{B}^T$ be opposite Borel subgroups and $U = B_u$, $U' = B'_u$. Then the product map $U' \times B \longrightarrow G$ is an isomorphism of $U' \times B$ onto an open subset of G. The group G is a rational variety.

By (14.12), we may assume that B, B' are the B and B^- of (14.11). Let w_0 be the element of W which maps Φ^+ onto Φ^-. Then, left translation by w_0 is an isomorphism of $U \cdot w_0 \cdot B$ onto $w_0 \cdot U \cdot w_0 \cdot B = U' \cdot B$, and the first assertion follows from (14.11).

T is isomorphic to a product of $\mathbb{GL}_1$'s over $\bar{k}$. In view of (13.18), the remark in (14.4) applies to U, U', hence both are isomorphic, as varieties, to affine spaces. Since B is isomorphic, as a variety, to $T \times U$

by (10.6), it follows that $U' \cdot B$ is a rational variety, hence so is G.

REMARK. We shall see in §18 that G is unirational over k, rational over a separable extension of k, and in (15.8) that any connected affine k-group is a rational variety over $\overline{k}$.

(14.14) LEMMA. We keep the notation of (14.11). Let $X_\alpha (\alpha \in S)$ be a non-zero element of $\underline{g}_\alpha$ and $X = \Sigma_{\alpha \in S} X_\alpha$. Then $Tr(X, \underline{b}) = \{g \in G, \ Ad\, g(X) \in \underline{b}\} = B$.

Let $g \in Tr(X, \underline{b})$. By (14.11), we may write $g = b' \cdot w \cdot b \quad (b, b' \in B, \ w \in W)$. Since B normalizes $\underline{b}$, we may assume $b' = e$. By (3.12), $Ad\, b(X) - X$ lies in the Lie algebra of the derived group (U, U) of U. It follows from (*) in (14.5) that (U, U) is directly spanned by the $U_\gamma (\gamma \in \Phi^+, \ \gamma \notin S)$. Since w permutes the $\underline{g}_\alpha$, we may then write

$$Ad\, g(X) = \Sigma_{\alpha \in \Phi} c_\alpha X_{w(\alpha)}, \qquad (X_{w(\alpha)} \in \underline{g}_{w(\alpha)}) .$$

The set of α's for which $c_\alpha \neq 0$ contains S, and the corresponding $X_{w(\alpha)}$ are linearly independent. Since $Ad\, g(X) \in \underline{b}$, it follows that $w(S) \subset \Phi^+$. By (14.7), (14.8), this yields $w = e$, $g \in B$.

(14.15) LEMMA. Let H be a connected k-group and M a closed subgroup of H. Assume that there exists

$X \in \underline{m} = L(M)$ such that the set $Tr(X, \underline{m})$ of $h \in H$ for which $Ad\, h(X) \in \underline{m}$ consists of finitely many left classes mod M. Then $N_H(\underline{m})^0 = M^0$, and $V = \bigcup_{h \in H} Ad\, h(\underline{m})$ contains a dense open set of $\underline{h}$. If H/M is complete, then $V = \underline{h}$.

$N_H(\underline{m})$ is a closed subgroup of H contained in $Tr(X, \underline{m})$, hence its identity component is equal to M^0.

The proof is quite similar to that of (11.9). We consider the morphisms

$$H \times \underline{h} \xrightarrow{\alpha} H \times \underline{h} \xrightarrow{\beta} (H/M) \times \underline{h} \ ,$$

where $\alpha(x, Y) = (x, Ad\, x(Y))$ and $\beta = \pi \times Id$, with $\pi : H \longrightarrow H/M$ the canonical morphism. Let $Q = \beta\alpha(H \times \underline{m})$. By the same argument as in (11.9), it is seen that Q is closed. By definition, $V = pr_2(Q)$, where pr_2 is the projection on the second factor, hence V is closed if H/M is complete. The fibre of pr_2 over an element Z of V is the set of cosets $x \cdot H$ fixed under $\pi(Tr(Z, \underline{m})^{-1})$. In particular, the fibre over X is finite. On the other hand, by using the projection pr_1 on the first factor, one sees again that $\dim Q = \dim H$, hence pr_2 is dominant.

(14.16) PROPOSITION. Let H be a k-group. Then $\underline{h}$ is the union of its Borel subalgebras.

(By definition, a Borel subalgebra of $\underline{h}$ is the Lie algebra of a Borel subgroup of H^0.)

We may assume H to be connected. Let R be its radical. The canonical projection $H \longrightarrow H/R$ defines a bijection between Borel subgroups (11.14). This reduces us to the case where H is semi-simple. Let B be a Borel subgroup of H. In view of (14.14) and (14.15), the set V of conjugates of $\underline{b}$ contains a dense open set of $\underline{h}$. But, since H/B is complete, it is closed by (14.15), whence the proposition.

(14.17) PROPOSITION. Let H be a k-group and $X \in \underline{h}$. Then X is nilpotent if and only if it belongs to the Lie algebra of a closed unipotent subgroup.

PROOF. For the "if" part, see (4.8). Let now X be nilpotent. By (14.16), it belongs to the Lie algebra of a Borel subgroup of H, which reduces us to the case where H is connected, solvable. But then, (10.6)(4) yields $X \in L(H_u)$.

BIBLIOGRAPHICAL NOTE

Up to (14.13), the results of this paragraph are due to Chevalley [8]. In particular, see Exp. 13 for (14.11), Exp. 16 for (14.8), and Exp. 17 for (14.9), (14.10). The main deviation here from [8] is that the integrality condition (14.6) is proved more directly, without recourse to representation theory. (14.16) is due to Grothendieck ([9], Exp. XIV, Thm. 4.11, p. 33). The proof given here is taken from [3].

CHAPTER V

RATIONALITY QUESTIONS

In this chapter, all algebraic groups are affine. G *is a* k*-group.*

§15. SPLIT SOLVABLE GROUPS AND SUBGROUPS

(15.1) DEFINITION. *Let* G *be connected solvable.* G *splits over* k, *or is* k*-split, if it has a composition series* $G = G_0 \supset G_1 \supset \ldots \supset G_s = \{e\}$ *consisting of connected* k*-subgroups such that* G_i/G_{i+1} *is* k*-isomorphic to* $\mathbb{G}_a$ *or* $\mathbb{GL}_1 (0 \leqq i < s)$.

EXAMPLES. (1) The group $\mathbb{D}_n$ of invertible diagonal matrices of degree n splits over the prime field. More generally, if a k-torus splits over k in the sense of (8.2), then it is k-isomorphic to a product of $\mathbb{GL}_1$ ((8.2), (8.3)), hence is k-split in the present sense. The converse then follows from ((8.14), Cor.).

(2) Since a connected one-dimensional k-group is

$\bar{k}$-isomorphic to $\mathbb{G}_a$ or $\mathbb{GL}_1$ (10.9), it follows from (10.6) that if k is algebraically closed, then any connected solvable k-group is k-split.

(15.2) PROPOSITION. _Let_ G _be connected, solvable and_ k-_split, and_ V _a complete_ k-_variety on which_ G _acts_ k-_morphically_. _If_ $V(k) \neq \phi$, _then_ G _has a fixed point in_ V(k).

Proof by induction on dim G. Let N be a normal connected k-subgroup of G such that G/N is isomorphic to $\mathbb{G}_a$ or $\mathbb{GL}_1$. By induction, there exists $x \in V(k)$ fixed under N. The orbit map $g \longmapsto g.x$ is defined over k, and induces a k-morphism $f : G/N \longrightarrow V$, whose image is the orbit G(x) of x. By assumption, G/N is k-isomorphic, as a variety, to $\mathbb{P}_1 - A$ where A consists of one or two points rational over k. Since V is complete, f extends to a k-morphism of $\mathbb{P}_1$ into V. Then $f(\mathbb{P}_1) = G(x) \cup f(A)$ is complete, hence is the Zariski-closure of G(x), hence is stable under G. The set f(A) consists of one or two points rational over k, each of which is fixed under G since otherwise its orbit would meet G(x). Q. E. D.

(15.3) DEFINITION. _A_ k-_subgroup_ H _of_ $\mathbb{GL}_n$ _is trigonalizable over_ k _if there exists_ $x \in \mathbb{GL}(n, k)$ _such that_ $x.H.x^{-1}$ _consists of upper triangular matrices_.

A flag F in K^n is rational over k if it consists

of subspaces defined over k. This is the case if and only if F is the transform by an element of $\mathbb{GL}(n, k)$ of the standard flag $F_0 : [e_1] \subset [e_1, e_2] \subset \ldots$. Thus, H is trigonalizable over k if and only if it leaves stable a flag rational over k. More intrinsically, we may say therefore that if V is a k-vector space, a k-subgroup H of GL(V) is trigonalizable over k if and only if it leaves stable a point rational over k of the flag manifold $\mathcal{F}(V)$.

A trigonalizable group is necessarily solvable. If k is algebraically closed, any connected solvable k-subgroup of $\mathbb{GL}_n$ is trigonalizable over k by the Lie-Kolchin theorem (10.5).

(15.4) THEOREM. Let G be connected, solvable.

(i) If G splits over k, then every image of G under a k-morphism f (resp. under a k-morphism into GL(V)) splits over k (resp. is trigonalizable over k).

Assume G to be linear.

(ii) The following conditions are equivalent: (a) G is trigonalizable over k; (b) G_u is defined over k and G/G_u splits over k; (c) $X(G) = X(G)_k$.

(iii) If k is perfect, G splits over k if and only if it is trigonalizable over k.

(i) We show first that $G' = f(G)$ is k-split. To start with, assume G to be of dimension one, and $G' \neq \{e\}$, hence of dimension one, too. If $G = \mathbb{GL}_1$, then G' is k-isomorphic to $\mathbb{GL}_1$ by (8.2). Let $G = \mathbb{G}_a$. The group G' is then unipotent; it acts faithfully and k-morphically on the projective line $\mathbb{P}_1$; it has exactly one fixed point, say P, which is rational over $k^{p^{-\infty}}$, and one open orbit ((10.9), Remark). Then G acts k-morphically on $\mathbb{P}_1$ via f, with P as its only fixed point. By (15.2), P is then rational over k, hence ((10.9), Remark), G' is k-isomorphic to $\mathbb{G}_a$.

In the general case, we have a composition series (G_i) of G as in (15.1). Then $(f(G_i))$ is a composition series for G', and f induces a surjective k-morphism of G_i/G_{i+1} onto $f(G_i)/f(G_{i+1})$, $(i = 0, \ldots, s-1)$. Our assertion now follows from the one-dimensional case.

Let now G' be a k-subgroup of $\mathbb{GL}_n$ and $\mathcal{F}_n$ the flag manifold of K^n. Since G' splits over k, and $\mathcal{F}_n(k) \neq \phi$, the group G' has a fixed point in $\mathcal{F}_n(k)$ by (15.2), hence is trigonalizable over k (15.3).

(ii) We prove first that (a) $\Longrightarrow$ (b). Let G be contained in the group $\mathbb{T}_n$ of upper triangular matrices of degree n, and let $\mathbb{U}_n$ be the unipotent part of $\mathbb{T}_n$. Then $G_u = G \cap \mathbb{U}_n$. By (10.6)(4), the Lie algebra of G_u consists of all the nilpotent elements in L(G), hence $L(G_u) = L(G) \cap L(\mathbb{U}_n)$, and G_u is defined over k by (6.12). The k-morphism of $\mathbb{T}_n$ onto $\mathbb{D}_n$ with kernel $\mathbb{U}_n$ induces an injective k-morphism of G/G_u into $\mathbb{D}_n$, hence G/G_u is k-isomorphic to a direct product of $\mathbb{GL}_1$ (8.1).

(b) $\Longrightarrow$ (c) Since G is $\bar{k}$-isomorphic to the semi-direct product of G/G_u and G_u (10.6), and $X(G_u) = \{1\}$, it is clear that the map $\pi^*: X(G/G_u) \longrightarrow X(G)$ induced by the projection $\pi: G \longrightarrow G/G_u$ is an isomorphism. If G_u is defined over k, then so is π, hence π^* maps $X(G/G_u)_k$ into $X(G)_k$. Therefore $X(G/G_u) = X(G/G_u)_k$ implies $X(G) = X(G)_k$.

(c) $\Longrightarrow$ (a) Let $\lambda: G \longrightarrow GL(V)$ be a k-morphism. By the Lie-Kolchin theorem, there exists $\chi \in X(G)$ such that the eigenspace V_χ is $\neq 0$. Since, by assumption, χ is defined over k, the space V_χ is defined over k (5.2). Using induction on dim V, we see then that $\lambda(G)$ is trigonalizable over k, whence our contention.

(iii) Let now k be perfect. In view of (i), there remains to show that if G is trigonalizable over k, then it splits over k. Let $G \subset \mathbb{T}_n$. By taking the identity components of the intersections of G with the standard normal series of $\mathbb{T}_n$ (see (10.2)), we get a normal series (G_i) consisting of connected one-dimensional k-groups, whose successive quotients are either k-isomorphic to images of subgroups of $\mathbb{D}_n$, hence are k-isomorphic to $\mathbb{GL}_1$ ((8.2), (15.1)) or are unipotent, one-dimensional. Since k is perfect, the latter quotients are k-isomorphic to $\mathbb{G}_a$ by ((10.9), Remark). Thus G splits over k.

REMARK. By (15.4)(ii), a linear k-torus is k-split if and only if it is trigonalizable over k. On the other hand, by the same result, a connected unipotent k-group is always trigonalizable over k, while it need not be k-split. In fact, [17, p. 46] gives an example of a one-dimensional such group, over a field of characteristic > 2 (which is necessarily imperfect in view of (15.4)(iii)).

(15.5) COROLLARY. (i) Let G be linear and trigonalizable over k. Then the image of G under a k-morphism $f : G \longrightarrow GL(V)$ is trigonalizable over k.

(ii) Let G be unipotent. Then G is trigonalizable over k. If k is perfect, G splits over k.

(i) Let $G' = f(G)$. Then $G'_u = f(G_u)$ and f induces a surjective k-morphism of G/G_u onto G'/G'_u. Our assertion follows from (15.4)(i), (ii).

(ii) This follows from (15.4)(ii), (iii).

(15.6) PROPOSITION. Let $G = \mathbb{G}_a, \mathbb{GL}_1$. Let X be a (non-empty) k-variety on which G acts k-morphically and transitively. Then $X(k) \neq \phi$.

The variety X is irreducible. If $\dim X = 0$, then X is reduced to a point, necessarily rational over k. Otherwise, $\dim X = 1$, and for $x \in X$, the orbit map $f_x : g \longmapsto g.x$ is surjective (with finite fibres), hence its comorphism is an injective homomorphism of $K(X)$ into $K(G)$. But, here, $K(G) = K(T)$, where T is an indeterminate, hence, by Lüroth's theorem, $K(X)$ is also a purely transcendental extension of K, of dimension one. In other words, X is a rational curve; it is obviously smooth. There exists therefore a k-isomorphism of X onto a k-open subset of a smooth complete curve Y of genus 0. The action of X on itself by right translations extends to a k-morphic action of G on Y, and Y-X consists of finitely many fixed points of G.

We have $\mathbb{P}_1 = G \cup A$ where either $A = \{0\}$ or $A = \{0\} \cup \{\infty\}$. The orbit map f_x extends to a morphism of $\mathbb{P}_1$ into Y, which is then surjective, since its image is closed, one-dimensional. It follows that $Y - X = f_x(A)$. The morphism f_x is defined over k(x), so $f_x(A) \subset Y(k(x))$. This is true for any point $x \in X$. But we may find two points $x, y \in X(K)$ such that $k(x) \cap k(y) = k$, e.g. two "independent generic points," or a generic point x and an algebraic point y. Therefore $f(A) \subset Y(k)$ and the latter set is not empty. Since Y is of genus zero, it is then k-isomorphic to $\mathbb{P}_1$ ((10.9), Remark). As a consequence, Y has at least three rational points (corresponding to 0, 1, ∞). Since f(A) consists of at most two points, this proves that $X(k) \neq \phi$.

(15.7) COROLLARY. Let H be a k-group, L a connected solvable k-split subgroup, and $\pi : H \longrightarrow H/L$ the canonical projection. Then $\pi(k) : H(k) \longrightarrow (H/L)(k)$ is surjective.

Proof by induction on dim L. Let N be the first non-trivial term of a composition series splitting L. Thus N is k-split, of codimension one, and L/N is k-isomorphic to $\mathbb{GL}_1$ or $\mathbb{G}_a$. The map π is the composition of the canonical projections

$$H \xrightarrow{\alpha} H/N \xrightarrow{\beta} H/L \ .$$

Let $x \in (H/L)(k)$ and $X = \beta^{-1}(x)$. Since β is separable, X is defined over k. The group L normalizes N, hence the right translations on H/N define a k-morphic action of L/N on H/N (6.11). Obviously, its orbits are the fibres of β. Therefore, (15.6) shows that $X(k) \neq \phi$. Since, by induction assumption $\alpha(k)$ is surjective, the corollary is proved.

(15.8) REMARK. Assume H to be a connected k-group. Let x be a generic point over k of H/L. By the corollary $\pi^{-1}(k(x))$ has a point y rational over $k(x)$, whence an embedding of $k(H/L)$ into $k(H)$, i.e. a "rational map, defined over k" of H/L into H. Otherwise said, there exists a dense k-open subset U of H/L and a k-morphism $s : U \longrightarrow H$ such that $\pi \circ s = \mathrm{id}$. This can also be expressed by saying that the fibration of H over H/L admits a local cross-section defined over k. The open set $\pi^{-1}(U)$ is k-isomorphic to $U \times L$, hence H is birationally isomorphic to $L/H \times L$ over k. In particular, if H is solvable and k-split, then H is a rational variety over k.

Assume now k to be algebraically closed. Then the unipotent radical $R_u(H)$ of H splits over k. The preceding remark and (14.13) show then that H <u>is a rational variety over</u> k, if k is algebraically closed.

(15.9) THEOREM. Let k be perfect and G be connected. The maximal connected solvable k-split subgroups (resp. maximal connected unipotent k-subgroups, resp. maximal k-split tori) of G are conjugate by elements of G(k). If R is one of them, (G/R)(k) is the set of rational points of a projective k-variety V containing G/R as k-open subset, on which G acts k-morphically.

Let R be a maximal connected solvable k-split subgroup of G. Let $\pi : G \longrightarrow GL(V)$ be a faithful k-morphism, such that $d\pi$ is injective, and V contains a line D defined over k whose isotropy group in G (resp. algebra in L(G)) is R (resp. L(R)) (see (5.1)). The image of R in GL(V/D) under the natural representation is trigonalizable over k (15.4). Therefore, there exists a flag P in V rational over k, whose one-dimensional subspace is D, and which is stable under R. Let $\mathcal{F}(V)$ be the flag manifold of V and $f : g \longmapsto g(P)$ the orbit map of G into $\mathcal{F}(V)$. Let $X = \overline{G(P)}$. This is a projective k-variety on which G operates k-morphically, and it is the union of G(P) and of orbits of strictly smaller dimension. Let $Q \in X(k)$, and H its isotropy group. It is defined over k (since k is perfect), trigonalizable over k, since it leaves fixed an element of $\mathcal{F}(V)(k)$, hence split over k ((15.4)(iii)). Consequently, $\dim H \leqq \dim R$, and $\dim G(Q) \geqq \dim G(P)$. It follows that $Q \in G(P)$, hence $X(k) = G(P)(k)$. In view of the construction of P, the isotropy group (resp. algebra) of

P is R (resp. L(R)), hence f is separable, and $G(P) = G/R$, whence $(G/R)(k) = X(k)$.

Let now H be a connected solvable k-split subgroup of G. By (15.2), it has a fixed point in $x \in X(k)$. By the above, $x \in G(P)(k) = (G/R)(k)$. It follows from (15.7) that x is the image of an element $g \in G(k)$ under the orbit map f. But, then, $x.H.x^{-1} \subset R$, and, if H is unipotent $x.H.x^{-1} \subset R_u$. This shows that any maximal connected solvable k-split subgroup (resp. connected unipotent k-subgroup) of G is conjugate under G(k) to R (resp. R_u), and that a k-split torus H is conjugate under G(k) to a subtorus of R. We already know that the k-tori of R are k-split (15.4). There remains to show that two maximal ones T, T' are conjugate by an element of R(k). We proceed by induction on dim R. Let Q be a connected one-dimensional k-subgroup of R_u normal in R. It is trigonalizable over k and, since k is perfect, it is k-split, k-isomorphic to $\mathbb{G}_a$. Using induction, and (15.8), we see that we are reduced to the case where $T' \subset T.Q$, i.e. where $R_u = \mathbb{G}_a$ is one-dimensional. If R_u commutes with T, then $R = T \times Q$ is nilpotent, and $T = T'$. If not, then $Z(T) = T$ and $R_u = (T, R)$ (see (9.3)). Let S be the identity component of the centralizer of R_u in T. It has codimension one, is defined over k, normal in R. The groups T, T' are conjugate under R_u (10.6), therefore $S \subset T'$, and, dividing out by S, we may assume $T = \mathbb{GL}_1$. Let $Y = \{n \in R_u, n.T.n^{-1} = T'\}$. This is a closed set, not empty (10.6), defined over k. If $x, y \in Y$, then $y^{-1}.x \in N(T)$, hence $y^{-1}.x \in Z(T) = T$ (10.6), and finally $x \in y.T$. Thus T acts transitively on Y by right translations, and $Y(k) \neq \phi$ by (15.6).

REMARK. Much more generally than in the last part of the proof, it can be shown for arbitrary k that in a solvable connected k-group H, any two maximal tori defined over k are conjugate by an element of H(k). This result is due to Rosenlicht (Annali di Mat. (IV) 61 (1963), 97-120, Theor. 4). For another proof, see [4, 11.4].

BIBLIOGRAPHICAL NOTE

Up to (15.5), the results of this section are proved in [17], which is one of the first papers devoted to rationality questions on affine algebraic groups. (15.6) is also due to M. Rosenlicht [16, p. 425]. For another proof see M. Rosenlicht, Pacific J. M. 20 (1967), 129-133. For (15.9), see [4, Théor. 8.2].

§16. GROUPS OVER FINITE FIELDS

In this section, k *is a finite field,* $q = p^s$ *the number of elements of* k; *and* $F_q : x \longmapsto x^q$ *the Frobenius homomorphism of a field of* char p.

(16.1) Let V be a k-variety. We denote by $v^{(q)}$ the image of $v \in V$ under the "Frobenius morphism" $V \longrightarrow V$, also to be denoted by F_q. We recall that if $V \subset K^n$ is affine, then the coordinates of $v^{(q)}$ are obtained by applying F_q to those of v, and the comorphism $F_{q,o} : k[V] \longrightarrow k[V]$ is the q-th power homomorphism $f \longmapsto f^q$.

The map F_q is a purely inseparable isogeny. It is bijective, and its differential at any point is the zero map. The fixed point set of F_q is $V(k)$, hence is finite. If V is a k-group, then F_q is a homomorphism.

(16.2) Let $f : G \times G \longrightarrow G$ be defined by $f(g, h) = g^{-1}.h.g^{(q)}$, and let f_g be the map $h \longmapsto f(g, h)$. Then $f_{gh} = f_h \circ f_g$, and f is defined over k. Hence G operates on itself by means of the f_g's, and this is a right k-morphic action.

(16.3) THEOREM (Lang). Let $a \in G$. Then the orbit map $s_a : g \longmapsto g^{-1}.a.g^{(q)}$ is separable. Its image is open and closed.

For the second assertion, it suffices to show that $s_a(G^0)$ is the connected component of a in G. We may therefore assume G to be connected. Let $i : x \longmapsto x^{-1}$. Then (3.2):

$$(ds_a)_e(X) = di_e(X)a + a.dF_q(X), \qquad (X \in \underline{g}) .$$

But $(di) = -\mathrm{Id}.$ (3.2) and $dF_q \equiv 0$ (16.2) hence

$$(ds_a)_e(X) = -X.a \quad ,$$

which shows that ds_a is an isomorphism. As a consequence, s_a is dominant, separable. The orbit $s_a(G)$ of a then contains a non-empty open set, hence is open by homogeneity. This being true for any $a \in G$, the orbit is also closed.

(16.4) COROLLARY. Let G be connected. Then the map $g \longmapsto g^{-1}.g^{(q)}$ is surjective, separable.

Apply (16.3) to the case $a = e$.

(16.5) COROLLARY. Let G be connected, and V be a non-empty k-variety on which G acts k-morphically and transitively. Then $V(k) \neq \phi$.

Let $v \in V$. By assumption, there exists $g \in G$ such that $g.v^{(q)} = v$. By (16.4), we may write $g = h^{-1}.h^{(q)}$ for some $h \in G$. We have then $h.v = h^{(q)}.v^{(q)} = (h.v)^{(q)}$, hence $h.v \in V(k)$.

(16.6) PROPOSITION. G^0 has a Cartan subgroup (resp. a maximal torus, resp. a Borel subgroup) defined over k. Two Borel subgroups defined over k are conjugate by an element of $G^0(k)$.

Let H be a Cartan subgroup (resp. maximal torus, resp. Borel subgroup) of G^0. Then so is its transform $H^{(q)}$ under the Frobenius map. Hence there exists

$g \in G^0$ such that

$$g.H^{(q)}.g^{-1} = H$$

((11.1), (11.3)). By (16.4), we may find $a \in G^0$ such that $g = a^{-1}.a^{(q)}$. Consequently

$$aHa^{-1} = a^{(q)}H^{(q)}a^{(q)^{-1}} = (a.H.a^{-1})^{(q)}$$

hence aHa^{-1} is defined over k.

Let B, B' be two Borel subgroups defined over k. The variety $V = Tr(B, B') = \{x \in G | xBx^{-1} = B'\}$ is defined over k (since k is perfect), not empty (11.1). Since B is equal to its normalizer (11.15), B acts transitively by right translations on V. By (16.5), $V(k) \neq \phi$.

REMARK. The last assertion is in fact valid over an arbitrary field [4, Th. 4.13].

(16.7) PROPOSITION. <u>Let</u> H <u>be a connected</u> k-<u>group and</u> $f : G^0 \longrightarrow H$ <u>a surjective</u> k-<u>morphism</u>. <u>Then a Cartan subgroup (resp. a maximal torus, resp. a Borel subgroup) of</u> H <u>defined over</u> k <u>is the image of such a subgroup of</u> G^0

Let M be a Cartan subgroup of H, defined over k, and $M' = f^{-1}(M)^0$. Then M' is defined over k (since it is k-closed, and k is perfect), and $M = f(M')$, since M is connected. By (16.6), M' has a Cartan subgroup C' defined over k. By (11.14), the group f(C') is a Cartan subgroup of $f(M') = M$. Hence $f(C') = M$. The proof in the other two cases is the same.

(16.8) PROPOSITION. Let G be connected, H a connected k-group and $f : G \longrightarrow H$ a k-isogeny. Then G(k) and H(k) have the same number of elements.

Given an isogeny $r : M \longrightarrow N$ of connected algebraic groups, we let deg r denote the degree of the field extension k(M) over $r_0 k(N)$. The degree of separability of this extension is the order of ker r.

Let a_G be the map $g \longmapsto g^{-1} . g^{(q)}$. It is separable, surjective (16.4) of degree equal to the number [G(k)] of elements in G(k). Similarly the analogous map a_H has degree [H(k)]. But $f \circ a_G = a_H \circ f$, therefore

$$\deg(f \circ a_G) = \deg f . \deg a_G = \deg f . \deg a_H .$$

Since $\deg f \neq 0$, this proves the proposition.

(16.9) Without giving any details, we mention that (16.4) has an interpretation in Galois cohomology. It is equivalent to the following fact: if L is a finite (Galois) extension of k, then

$$H^1(\mathrm{Gal}(L/k)), G(L)) = 0 .$$

(For the definition of H^1, see e.g. [19].)

BIBLIOGRAPHICAL NOTE

Except for (16.6), (16.7) the results of this section

are due to S. Lang [13]. That (16.6) was a consequence of Lang's theorem (16.3) was noticed by Serre (and mentioned in [17, footnote, p. 45]).

§17. QUOTIENT OF A GROUP BY A LIE SUBALGEBRA

In this paragraph, char $k = p > 0$. We put $A_k = k[G]$ and $A_K = K[G]$. We recall (3.3) that $\underline{g}$ may be identified with the algebra of left-invariant K-derivations of A_K by means of the map $X \longmapsto {}^*X$, and that $\underline{g}(k) = \underline{g} \cap Der_k(A_k, A_k)$.

In §6, we introduced the quotient G/H of G by a closed subgroup. Of course, both G and H were "reduced," since only such groups have been dealt with in this course. However, this quotient can be (and has been) defined in the broader category of group schemes [9]. In this paragraph, we discuss another special case of this situation, where H is a restricted subalgebra of $\underline{g}$, i.e. is of the simplest type among non-reduced groups of dimension zero. Our main objective here is (17.8), which will play an essential role in §18.

(17.1) LEMMA. Let $\underline{m}$ be a restricted Lie subalgebra of $\underline{g}$, which is defined over k. Let B be the set of elements of A_k annihilated by $\underline{m}(k)$. Then B contains A_k^p and is a finitely generated k-algebra. Moreover, $\underline{m} = \{X \in \underline{g},\ X.B = 0\}$.

Since $\underline{g}$ acts via derivations on A_K, it annihilates

A_K^p, hence $B \supset A_k^p$. Therefore A_k is integral over B. The latter is then finitely generated by a known result (see e.g. Serre, Groupes algébriques et corps de classes, Hermann, Paris, 1959, lemme 10, p. 58).

To prove the second assertion, it suffices to consider the case where G is connected. Let $L = K(G)$ and M be the quotient field of B_K. Then $L \supset M \supset L^p$, hence L is a purely inseparable extension of M, of height one. The given action of $\underline{g}$ on A_K extends in the obvious way to make $\underline{g} \otimes_K L$ into a restricted Lie algebra over L of derivations of L. The field M is the field of invariants of $\underline{m} \otimes_K L$. (If $D(a/b) = 0$, where D is a derivation, then $D(a.b^{p-1}) = 0$, hence $a/b = a.b^{p-1}/b^p$ is the quotient of two D-invariants.) But then, by Jacobson Galois theory of inseparable extensions of height one (Jacobson, Lectures in Abstract Algebra III, van Nostrand, Chap. IV, Theor. 19, p. 186), $\underline{m} \otimes_K L$ is the algebra of all derivations of L which are zero on M, whence our second assertion.

(17.2) PROPOSITION. _Let_ $\underline{m}$ _be a restricted subalgebra of_ $\underline{g}$, _which is defined over_ k. _There exists an affine_ k-_variety_ $G/\underline{m}$, _and a_ k-_morphism_ $\pi : G \longrightarrow G/\underline{m}$ _having the following properties:_

(i) π _is bijective_, $\ker(d\pi)_x = x.\underline{m}$ $(x \in G)$. _The comorphism_ π_0 _induces an isomorphism of_ $k[G/\underline{m}]$ _onto the algebra_ B _of elements in_ A_k _annihilated by_ $\underline{m}(k)$.

(ii) _If_ Z _is an affine_ k-_variety and_ $s : G \longrightarrow Z$ _a_ k-_morphism such that_ $\ker(ds)_x \supset x.\underline{m}$ $(x \in G)$, _then_ *there exists a unique* k-*morphism* $f : G/\underline{m} \longrightarrow Z$ *such that* $s = f \circ \pi$.

The pair $(G/\underline{m}, \pi)$ *is unique up to a* k-*isomorphism*.

Let $(V_i, \pi_i)(i = 1, 2)$ be two pairs verifying the conditions imposed on $(G/\underline{m}, \pi)$ in (i), (ii). Then we have unique k-morphisms $f : V_1 \longrightarrow V_2$ and $h : V_2 \longrightarrow V_1$ such that $\pi_2 = f \circ \pi_1$ and $\pi_1 = h \circ \pi_2$. It follows then immediately that f, h are bijective and that the comorphisms f_0, h_0 are isomorphisms. There remains to show the existence.

Let $b_1, \ldots, b_s$ be a generating set for B as a k-algebra (17.1). By (1.9), we can find a finite dimensional subspace W_i of A_K, stable under G under right translations, defined over k, and containing b_i $(1 \leqq i \leqq s)$. Let $E = \coprod W_i$, and $b = b_1 + \ldots + b_s$. We claim that the orbit $V = G.b$ of b, under the natural representation of G in E, and the orbit map $\pi : g \longmapsto g.b$ verify our conditions.

If $g.b = b$, then $b_i(g) = b_i(e)$ $(1 \leqq i \leqq s)$. Since the b_i's generate B and B contains A_k^p, this implies $f(g) = f(e)$ for any $f \in A_k$, hence $g = e$, and π is bijective. Let $X \in \underline{g}$. Then by (3.10), $X \in \ker(d\pi)_e$ if and only if $b_i{*}X = 0$, i.e., by (17.1), if and only if $X \in \underline{m}$. Thus $\ker(d\pi)_e = \underline{m}$. The equality $\ker(d\pi)_x = x.\underline{m}$ follows then from the fact that the orbit map is equivariant.

The orbit map being bijective, and V being normal, V is affine (AG.18.3) and π_0 is injective. The relation $\ker(d\pi)_e = \underline{m}$ implies that $\pi_0(k[V]) \subset B$. To establish the reverse inclusion, it suffices to prove that $b_i \in \operatorname{Im} \pi_0$ $(1 \leqq i \leqq s)$. Fix i. Let $u_1, \ldots, u_t$ be a basis of $W_i(k)$ and $a_1, \ldots, a_t$ the dual basis of $W_i^*(k)$. The restriction of $a_j \in W_i^* \subset E^*$ to V is an element of $k[V]$. If we denote it also by a_j, we have:

$$b_i(g) = g.b_i(e) = \Sigma_j\ a_j(g.b_i).u_j(e) = \Sigma_j\ \pi_0 a_j(g).u_j(e) ,$$

which proves our contention.

Let now s and Z be as in (ii). Then $s_0(k[Z])$ is annihilated by $\underline{m}(k)$, hence contained in B. Consequently, the unique k-morphism $f : V \longrightarrow Z$ whose associated comorphism is $s_0 : k[Z] \longrightarrow B$ verifies the relation $s = f \circ \pi$.

REMARK. To show that V is affine, we have quoted (AG.18.3). In fact, this can be avoided. With a little more work, one can show directly that V is closed in E. (For a similar argument, see e.g. A. Borel, Introduction aux groupes arithmétiques, Hermann, Paris, 1969, Prop. 7.7.)

(17.3) LEMMA. <u>We keep the notation of</u> (17.2) <u>and</u> §3. <u>Let</u> $f \in A_K$, $g \in G$, $X \in \underline{g}$. <u>Then</u>

(i) $(i_0 f) * X = -i_0(X * f)$;

(ii) $(f * X)(g) = (\operatorname{Ad} g(X) * f)(g)$.

Let $f_i, h_i \in A_K$ be such that $\mu_0 f = \Sigma_i f_i \otimes h_i$. We have then

$$i_0 f(g.x) = f(x^{-1}.g^{-1}) = \Sigma_i\, i_0 f_i(x) \,.\, h_i(g^{-1}) \,.$$

Since $(i_0 f * X)(g) = X(\lambda_{g^{-1}} . i_0 f)$ (see (3.4)), this yields

$$(i_0 f * X)(g) = \Sigma_i X(i_0 f_i) \,.\, h_i(g^{-1}) \,,$$

hence, by (3.4),

$$(i_0 f * X)(g) = -\Sigma_i X f_i \,.\, h_i(g^{-1}) = -(X * f)(g^{-1}) \,,$$

which proves (i). The equality $f(g.x) = f(gxg^{-1}.g)$ gives

$$\Sigma_i f_i(g) \,.\, h_i(x) = \Sigma_i f_i(gxg^{-1}) \,.\, h_i(g) \,.$$

Therefore

$$(f * X)(g) = \Sigma_i X(f_i \circ \mathrm{Int}\ g) \,.\, h_i(g) \,.$$

Since the differential of Int is Ad by definition (3.3), the definition of the differential of a map, and (3.4), yield

$$(f * X)(g) = \Sigma_i (\mathrm{Ad}\ g(X).f_i) \,.\, h_i(g) = (\mathrm{Ad}\ g(X) * f)(g) \,.$$

(17.4) PROPOSITION. Let $\underline{m}$ be a restricted subalgebra of $\underline{g}$ which is defined over k and is stable under Ad G. Then the variety $G/\underline{m}$ of (17.2) admits a canonical structure of k-group such that $\pi : G \longrightarrow G/\underline{m}$ is a k-isogeny. If G' is a k-group and $s : G \longrightarrow G'$ a k-morphism whose differential annihilates $\underline{m}$, then there is a unique k-morphism $f : G/\underline{m} \longrightarrow G'$ such that $s = f \circ \pi$.

We keep the previous notation. Since $\underline{m}$ is stable under Ad G, (17.3)(i) shows that B_K is also the set of invariants of the left convolutions $X *$ ($X \in \underline{m}$). In view of (17.3)(ii), it follows then that $i_0 B = B$. Let $f \in B$, and write $\mu_0 f = \Sigma f_i \otimes h_i$ ($f_i, h_i \in A_k$). We may assume the f_i's (resp. h_i's) to be linearly independent over k. For $X \in \underline{g}$, we have

$$f * X = \Sigma f_i \,.\, Xh_i, \quad X * f = \Sigma Xf_i \,.\, h_i \,.$$

If $X \in \underline{m}$, both left hand sides are zero. Consequently $Xf_i = Xh_i = 0$ for all i, which shows that $\mu_0 B \subset B \otimes B$. Thus, B, endowed with μ, i_0, ε, satisfies all conditions of (1.5) for the coordinate ring over k of an affine k-group. This yields a group structure on $G/\underline{m}$. Since it is compatible with the inclusion $B \subset A_k$, the map π of (17.2) is a k-isogeny. This proves the first assertion of (17.4). The second one follows from (17.2)(ii).

(17.5) EXAMPLES. (1) If $\underline{m} = \underline{g}$, then $k(G/\underline{m}) = A_k^p$. The Frobenius isogeny of (16.1) may be viewed as the k-isogeny π of G onto $G/\underline{g}$.

(2) Let $p = 2$ and $G = \mathbf{SL}_2$. Then $\underline{g} = \underline{sl}_2$ is the Lie algebra of 2×2 matrices with trace zero. It contains the one-dimensional space $\underline{m}$ of multiples of the identity, which is a restricted ideal, normalized (in fact centralized) by $\mathbf{SL}_2$. It can be seen easily that $G/\underline{m} = \mathbf{PGL}_2$. The morphism $\pi : G \longrightarrow G/\underline{m}$ is realized by the natural action of G on $\mathbf{P}_1$ (see (10.8)). Then $\text{Im}\, d\pi = \underline{n}$ is a two

dimensional ideal of $L(G/\underline{m})$, stable under p-power operation and $Ad(G/\underline{m})$. It can be checked that $\mathbb{P}\mathbb{G}\mathbb{L}_2/\underline{n} \cong \mathbb{S}\mathbb{L}_2$ and that the composition of the projections $G \longrightarrow G/\underline{m} \longrightarrow (G/\underline{m})/\underline{n}$ is the Frobenius isogeny of G.

(17.6) A character of $\mathbb{G}\mathbb{L}_1$ is of the form $x \longmapsto x^m$ $(m \in \mathbb{Z})$. Its differential is $X \longmapsto m.X$. Let now T be a torus. From this remark, it follows that $L(T) \cong X_*(T) \otimes k$, $L(T)^* \cong X(T) \otimes k$. In particular, $a \in X(T)$ has a zero differential if and only if $a \in p.X(T)$.

(17.7) LEMMA. Let G be connected. Assume all semi-simple elements of $\underline{g}$ are central. Then the set of semi-simple elements of $\underline{g}$ is a subspace defined over k, and is the Lie algebra of any maximal torus of G.

Let T be a maximal torus of G. Let $X \in \underline{g}$ be semi-simple. It is tangent to a torus (11.8), say S, and (11.3), there exists $g \in G$ such that $g.S.g^{-1} \subset T$. By assumption, X is central in $\underline{g}$, and therefore also in G (9.1). Hence $Ad\, g(X) = X$, and $X \in \underline{t}$. But $\underline{t}$ consists of semi-simple elements ((8.2), Cor.), hence $\underline{t}$ is the set of all semi-simple elements of $\underline{g}$. There exists a power $q = p^s$ of p such that the s-th iterate [q] of [p] annihilates all nilpotent elements of $\underline{g}$ (if $G \subset \mathbb{G}\mathbb{L}_n$, $s = n$ will do). If $X = X_s + X_n$ is the Jordan decomposition of $X \in \underline{g}$, we have then $X^{[q]} = X_s^{[q]}$, which shows that [q] maps $\underline{g}$ into $\underline{t}$. Since [q] is bijective on $\underline{t}$, as follows from (3.3(2)), $\underline{t}$ is in fact the image of [q]. But [q] is a k-morphism of varieties (if $G \subset \mathbb{GL}_n$, $X^{[q]}$ is the matrix product of q copies of X, see (3.6)), hence $\underline{t} = \mathrm{Im}[q]$ is defined over k.

(17.8) PROPOSITION. Let G be connected, not nilpotent, and assume that every semi-simple element of $\underline{g}$ is central. Let T be a maximal torus of G. Then there exists a k-group G', such that not all semi-simple elements of $\underline{g}'$ are central, and a purely inseparable k-isogeny $\pi : G \longrightarrow G'$ such that $\ker d\pi = \underline{t}$ and $\mathrm{Im}\, d\pi$ is a supplementary subspace in $\underline{g}'$ to the Lie algebra of any maximal torus.

Let $\Phi = \Phi(T, G)$ be the set of roots of G with respect to T (8.17). Since G is not nilpotent, T is not central in G (11.5) and Φ is not empty ((9.2), Cor.). Let c be the greatest positive integer such that $\Phi \subset p^c X(T)$. In view of (17.6), $\underline{t}$ is central in $\underline{g}$ if and only if $c \geqq 1$. By (17.7) and the assumption, we have then $c \geqq 1$. The proof is carried out by descending induction on c.

By (9.1) all elements of $\underline{t}$ are centralized by G. Of course, $\underline{t}$ is restricted and invariant under Ad G, hence we may apply (17.4), which yields a k-group $G_1 = G/\underline{t}$ and a k-isogeny $\pi_1 : G \longrightarrow G_1$ such that $\ker d\pi_1 = \underline{t}$. Let T' be a maximal torus of G_1. By (11.14), dim T = dim T'. By (17.7), $d\pi_1$ annihilates all semi-simple elements of $\underline{g}$, hence (4.4), $d\pi(\underline{g})$ consists of nilpotent elements. If T' is a maximal torus of G_1, we have then $d\pi(\underline{g}) \cap L(T') = \{0\}$, hence

$$(1) \qquad L(G_1) = d\pi_1(\underline{g}) \oplus L(T') ,$$

for dimensional reasons. Let now $T' = \pi_1(T)$. Since $d\pi_1$ annihilates $\underline{t}$, it follows from (17.6) that the induced homomorphism $\pi_1^* : X(T') \longrightarrow X(T)$ maps $X(T')$ into $p.X(T)$. On the other hand, $d\pi$ is injective on the sum of the root spaces $\underline{g}_\alpha (\alpha \in \Phi)$. It follows then from equivariance and (1) that π_1^* induces a bijection of $\Phi(T', G_1)$ onto Φ. Since $\pi_1^* X(T') \subset p.X(T)$, this shows that if d is the greatest integer such that $\Phi(T', G_1) \subset p^d X(T')$, then $d < c$. If $d = 0$, then we take $G_1 = G'$, $\pi_1 = \pi'$. If not, by induction, we choose G' and π_2 which verify our conditions with respect to G_1. It is then clear that $(G', \pi' = \pi_2 \circ \pi_1)$ satisfy our requirements.

BIBLIOGRAPHICAL NOTE

As was already mentioned, (17.2), (17.4) are contained in much more general results of [9]. (17.3) was first proved by Serre (Am. J. M. 80 (1958), 715-739), and Barsotti. See also P. Cartier (Bull. S. M. France 87 (1959), 191-220, §7). (17.8) is Prop. 2.2 of [2]. For a slightly more general version, see [3, §5.3].

§18. CARTAN SUBGROUPS OVER THE GROUNDFIELD. UNIRATIONALITY. SPLITTING OF REDUCTIVE GROUPS.

(18.1) Regular elements. Let nil X ($X \in \underline{g}$) be the multiplicity of the eigenvalue zero of ad X, and let $n(\underline{g})$ be the minimum of nil X, as X ranges through $\underline{g}$. The element X is regular if nil $X = n(\underline{g})$, singular otherwise. Clearly, nil X = nil X_s, hence X is regular if and only if its semi-simple part X_s is. If $p \neq 0$, then X is regular if and only if $X^{[p]}$ is so.

Taking coordinates in $\underline{g}$ with respect to a base of $\underline{g}(k)$, we can write

$$\det(\mathrm{ad}\, X - T) = T^{n(\underline{g})}(c_0(X) + c_1(X)T + \ldots + c_q(X).T^q) ,$$

where the c_i's are homogeneous polynomials with coefficients in k, and $q = \dim \underline{g} - n(\underline{g})$. By the definition of $n(\underline{g})$, the polynomial c_0 is not identically zero. The singular elements are the zeros of c_0, hence they form a proper k-closed algebraic subset of $\underline{g}$, and the regular elements form a dense open set.

Let k be infinite. Then there always exists a semi-simple $X \in \underline{g}(k)$ which is regular. In fact, since $\underline{g}(k)$ is Zariski dense in $\underline{g}$ (k infinite), there exists a regular $X \in \underline{g}(k)$. Let $X = X_s + X_n$ be its Jordan decomposition (4.4). Then X_s is regular. If k is perfect, then $X_s \in \underline{g}(k)$. Let $p \neq 0$. There exists a power [q] of [p] which annihilates X_n. Then $X_s^{[q]} = X^{[q]}$ will do.

(18.2) THEOREM. *Let* G *be connected.*

(i) G *contains a maximal torus and a Cartan subgroup defined over* k.

(ii) *If* G *is reductive or* k *is perfect,* G *is unirational over* k.

(i) A Cartan subgroup is the centralizer of a maximal torus T, and is defined over k if T is ((9.2), Cor.). It suffices therefore to show the existence of a maximal torus defined over k. If G is nilpotent, see (10.6)(3). If k is finite, see (16.6). In the general case, we shall use induction on dim G.

Let now k be infinite, and G be not nilpotent.

Let T be a maximal torus of G. Since G is not nilpotent, T is not central (11.5). If $p = 0$, then a non-zero character of T has a non-zero differential, therefore $\underline{t}$ is not central in $\underline{g}$, and $\underline{g}$ has non-central semi-simple elements. We now let G' and $\pi : G \longrightarrow G'$ be as in (17.8) if all semi-simple elements of $\underline{g}$ are central (and hence $p \neq 0$), and $G' = G$, $\pi = \mathrm{Id}$. otherwise. By (18.1), $\underline{g}'(k)$ contains a regular semi-simple element Y. By construction, $n(\underline{g}') \neq \dim \underline{g}'$, hence $\underline{z}(Y) \neq \underline{g}'$. We let G operate on $\underline{g}'$ via $\mathrm{Ad} \circ \pi$ and, for $Z \in \underline{g}'$, denote by G_Z the stability group of Z in G. Clearly, $\pi(G_Z) = Z_{G'}(Z)$. In particular, by (9.1), $\dim G_Y = \dim \underline{z}_{\underline{g}'}(Y) \neq \dim \underline{g}'$ hence $G_Y \neq G$. We claim that G_Y is defined over k. This is clear if k is perfect, or, by (9.1), if π is the identity. In the remaining case, it suffices to show that the orbit map $f : g \longmapsto g(Y) = \mathrm{Ad}\,\pi(g)(Y)$ is separable (6.7). This amounts to proving that df_e is surjective. By (3.9)(2) and (9.1), the tangent space at Y to the orbit $\mathrm{Ad}\,G'(Y) = G.Y$ is $Y + [Y, \underline{g}']$. On the other hand, by (3.9)(2):

$$df_e(X) = Y + [d\pi(X), Y], \qquad (X \in \underline{g}) .$$

By (17.8), $d\pi(\underline{g})$ is supplementary in $\underline{g}'$ to the Lie algebra of any maximal torus. We know Y is in the Lie algebra of a maximal torus (see (11.8)). Since the latter commutes with Y, we get $[Y, d\pi(\underline{g})] = [Y, \underline{g}']$, which proves our contention.

Since Y is tangent to a maximal torus, $Z_{G'}(Y)$ contains a maximal torus of G', and therefore G_Y^0 contains a maximal torus of G. By conjugacy, all maximal tori of G_Y^0 are maximal tori of G. By induction assumption, one of them is defined over k, whence (i).

(ii) Recall first ((8.13)(2)) that an irreducible k-variety V is unirational over k if its function field $k(V)$ is contained in a purely transcendental extension of k. If (V_i) $(1 \leqq i \leqq m)$ are unirational over k, and $f : V_1 \times \ldots \times V_m \longrightarrow V$ is a dominant k-morphism, then, clearly, V is unirational over k.

Let k be perfect. Then the unipotent radical $R_u(G)$ of G, which is always k-closed, is defined over k. It splits over k (15.4), hence is a rational variety over k (15.8). Moreover, also by (15.8), G is birationally k-isomorphic, as a variety, to $G/R_u(G) \times R_u(G)$. This reduces the proof of (ii) to the case where G is reductive.

From now on, G is reductive. If G is a torus, see (8.13)(2). We now consider the case where k is infinite, and argue by induction on dim G. We keep the notation of the proof of (i) and let H be the group generated by the groups G_Y^0, as Y ranges through the regular semi-simple elements of $\underline{g}'(k)$. We claim that H = G. Assume this is not the case. Then $\underline{h}' = L(\pi(H))$ is a proper subalgebra of $\underline{g}'$. Since k is assumed to be infinite, there exists $Z \in \underline{g}'(k)$ which is regular, and not contained in $\underline{h}'$. Let $Z = Z_s + Z_n$ be its Jordan decomposition. For some iterate [q] of [p], we have $Z_s^{[q]} = Z^{[q]}$, and the element $U = Z_s^{[q]}$ is regular, semi-simple, rational over k. It commutes with Z (since Z_s does, and $Z_s^{[q]} = Z_s^q$ in a matrix realization of G'), hence $\underline{z}_{\underline{g}'}(U) \not\subset \underline{h}'$. But (9.1) $\underline{z}_{\underline{g}'}(U)$ is the Lie algebra of $Z_{G'}(U)^0 = \pi(G_U)$. As a consequence, $G_U \not\subset H$, a contradiction. Thus H = G. There exists then in the set of G_Y^0's finitely many groups $H_1, \ldots, H_t$ such that the product map $H_1 \times \ldots \times H_t \longrightarrow G$ is surjective. The groups H_i are $\neq G$, defined over k by (i), and reductive since their images under the isogeny π are so by (13.19). By induction, they are unirational over k, hence so is G.

Let now k be finite. Then (16.6) it has a Borel

subgroup B defined over k, and the latter contains a maximal torus T defined over k. Since k is perfect, the unique Borel subgroup B^- opposite to B and containing T is also defined over k, and the unipotent radicals U, U^- of B and B^- are defined over k. By (10.6), B is k-isomorphic to the semi-direct product T.U. By (14.13), G, as a variety, is then birationally k-isomorphic to $U^- \times T \times U$. By (15.5), U, U^- split over k, hence (15.8) are rational varieties over k. Since T is unirational over k ((8.13)(2)), G is unirational over k.

REMARK. It can be shown that any connected k-group is generated by its Cartan subgroups defined over k: for finite k, see [3, 2.9]. For infinite k, this follows from the fact that the variety of Cartan subgroups of G is rational over k, due to Grothendieck (over arbitrary fields) ([9], Exp. XIV, Th. 6.1, p. 39; this is also proved in [3], 7.9, 7.10). As a consequence G is unirational over k if its Cartan subgroups are; this includes both cases of (ii).

(18.3) COROLLARY. Let G be connected, k infinite. If either k is perfect, or G is reductive, G(k) is Zariski-dense in G.

The follows from unirationality. We note that Rosenlicht has given an example of a one-dimensional unipotent k-group over an infinite k, in which G(k) is finite [17, p. 46].

(18.4) COROLLARY. Let G be connected, solvable. Then G splits over an algebraic extension of k.

By (18.2), G has a maximal torus T defined over k. Its unipotent radical is k-closed, hence splits over a finite purely inseparable extension of k, in view of (15.5). Since T splits over a finite (separable) extension of k (8.11), the corollary follows.

(18.5) LEMMA. Let $\underline{h}$ be the Lie algebra of a closed subgroup H of G. Assume that $\underline{h}$ is defined over k and $\underline{h} = \underline{n}_{\underline{g}}(\underline{h})$. Then $N_G(\underline{h})$ is defined over k, the group H is of finite index in $N_G(\underline{h})$, defined over a finite separable extension of k, and H^0 is defined over k.

Let $N = N_G(\underline{h})$. Then N contains H, and L(N) contains $\underline{h}$ and normalizes $\underline{h}$. Thus $L(N) = \underline{h}$, dim N = dim H. Since $N \supset H$, this proves that $H^0 = N^0$ and H has finite index in N. Assume N to be defined over k. Then so is $H^0 = N^0$ (see (1.2)(b)), and H is defined over k_s by (AG.12.3). There remains to show that N is defined over k.

Let $d = \dim \underline{h}$, $E = \Lambda^d \underline{g}$ and $\pi = \Lambda^d \mathrm{Ad}$ the natural representation of G in E. Let D be the line representing $\underline{h}$. It follows from the assumptions and the lemma in (5.1) that N is the stability group of D, and L(N) is the stability algebra of D. Let $f : g \longmapsto g.D$ be the orbit map in the associated projective space $\underline{P}(E)$. Since π and D are defined over k, the map f is defined over k. The kernel of df_e is the Lie algebra of the stability group of D, hence f is separable (see proof of (6.8)). Consequently N is defined over k (6.7).

(18.6) Split reductive groups. Let G be reductive, connected, T a maximal torus of G, and $\Phi = \Phi(T, G)$ the set of roots of G with respect to T. For each $\alpha \in \Phi$ there exists a connected unipotent subgroup U_α of G, normalized by T, and an isomorphism $\theta_\alpha : \mathbf{G}_a \longrightarrow U_\alpha$ such that

$$(1) \qquad t.\theta_\alpha(x).t^{-1} = \theta_\alpha(t^\alpha.x) \qquad (x \in K,\ t \in T) .$$

The group U_α is the unique one-dimensional subgroup normalized by T satisfying this condition (see (13.18)). The group G is said to split over k, or to be k-split, if we can choose a T split over k (8.2) and isomorphisms θ_α defined over k.

Note that if θ' is an isomorphism of $\mathbf{G}_a$ onto U_α, then $f = \theta_\alpha^{-1} \circ \theta'$ is an automorphism of $\mathbf{G}_a$, hence there exists $c \in K^*$ such that $f(x) = c.x$ $(x \in K)$. Then θ' also verifies (1).

(18.7) THEOREM. Let G be connected, reductive. Then G splits over k if it has a maximal torus which splits over k.

Let T be a maximal torus which splits over k. Let U_α ($\alpha \in \Phi$) be the unipotent one-parameter subgroup normalized by T. In view of the end remark of (18.6) it suffices to show that each U_α is k-isomorphic to $\mathbb{G}_a$.

Let $\alpha \in \Phi(T, G)$ and $T_\alpha = (\ker \alpha)^0$. The group T_α is defined over k (8.4), hence so is $G_\alpha = Z(T_\alpha)$ ((9.2), Cor.). The group G_α is reductive, generated by T, U_α, $U_{-\alpha}$, and $T.U_\alpha$, $T.U_{-\alpha}$ are the Borel subgroups of G containing T (see (13.18)). This reduces us to the case where G has semi-simple rank equal to one. We shall prove first that U_α, $U_{-\alpha}$ are defined over k. Since they are the derived groups of $T.U_\alpha$ and $T.U_{-\alpha}$, it suffices to show that the two Borel subgroups $B = T.U_\alpha$ and $B^- = T.U_{-\alpha}$ containing T are defined over k. We have

$$\underline{g} = \underline{t} \oplus \underline{g}_\alpha \oplus \underline{g}_{-\alpha} \quad \underline{b} = \underline{t} \oplus \underline{g}_\alpha, \ \underline{b}^- = \underline{t} \oplus \underline{g}_{-\alpha} .$$

The group T is k-split, hence α is defined over k, and $\underline{g}_\alpha$, $\underline{g}_{-\alpha}$ are defined over k (5.2). Thus $\underline{b}$ and $\underline{b}^-$ are defined over k. Since B and B^- are the normalizers of $\underline{b}$ and $\underline{b}^-$ ((14.2), Cor. 2) they are k-closed. This finishes the proof when k is perfect. Let now k be infinite, of non-zero characteristic. Assume first that $\underline{t}$ is not central in $\underline{g}$, which amounts to supposing that $d\alpha \neq 0$. We have then

$$[\underline{t}, \underline{g}_\alpha] = \underline{g}_\alpha \quad [\underline{t}, \underline{g}_{-\alpha}] = \underline{g}_{-\alpha} ,$$

which implies that $\underline{b}$ (resp. $\underline{b}^{-}$) is its own normalizer in $\underline{g}$. Then, B and B^{-} are defined over k by (18.5).

If now $\underline{t}$ is central in $\underline{g}$, we let G' and $\pi : G \longrightarrow G'$ be as in (17.8). The group $T' = \pi(T)$ is a maximal torus of G' and is k-split ((11.14), (8.4)). The groups $B' = \pi(B)$ and $B'^{-} = \pi(B^{-})$ are the two Borel subgroups of G' (11.14) containing T'. By the previous proof, they are defined over k. Let $\sigma : G' \longrightarrow G'/B'$ be the canonical projection, and $\tau = \sigma \circ \pi$. It follows from the equality ker $d\pi = \underline{t}$ that $d\pi$ maps $\underline{g}_{-\alpha}$ injectively onto a supplement of $L(B')$ in $\underline{g}'$. Therefore τ is separable, and (6.7) $B = \tau^{-1}(B')$ is also defined over k. Similarly, B^{-} is defined over k.

We now know that U_{α} and $U_{-\alpha}$ are defined over k. Since $d\pi$ is injective on $\underline{g}_{\alpha}$ and $\underline{g}_{-\alpha}$, the map π is a k-isomorphism of U_{α} (resp. $U_{-\alpha}$) onto its image. It suffices then to prove that the latter is k-isomorphic to $\mathbb{G}_{a}$, which reduces us to the case where $\underline{t}$ is not central in $\underline{g}$. If k is perfect, our assertion has already been proved ((10.9), Remark). Let now k be infinite. We may then find $H \in \underline{t}(k)$ such that $d\alpha(H) \neq 0$. We have then $\underline{z}(H) = \underline{t}$, hence (9.1) $Z_{G}(H)^{0} = T$. Using (10.6), we get then $Z_{B}(H) = T$. In particular, the map $f : u \longmapsto Ad\ u(H) - H$ of U_{α} into $\underline{g}$ is injective. Let X be a non-zero element of $\underline{g}_{\alpha}(k)$. Since B/U_{α} is commutative, we can write

$$Ad\ u(H) = H + c(u).X, \qquad (u \in U_{\alpha}) ,$$

where $c : u \longmapsto c(u)$ is clearly an injective k-morphism of U_α into $\mathbb{G}_a$. It is then bijective. By (3.9)(2), $dc(X) = -[H, X] = -\alpha(H).X \neq 0$. Hence c is separable, and yields the desired k-isomorphism of U_α onto $\mathbb{G}_a$. The argument is the same for $U_{-\alpha}$, which ends the proof.

(18.8) COROLLARY. Let G be connected, reductive. Then G splits over a finite separable extension of k.

G has a maximal torus T defined over k (18.2). The latter splits over a finite separable extension k' of k (8.11). G splits over k' by the theorem.

BIBLIOGRAPHICAL NOTE

In characteristic zero, (18.2) is due to Chevalley: (18.2)(i) is proved in [7b] and (18.2)(ii) in J.M.S. Japan 6 (1954), 303-324. It has been established by Rosenlicht [17] over infinite perfect fields, and by Grothendieck ([9], Exp. XIV) in general. The proof given here is taken from [2]. The paper of Chevalley quoted above also contains a result (Proposition 3) which appears to be essentially equivalent to the rationality over k of the variety of Cartan subgroups of G, when k is of characteristic zero (see remark to (18.2) for references to the general case of this theorem).

(18.7) is due to Cartier (unpublished). More general results can be found in [9, Exp. XII]. Here, we have followed [3].

REFERENCES

The numbered list below is limited to papers or books referred to in the text. In addition, we mention three papers which give surveys on algebraic groups over an algebraically closed groundfield, affine algebraic groups over a field, and affine group schemes respectively.

C. CHEVALLEY - La théorie des groupes algébriques. Proc. Int. C. M. Edinburgh 1958, Cambridge University Press 1960, 53-68.

A. BOREL - Linear algebraic groups. Proc. Symp. Pure Math. 9, A.M.S. 1966, 3-19.

M. DEMAZURE - Schémas en groupes réductifs. Bull. S.M.F. 93 (1965), 369-413.

[1] A. BOREL - Groupes algébriques linéaires. Annals of Math. (2) 64 (1956), 20-82.

[2] ———— and T. A. SPRINGER - Rationality properties of linear algebraic groups. Proc. Symp. Pure Math., vol. IX (1966), 26-32.

[3] ———— and T. A. SPRINGER - Rationality properties of linear algebraic groups II, Tohoku Math. Jour., vol. 13 (1969)

[4] ———— et J. TITS - Groupes réductifs. Publ. Math. I.H.E.S. 27 (1965), 55-150.

[5] N. BOURBAKI - Groupes et algèbres de Lie. Chapitre 1: Algèbres de Lie, Paris (1960), Hermann éd.

[6] ———— Groupes et algèbres de Lie, Chap. VI: Systèmes de racines, Paris (1969), Hermann éd.

[7] C. CHEVALLEY - Théorie des groupes de Lie. (a) Tome II: Groupes algébriques, Paris 1951, (b) Tome III: Groupes algébriques, Paris 1955, Hermann éd.

[8] ———— Séminaire sur la classification des groupes de Lie algébriques (Mimeographed Notes), Paris 1956-58.

[9] M. DEMAZURE et A. GROTHENDIECK - Schémas en groupes (Mimeographed Notes), I. H. E. S. 1964.

[10] N. JACOBSON - Lie algebras. Interscience Tracts in pure and applied math. 10, New York 1962, Interscience Publ.

[11] E. R. KOLCHIN - Algebraic matric groups and the Picard-Vessiot theory of homogeneous linear differential equations. Annals of Math. (2) 49 (1948), 1-42.

[12] ———— On certain concepts in the theory of algebraic matric groups. Ibid. 774-789.

[13] S. LANG - Algebraic groups over finite fields. Amer. Jour. Math. 78 (1956), 555-563.

[14] D. MUMFORD - Introduction to algebraic geometry. Harvard Lecture Notes.

[15] T. ONO - Arithmetic of algebraic tori. Annals of Math. (2) 74 (1961), 101-139.

[16] M. ROSENLICHT - Some basic theorems on algebraic groups. Amer. Jour. Math. 78 (1956), 401-443.

[17] ——————— Some rationality questions on algebraic groups. Annali di Mat. (IV) 43 (1957), 25-50.

[18] ——————— On quotient varieties and the affine embedding of certain homogeneous spaces. Trans. Amer. Math. Soc. 101 (1961), 211-223.

[19] J-P. SERRE - Cohomologie galoisienne. Springer Lecture Notes 5 (1965), Springer ed.

[20] ——————— Algèbres de Lie semi-simples complexes. New York 1966, Benjamin ed.

[21] A. WEIL - On algebraic groups and homogeneous spaces. Amer. Jour. Math. 77 (1955), 493-512.

INDEX TO CHAPTERS I TO V